DATE DUE

FEB 2 0 1993			
GAYLORD			PRINTED IN U.S.A.

Optical Fiber Sensors: Principles and Components

VOLUME ONE

The Artech House Telecommunication Library

Vinton G. Cerf, *Series Editor*

Digital Cellular Radio by George Calhoun

E-Mail by Stephen A. Caswell

Communication Satellites in the Geostationary Orbit by Donald M. Jansky and Michel C. Jeruchim

World Atlas of Satellites, Donald M. Jansky, ed.

Handbook of Satellite Telecommunications and Broadcasting, L. Ya. Kantor, ed.

Introduction to Telecommunication Electronics by A.Michael Noll

Introduction to Telephones and Telephone Systems by A. Michael Noll

Integrated Services Digital Networks by Anthony M. Rutkowski

Signal Theory and Processing by Frederic de Coulon

Digital Signal Processing by Murat Kunt

Principles of Secure Communication Systems by Don J. Torrieri

Digital Image Signal Processing by Friedrich Wahl

Advances in Computer Systems Security: 3 volume set, Rein Turn, ed.

Techniques in Data Communications, by Ralph Glasgal

Measurement of Optical Fibers and Devices by G. Cancellieri and U. Ravaioli

Codes for Error Control and Synchronization by Djimitri Wiggert

Mathematical Methods of Information Transmission by K. Arbenz and J.C. Martin

Telecommunication Systems by Pierre-Girard Fontelliet

Optical Fiber Transmission Systems by Siegried Geckeler

Traffic Flow in Switching Systems by G. Hebuterne

Optimization of Digital Transmission Systems by K. Trondle and G. Soder

Quality Measures and the Design of Telecommunications Systems by John H. Fennick

Troposcatter Radio Links by G. Roda

Innovation in Internetworking, Craig Partridge, ed.

Principles of Signals and Systems: Deterministic Signals by B. Picinbono

Television Technology: Fundamentals and Future Prospects by A. Michael Noll

Voice Teletraffic System Engineering by James R. Boucher

Advances in Fiber Optics Communications, Henry F. Taylor, ed.

Optical Fiber Sensors:
Principles and Components

by

John Dakin and Brian Culshaw

VOLUME ONE

Artech House
Boston and London

British Library Cataloguing in Publication Data
Optical fiber sensors: principles
and components.
  1. Fibre-optic sensors
  I. Dakin, John, *1947*—II. Culshaw, B.
  (Brian)
  620′.0044

ISBN 0–89006–317–6

Library of Congress Cataloging-in-Publication Data
Optical fiber sensors.
  Bibliography: v. 1, p.
  Includes index.
  1. Optical fibers.   2. Optical detectors.
I. Dakin, John, 1947–   . II. Culshaw, B.
TA1800.0666   1988   621.36′92   88–7611

ISBN 0–89006–317–6 (v. 1)

Copyright © 1988

ARTECH HOUSE, INC.
685 Canton Street
Norwood, MA 02062

International Standard Book Number: 0–89006–317–6 (v. 1)
Library of Congress Catalog Card Number: 88–7611

10 9 8 7 6 5 4 3 2

Contents

Dedication

To Pat, Shauna and Kacie
for support and understanding
To Aileen for patience, tolerance and good
humor
beyond every call of duty

B.C.

To my wife Susan
for her understanding and help with the book
J.P.D.

Preface

Over 20 years have elapsed since the concept of combining fiber optic technology with environmental sensing was first mooted. During that interval the underlying building blocks, comprising fiber optic and related components, have evolved from very simple light-guiding bundles of glass fibers into a range of extremely elegant, rugged and relatively inexpensive devices. These, in turn, have stimulated an ever-increasing interest in the exploration of fiber optic techniques for sensing media which has generated a range of proven devices and subsystems that exploit an extremely wide range of optical concepts in transduction mechanisms. In parallel with the technological evolution, an appreciation of a significant commercial potential for this new approach to sensing has matured and new instrumentation application areas have emerged.

The basic techniques which can be exploited have now been well defined and cover almost every aspect of guided wave and classical optics. The range of available sensors is bewildering and many have found quite specific application niches. The major current problems are in engineering the concepts into rugged, reliable and economically competitive devices and these problems, together with a related discourse centered on identifying optimum materials for use in fiber optic sensors, are now being addressed. This background of known well-characterized science and identified (if speculatively) applications provides an ideal environment in which to produce a book with the aim of providing a definitive statement of the science and technology underlying the field of fiber optic sensors. It is with this in mind that we sought to produce these volumes.

To achieve such an objective requires access to a diversity of expertise since, in common with all transducer technologies, fiber optic sensors are very much a multidisciplinary area. Consequently, a multi-author format has been adopted and we have been fortunate to persuade many of the world's experts in the field to contribute. We have been even more fortunate in that the enthusiasm of the contributors has surpassed all expectations and the result has been these two volumes which convey some impressions not only of the underlying science but also of the excitement and stimulation which has been shared over the last decade or so by those researchers who have been actively conducting research in the area. This first volume covers underlying principles and baseline technology and the second covers systems and applications.

In addition to the acknowledgments made by individual contributors, we, the editors, must thank all the friends and colleagues who have contributed to the growth of this intriguing subject area. We also gratefully acknowledge the companies and organizations with whom we have worked, whose support has enabled us to develop our knowledge of optical fiber sensors.

The result is, we hope, a valuable statement of the art in fiber optic sensors and a reference book which will serve to describe the underlying principles and principal applications which will continue to be valuable for many years to come.

Brian Culshaw   **John Dakin**
Glasgow   *Romsey*

Author's Biographies

Andrew **CARTER** was born in Helensburgh, Scotland, in 1951. He graduated with honors in physics from the University of Oxford in 1973, where he carried out research for his D.Phil. in semiconductor physics. He joined the Plessey Company at the Allen Clark Research Centre, Caswell, England, in 1977, since when he has carried out research into optoelectronic devices, subsystems and integrated optoelectronic circuits. He is currently the manager of the Optoelectronic Devices and Subsystems Department at Caswell.

Brian **CULSHAW**, currently Professor of Electronics at Strathclyde University, was born in 1945. His interests in fiber optic sensors started in the mid-1970s while he was a lecturer at University College London and followed his earlier activities in microwave semiconductor devices. His previous posts include a period with Bell Northern Research in Ottawa, Canada, and visiting appointments at Cornell and Stanford Universities. He has been author or co-author of well over 100 technical papers and two other textbooks as well as several patents. His current interests include fiber optic gyroscopes, sensor multiplexing systems, optical waveguides and waveguide technology, smart structure research and silicon micromachining especially for optical transducers.

John **DAKIN** graduated in electronics at Southampton University, England, in 1968, and remained as a research student and research fellow until 1972, researching on loss mechanisms in glass and glass fiber. He joined AEG Telefunken Research Institute in Ulm, West Germany, in 1973, where he spent 2 years working on glass fiber measurements and researching into new fiber fabrication techniques. In 1975 he joined Plessey Electronic Systems Research and has since then established an active research team working on optical fiber sensors and specialized optical fiber communication systems. He is the author of over 90 technical papers and over 100 patent applications and was responsible for novel inventions with regard to multiplexed optical fiber hydrophone arrays, distributed fiber temperature sensors using Raman scattering and a wide variety of other transduction methods for simplex incoherent sensors. He has recently been appointed a visiting Professor of

Strathclyde University, and has just joined York Ltd, of Chandlers Ford, Eastleigh, England, as a senior consultant on optical and fiber optical systems.

Anthony **DANDRIDGE** was born in Kent, England. He received his B.Sc. and Ph.D. degrees in physics from the Sir John Cass School of Science and Technology, City of London Polytechnic. His postgraduate and postdoctoral research work included flow-birefringence, viscometric and light-scattering studies of short-chain polymers. In 1979 he was a lecturer in physics at the University of Kent, Canterbury, England. Since 1980 he has been associated with Georgetown University, Washington, DC, John Carrol University, Cleveland, OH, and the Naval Research Laboratory, Washington, DC. In 1984 he became head of the Optical Sensor Section at the Naval Research Laboratory. His research work covers fiber optic sensor systems as well as the noise and spectral characteristics of semiconductor lasers. He has authored and co-authored over 150 journal and conference publications.

Michel **DIGONNET** was born in Paris, France, in 1955. He received his Engineering Degree in physics and chemistry from Ecole Supérieure de Physique et de Chemie Industrielle de la Ville de Paris and the Diplôme d'Etudes Approfondies in coherent optics from the University of Paris, Orsay, in 1978. He received the M.S. degree in 1980 and the Ph.D. degree in 1983 in applied physics from Stanford University, CA. His graduate research included the development of single-mode fiber couplers and single-crystal fiber devices. From 1983 to 1986 he was with Litton Guidance and Control, Chatsworth, CA, doing research at Stanford University as a Visiting Scholar in the areas of single-crystal lasers, miniature solid state lasers and integrated optics devices for optical sensors. Since 1987 he has been involved in the development of fiber delivery and sensor systems for laser angioplasty with MCM Laboratories, Mountain View, CA. He is also pursuing his research activities on Nd:silica fiber lasers at Stanford University on a part-time basis.

Brian **DEBNEY** was born in Birmingham, England, in 1951. He attended the University of Birmingham between 1970 and 1976, during which time he was awarded a first class honors degree in mathematical physics and a Ph.D. for research in theoretical solid state physics. In 1976 he joined the Plessey Company at Plessey Research Caswell where his research included detectors and receivers for fiber optic systems. In 1985 he joined the Optoelectronics Department where he is now a group leader responsible for the research and development of advanced components and subsystems for direct detection, coherent detection and wavelength-multiplexed systems.

Alec **GAMBLING** is Head of the Optical Fibre Group in the Electronics and Computer Science Department at Southampton University. For his many contributions to optical electronics he has been awarded the J. J. Thomson and Faraday Medals of the Institution of Electrical Engineers and the Churchill Medal of the Society of Engineers. He has received a number of other prizes and premiums for his published work. He is a Fellow of the Royal Society, Selby Fellow of the Australian Academy of Science, a foreign member of the Polish Academy of Sciences, an honorary professor at Huazhong University of Science and Technology and at the Beijing Institute of Telecommunications, China, an honorary director of the Beijing Optical Fibre Institute, China, and a founding director of York Ltd, England, a company manufacturing instruments and components for the optical fiber industry.

Ralf **KERSTEN** was born in Halle/Saale, West Germany, in 1947. He studied physics at the Technical University of Munich, West Germany, and the University of Innsbruck, Austria. In 1973 he finished his Ph.D.thesis, which was the first experimental work on integrated optics in West Germany. After 4 years as a staff member of Siemens Research Laboratories, Munich, he joined the Technical University of Berlin as a professor working on optical communications and integrated optics. In 1982 he went to Fraunhöfer Gesellschaft at Freiburg, heading a research group on fiber and integrated optic sensors. Since 1985 he has been responsible for quartz glass fiber fabrication and its industrial applications at Schøtt Glaswerke, Mainz. He has published more than 50 papers, is author of a book on optical communications and editor-in-chief of the *Journal of Optical Communications*. He is a member of the Optical Society of America.

Yuan **KIM** was born in Seoul, Korea. He received the B.S. degree from Seoul National University in 1977 and the M.S. degree from Korea Advanced Institute of Science in 1979, both in physics. He received the Ph.D. degree in applied physics from Stanford University, Stanford, CA, in 1985. From 1979 to 1982 he was a member of the research staff at the Korea Institute of Science and Technology, Seoul, where he worked on the fabrication and characterization of optical fibers, fiber optic gyroscopes, polarization optical time domain reflectometry and high precision laser interferometry. From 1985 to 1986 he was employed as a research associate at the Edward L. Ginzton Laboratory, Stanford University, where he is currently an acting assistant professor of electrical engineering. His current research interests are fiber optic sensors and related components, optical signal processing and guided wave modulators.

Simon **POOLE** was born in Watford, England, in 1958. He received a B.Sc. in electronic engineering from the University of Nottingham in 1979. In 1981 he joined the Optical Fibre Group at Southampton University as a research student working on optical fiber fabrication and characterization. He is now the Pirelli Senior Research Fellow within the group. His current research interests include fiber fabrication and characterization, active fiber devices and planar guided wave structures. He has published over 50 papers in the field of optical fibers and is the holder of four patents relating to rare-earth-doped fibers and fiber lasers.

Alan **ROGERS** studied for his degrees at Cambridge University, obtaining his Ph.D. in radio astronomy and space physics in 1966. He then spent 3 years as a lecturer in physics at the University of London while pursuing research into ionospheric structure and solar–terrestrial interactions. In 1969 he joined the Central Electricity Research Laboratories of the CEGB, where he researched, at various times, in the areas of microwave communications, signal processing, mobile radio communications, optical communications, optical sensing and laser diagnostics. In 1985 he became professor of electronics at King's College London, where he is engaged in research primarily in the areas of nonlinear optics and distributed optical fiber sensors.

Martin **SMITH** studied physics at Exeter College, Oxford, and then worked at the Central Electricity Research Laboratories on the application of single-mode optical fibers for current measurement. He gained a Ph.D. from King's College London on the basis of this work. Subsequently, he worked at PA Technology and Unilever Research on optical methods for sensing, particularly the use of evanescent wave methods for monitoring immunological reactions. Since 1987 he has worked for ICI Diagnostics on the commercialization of biosensors. Dr Smith has written a number of publications on the technical and commercial aspects of sensing, and several patents.

Aileen **YUREK** was born in St Paul, MN. She received her BSEE at the University of Minnesota and her M.S. and Ph.D. degrees in electrical engineering from the University of Maryland. Her postgraduate and postdoctoral work included laser-pumped bulk GaAs lasers, optically controlled millimeter-wave devices, noise properties of semiconductor lasers and superluminescent diodes, and optical fiber sensors. Since 1984 she has been associated with the Naval Research Laboratory, Washington, DC, where she is presently group leader for the acoustic sensor project.

Chapter 1

Introduction: Sensor Systems and Fiber Optics

BRIAN CULSHAW AND JOHN DAKIN

Most, if not all, electronic systems consist of three major parts: an input derived from a sensor, an electronic device which performs some processing on this input, perhaps in parallel with inputs from other sources, and finally an output device, typically an actuator. The input device can range from a keyboard to a television camera to a blood gas monitor. The output device— the actuator—may take the form of a visual or audible display or an electrically activated valve, switch or positional translator. The signal processing element is, of course, based on the ubiquitous chip. Of these three elements the signal processing is extremely refined whilst the remainder have received relatively scant attention.

This book is about sensors and concentrates upon one particular implementation of sensors—that using fiber optics. Perhaps one of the most important messages which the book serves to emphasize, but which is also general to the entirety of sensor technology, is that the conversion of one type of signal into another via a sensing element is a very multidisciplinary art involving electronics, mechanical engineering, chemistry, packaging and, in this case, fiber optics as well. The combination presents a considerable challenge and perhaps this explains why the sensor is the Cinderella of the information age—the design problems are simply very difficult. Inevitably this leads to speculation as to what may play the role of the Ugly Sisters.

The essential function of a sensor is to cause a change in one form of input energy (the measurand) to result in a corresponding single-valued change in another or the same form of energy (the signal). Thus, for example, changes in acoustic pressure produce changes in electric current in a microphone, changes in temperature produce an electrical voltage in a thermocouple and changes in the spatial features of a scene produce changes in the electric current in a television camera. The signal can be produced in other domains, and perhaps the most common example is the brake servomechanism in an automobile in which changes in the position of the pedal are sensed as changes in the pressure of the brake fluid.

Measurands can be classified into six groups. These include the following:

1

(a) radiant signals embracing the intensity, wavelength, state of polarization and phase of electromagnetic or acoustic radiation;

(b) mechanical signals which include force, pressure torque, flow, mass etc.;

(c) thermal signals which include temperature, temperature differential measured in space and/or time and heat flow;

(d) electrical signals which include voltage, current, charge, resistance, inductance, capacitance, pulse duration, frequency and dielectric constant;

(e) magnetic signals which include magnetic flux density, magnetic field direction and permeability;

(f) chemical signals which include chemical composition, toxicity, oxidation–reduction potential, pH, pCO_2 etc.

Even this classification omits secondary inferential measurements such as the use of turbidity to monitor the presence and/or constitution of slurries and colloids. Furthermore, all these measurands can be configured as outputs, although some are more useful than others and the electrical quantities are often the preferred output signals. The transduction process involved in the sensor may be a direct single-stage interaction as, for example, when changes in temperature change the resistance of a wire in a platinum thermometer, or it may include an intermediate phase as, for example, when the intensity of

Scanning electron micrograph of an optically excited resonant beam sensor mounted on the reverse of a diaphragm. The whole assembly is micromachined from a single crystal.

infrared radiation is used to change the temperature of a platinum thermometer in order to measure infrared flux. Fiber optic sensors, which are the subject of this book, are almost always two-stage devices. In a fiber optic sensor the measurand is made to change the features of light transmitted along the fiber, and these changes in turn are used to modify an electrical signal in a receiver. This two-stage process is absolutely basic to the operation of fiber optic sensors and implies that great care has to be taken in the characterization of *both* phases of the interaction.

It is tempting to argue that the need for new sensor technology is limited since the explosion of signal processing capability implies that deficiencies in the current portfolio of sensors can be made good by appropriate signal processing. There is some validity in this approach and indeed "smart sensors" are beginning to make some impact. However, smart sensors rely upon direct or indirect information which monitors the state of interfering measurands and corrects the output signal from the sensor accordingly. In many situations—for example, in the presence of high and variable electromagnetic fields—sensors to provide the information to perform corrections on the outputs are simply not available and, in a rapidly changing technological world, there are more and more requirements in which the smart sensor approach is just not appropriate. In addition to the aforementioned example concerning high electromagnetic fields, there are applications in new complex avionic systems where weight and radar or radiation signatures from the instrumentation are very important considerations. There is an ever-increasing activity in medical instrumentation where safety, particularly for intravenous use, is paramount. Meanwhile the security industry has identified the attraction of nonmetallic nonradiative intruder alarm systems. All these applications, and more, can be addressed using fiber optic sensor technology.

This approach to sensing enjoys considerable advantages over other sensor techniques in that there is a substantial background activity in fiber optic communications. This serves a much larger marketplace and therefore can provide a range of components at relatively low cost, and, perhaps more importantly, provides a background science which can be modified for sensor applications. This feature is only shared by silicon micromachining approaches to sensing which can draw upon the background of the semiconductor industry. All other sensing techniques are highly application specific. Of course, there are still a large number of application-specific features in fiber optic sensor technology which are usually centered around the interface between the measurand and the optical modulator which is incorporated in the optical fiber link. However, a baseline technology which is capable of transmitting several hundred megabits per second at distances of hundreds of kilometers must have something to offer, especially when we consider the other well-developed aspects of fiber optics including imaging (endoscopy) and displays. Indeed, displays have already made a considerable mark in the automobile industry for simple remote "cold" indicator lamps. Usable fiber components must therefore be available at very low cost for otherwise these applications simply could not have been developed.

Trial optical fiber hydrophone array (Plessey). The sensor on the right of each horizontal arm on the gantry is one of six passively multiplexed fiber hydrophones. On the left is a reference piezoelectric sensor.

Optical fiber sensors exploit light as the information carrier, and light is remarkably versatile when viewed with this in mind. Light can be coherently modulated in phase and frequency and either coherently or incoherently modulated in amplitude and state of polarization. Furthermore its color can be used as an information carrier and it has the ability to carry highly detailed spatial information. Secondary modulation techniques can also be used, of which the most useful is probably subcarrier frequency modulation in which the frequency of an amplitude modulation is caused to vary and the necessary information is carried as the value of this frequency. All these modulation techniques have been used in other domains than sensing and there is a substantial background technology from which to draw the demodulation techniques. Fiber optic sensors, therefore, consist of a constant light source launched into an optical fiber and transmitted to another point at which a measurement is to be made. At this point, the parameter to be measured is used to modulate one of the above properties of the light and this modulated light is collected by the same or a different fiber and returned to a detector where it is converted into an electrical signal. The modulation process can proceed either within the fiber itself or in an external system usually coupled to the fiber through some kind of lens arrangement. The system has all the electromagnetic immunity and safety advantages alluded to earlier and in addition, with modern optical fibers, sensor regions can be addressed over considerable distances whilst the achievable signal-to-noise ratios imply that extremely high sensitivity to changes in the measurand can be engineered. Furthermore the very high information-carrying capacity of optical fiber networks implies that it is feasible to multiplex a large number of sensors passively onto one link.

The concept of fiber optic sensors is far from new. The first patents were taken out in the middle 1960s and included the Fotonic mechanical displacement sensor based upon fiber bundles and an early ultrasonic sensor based upon phase modulation. However, serious research effort on the much broader base which is now regarded as fiber sensor technology began about 10 years later, and since that time the technology has gone through the classic cycle of initial euphoria leading into increasing cynicism and followed by a settling-in process to a realistic assessment of what can really be done. The settling-in is now almost complete, most of the scientific principles of fiber sensors have been identified and characterized and much of the applications potential has been assessed. This book is then well timed and presents a statement of the art which should remain useful until the turn of the century and perhaps beyond.

In common with all other sensor technologies, this subject is highly interdisciplinary in nature and we aim to cover most aspects of the technology in this book. Consequently we have adopted a multi-author approach since it is only by this means that adequate coverage can be assured. The book provides a comprehensive coverage of the major aspects of the science and technology of fiber optic sensors by incorporating the collective talents of almost 30 internationally recognized experts. Even so, it is not possible to discuss everything in the 800 pages or thereabouts of the two volumes. In particular we have omitted to address anything other than the basic processes of detection and signal processing and we have barely covered the important questions of sensor mechanical engineering and tolerancing, much of which is commercially sensitive anyway. There are undoubtedly other stones which have also remained unturned.

The material in this book is largely aimed at graduate level and above. Even though we have endeavored to cover the basic principles underpinning the technology, the treatment cannot be self-contained and, in particular, a background in optics and electronics as well as a working knowledge of materials science are needed to convert the information presented here into practical devices and systems. In addition, many of the introductory chapters are by their very nature broad-brush discussions of substantial topics in their own right so that, for example, the chapter on integrated optics can only be a précis of the considerable literature which abounds on this subject.

The book is in two volumes which broadly cover principles and applications. In Volume 1 basic fiber optic sensor concepts are discussed in Chapter 2 which is really nothing more than a very brief statement of the essential features of the fiber optic sensor problem. In Chapter 3 by Alan Rogers the essential optics which must be brought to bear upon the design of fiber optic sensors are recapitulated. Detectors and detection are covered by Andy Carter and Brian Debny who concentrate on the practical issues surrounding the use of semiconductor diode detectors which are used in most fiber optic sensor systems. The next chapter on optical sources by Tony Dandridge and Aileen Yurek again concentrates on semiconductor diode optical generation although, since sensors utilize many other forms of optical source, these are briefly discussed as well. In Chapter 6 on materials for optical fiber sensors by Martin Smith techniques whereby a measurand can modulate the optical properties of a particular material are discussed and attention is focused on chemical and biochemical stimuli. Yoon Kim and Michel Digonnet present a review of fiber optic components in Chapter 7. Almost all sensor systems require means for temporal or spatial modulation of the light within the system in a guided wave format so that fiber optic components are particularly important. The optical fiber itself can have its properties tailored specifically for sensor applications and this is covered in Chapter 8 by Alec Gambling and Simon Poole who concentrate on specially modified optical properties. There is also a need in sensors for fibers with specially modified mechanical properties and this is covered very briefly in Chapter 2. In the final chapter in Volume 1 Ralf Kersten focuses on integrated optics in sensors and discusses technologies based on lithium niobate and glass in particular.

Volume 2 starts with a detailed discussion of fiber optic interferometric sensors presented by David Jackson and Julian Jones. Chapter 11, written by Hervé le Fevre, concentrates solely on the fiber optic gyroscope which is a

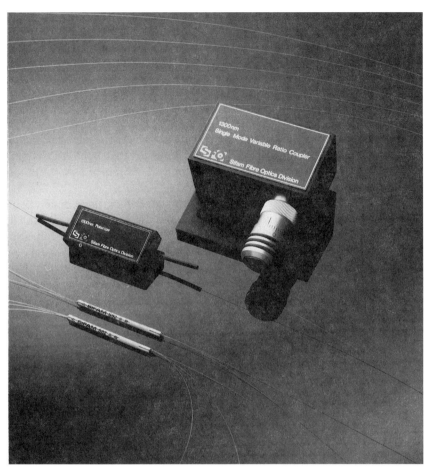

Typical passive fiber optic components for use in sensor or communications systems: from the top, an adjustable coupler, a fiber optic polarizer and a pair of fixed couplers.

particularly interesting class of sensor since it brings together a diverse range of optical principles. Intensity- and wavelength-based sensors are covered in Chapter 12 by Barry Jones, Reg Medlock and Ron Spooner who concentrate on the realization of relatively simple first-generation devices. Chapter 13 examines the role of silicon in fiber optic sensors as both a mechanical and an optical material. In Chapter 14 Rainer Kist discusses the basic principles of point sensor multiplexing and in Chapter 15 John Dakin examines distributed sensing schemes. These two chapters are particularly important since they represent the beginning of the evolution of a range of fiber optic sensor multiplexers which many consider to be essential for the long-term implementation of the technology. The application section in Volume 2 starts with a discussion of chemical, medical and biomedical sensing by Alan Harmer and Annamaria Scheggi and continues with an examination of physical sensors of process control by Kazuo Kyuma. The avionic and military sector is particularly important for fiber optic sensor systems, and Brian Culshaw explores some of the possibilities in Chapter 18. Chapter 19 is a potpourri of other applications discussed by Dr Bruinsma who considers in particular possibilities in electrical measurement, laser velocimetry and industrial inspection. The eventual success or otherwise of fiber optic sensors is determined by the potential marketplace, and this is covered in the last chapter by Peter McGeehin who examines the past developments and future possibilities for fiber optic sensor technology.

The authors of all these chapters, without exception, have undertaken their task with commitment and enthusiasm, and the result is a book which conveys not only the technical status of an important technology but also much of the excitement which is shared by those who, after several years of research, are beginning to see the fruits of their endeavors put into action. The basic technology now is relatively mature and one of the major aims of this book is to convey this maturity and to stimulate its application in new disciplines. The next 10 years of fiber optic sensors will be considerably different from the first 20 in that we shall see an increasing emphasis on development and engineering. This book promises to serve as both a reference manual and technical stimulus throughout this forthcoming phase.

Chapter 2

Basic Concepts of Optical Fiber Sensors

BRIAN CULSHAW

2.1 Introduction

This chapter serves primarily as a very brief overview of the remainder of this book together with a rather cursory examination of the principal features of fiber optic sensors. Most, if not all, of the points raised in this chapter are covered in substantially more detail within these volumes. The principal aim is to produce a short chapter in which the detailed points discussed elsewhere are examined together in order to illustrate the technical linkage between the various chapters.

2.1.1 Optical fiber sensors—what are they?

Optical fiber sensors are essentially a means whereby light guided within an optical fiber can be modified in response to an external physical, chemical, biological, biomedical or similar influence. Light from an optical source whose relevant optical properties remain constant is launched into a fiber via a stable coupling mechanism and guided to the point at which the measurement is to take place. At this point either the light can be allowed to exit the fiber and be modulated in a separate zone before being relaunched into either the same or a different fiber—these are called *extrinsic* sensors—or the light can continue within the fiber and be modulated in response to the measurand whilst still being guided—these are known as *intrinsic* sensors. Some sensors function by causing the light guided in the fiber to couple to the measurand via the evanescent field—these are a halfway house but are perhaps best classified with the extrinsic devices. The basic concepts are indicated in Fig. 2.1.

The fact that the fiber itself can respond to an external influence immediately indicates that the optical fiber leads to and from the sensing region may also be accidentally responsive to external influences. This gives rise to the possibility for interference with the sensed signal along the fiber path. The need for "lead insensitivity" or "transmission line neutrality", an important prerequisite for a practical sensor, will be a recurrent theme

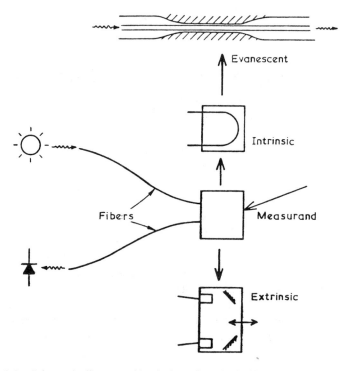

Fig. 2.1 Schematic diagram of intrinsic and extrinsic fiber optic sensors. The evanescent field device has features of both.

throughout the book. One approach is to modify the open-loop sensor system shown in Fig. 2.1 to a closed-loop format in which the detector signal is caused to modify the optical source, perhaps in its wavelength, in order to produce an apparent zero due to the measurand at the output. This does, of course, imply that the "accidental" signals along the fiber may also form part of the nulling signal, but in a well-designed system these effects can be minimized.

The measurand can be virtually any physical or chemical influence and the range of optical fiber sensors that have been demonstrated is extremely diverse. The property of the optical signal which can be modulated is also extremely diverse, embracing intensity, phase, Doppler shifts, state of polarization, subcarrier modulation function (for instance modulation frequency or pulse width) or color.

Since optical detectors only finally respond to optical intensity, which in turn is a parameter strongly dependent upon both temperature and aging, and since these dependences may also be a function of wavelength, the simplest coding mechanism will obviously be digital where the state of the sensor is transmitted as some form of pulse sequence. It is interesting to observe that, of the mechanisms mentioned, only modulation frequency and on–off intensity modulation will produce a digital signal, with 0°–180° and carrier frequency shift keying as further possibilities. The remaining sensors are all essentially analog in nature and this has important consequences for their design and use.

2.1.2 Optical fiber sensors—why use them?

The potential advantages of optical fiber sensors all stem from the fact that the modulated signal can be transmitted to and from the sensing region without recourse to electrical connection. This gives the following principal features: immunity from electromagnetic interference; electrical isolation, removing problems with ground plane separation and electrical safety regulations; chemical passivity; small size and low weight because of the fiber optic transmission medium; potentially high sensitivity and the ability to interface with a wide range of measurands.

There is also a considerable potential, as yet unrealized, for multiplexed fiber sensor systems in which the tremendous information-carrying capacity of the optical fiber link can be more fully exploited. A number of trial demonstration systems of this type have been evaluated and will be described in Volume 2. Furthermore, for intrinsic sensors, the fact that the fiber is sensitive to the measurand of interest can be used to advantage to form distributed networks which are very difficult, if not impossible, to realize using alternative technologies. Another interesting and longer-term development would involve the marriage of optical signal processing techniques and electronic signal processing to form a flexible high speed sensor network.

Perhaps the main advantage of optical fiber sensors is their ability to address measurement problems which are inaccessible using alternative technologies. Examples of these include the measurement of current and voltage in very high electromagnetic interference environments, the measurement of chemical constituents in the blood of patients undergoing surgical treatment and the ability to monitor parameters such as temperature in very high intensity radiofrequency fields such as those found in diathermy and microwave heating. The low weight properties of fiber interconnects are beginning to make their mark in aerospace applications where the next generation of aircraft are likely to be flown using optical sensors only.

2.1.3 Optical fiber sensor response functions

The final detected output in optical fiber sensors is influenced by many parameters along the way and it is important to appreciate how these arise. Again the details will be discussed more rigorously in the remainder of the book. The detected signal can be represented as follows:

$$\text{electrical output} = \text{SP} \times D \times \text{FT} \times M \times Q \times \text{FR} \times S \tag{2.1}$$

where SP represents the operations performed by signal processing within the detection electronics, D represents the signal generated by the photo-detector in response to the optical input to the detector, FT represents the transmission function of the fiber linking the sensor to the detector, M represents the modulation function applied to the optical signal as it passes through the modulator, Q represents the quantity to be measured as interpreted through the modulation characteristics of the modulator, FR represents the transmission function of the fiber linking the source to the modulator and S represents the output from the source itself coupled to the fiber.

There are numerous terms here and we could identify even more subunits in each of them, representing for example the coupling between the fiber and the detector, modulator and source. The reason for mentioning all these terms is to emphasize that any of them may be affected by aging in the system and most will also be affected by temperature. Some of the fiber transmission functions may also be affected by physical interference (e.g. bending or shaking) within the link itself.

It is also important when discussing noise in optical fiber sensors to appreciate that all these components could also influence the noise levels in the receiver; for example, source phase noise may influence the performance of any multipath network and $1/f$ noise in detectors will often restrict the performance of detection systems at relatively low frequencies. Values of these functions will be discussed in more detail later in the book.

2.2 Optical fiber sensor components

The purpose of this section is to give very brief consideration to all the parameters mentioned in eqn (2.1) and to discuss briefly the order-of-magnitude properties of the various components which are available.

2.2.1 Modulators

The means whereby light can be modulated in response to the physical measurand are numerous. For the purposes of this discussion it is convenient to divide the modulation functions into analog and digital (or quasi-digital) techniques.

Analog quantities include the following.
Intensity is the parameter to which all optical detectors finally respond. Precise repeatable measurement of optical intensity over a wide dynamic range is quite difficult and the basic shot noise performance, implying a signal-to-noise ratio of $N^{1/2}$ where N is the number of photons arriving at the detector in the system response time (see Chapter 3), is very rare. Even when

this signal-to-noise ratio is achieved, the stability of long-term measurements of intensity is considerably worse than this value. Intensity-modulated sensors typically respond to the position of a mask which varies the aperture and in turn the transmission through an extrinsic sensor or to the position of a movable mirror reflecting light back into a fiber. Such sensors generally have relatively poor stability, 0.1% being as good as can be realistically achieved. Variations in the intensity response of the detection system may manifest themselves simply as changes in scale factor rather than changes in absolute reading, although sometimes these two features may become confused.

Optical phase, which is detected interferometrically, is one of the most sensitive ways of measuring physical changes. Small fractions of a microradian can be detected with moderate care. Fiber optic sensors—usually intrinsic for phase modulation—are no exception to this, and optical-fiber-based magnetometers are the most sensitive means known (except for superconducting quantum interference devices (SQUIDS)) for monitoring magnetic fields. Similarly, the fiber optic gyroscope is an extremely sensitive means of measuring rotation. Optical phase in fibers is affected by temperature $(100 \, \text{rad} \, \text{m}^{-1} \, ^\circ\text{C}^{-1})$, pressure $(10 \, \text{rad} \, \text{m}^{-1} \, \text{bar}^{-1})$, strain $(10 \, \text{rad} \, \text{m}^{-1} \, (\text{micro-strain})^{-1})$ and rotation $(0.05 \, \text{rad} \, \text{m}^{-2} \, \text{rad}^{-1} \, \text{s}^{-1})$, where the values in parentheses are typical for wavelengths in the region of $1 \, \mu\text{m}$. It should be clearly appreciated that these phase measurements are usually indirect measurements of another parameter. Typically this is the differential time delay between two paths in an interferometer, so that the wavelength of the source and (sometimes) the refractive index of the medium through which the light is propagating will appear in the final phase-delay relationships. These parameters will in turn influence the scale factor of the sensor. Furthermore, many phase detection systems implicitly rely upon knowing the value of the optical intensity, and again variations in this or indeed of the response function of the detector can manifest themselves as spurious fluctuations in scale factor.

Polarization modulation is, in practice, very similar to interferometry. Light is launched along the two principal axes of a delay medium, which may be a fiber or a crystal, with equal intensities in each axis and is detected using a polarization analyzer which is usually located to receive equal intensities from each principal axis in the neutral state. The signal obtained through this analyzer will behave exactly as the signal through an interferometer, depending upon the differential phase between the two principal axes of the birefringent medium. In the case of all fiber devices where birefringent fibers may be used, the sensitivity to temperature or pressure, for example, is typically two orders of magnitude below that of a direct interferometer. When birefringent crystals are used as the sensing element, the response will depend upon the characteristics of the crystal. Very successful pressure transducers based upon the observation of birefringence in quartz have been produced, although these are only useful at very high input pressures. At the other extremes some types of epoxy resin can be made both to be birefringent and to have very sensitive birefringent properties. However, these substances are highly temperature sensitive and are susceptible to variations due to the absorption of moisture.

Color is a useful function to modulate since its detection can be unambiguous provided that detailed knowledge of the variations in intensity with wavelength at the detector is not required. For example, birefringent crystals can also be configured as filters and, provided that the crystal is well defined, the filter response can produce a notch which is sensitive to environmental variations and measurement of the position of the notches is all that is required. However, perhaps the most successful exploitation of color has been in the use of temperature-sensitive luminescence from optically excited rare earth phosphors, direct-bandgap semiconductors and similar materials. Here, however, some knowledge of the intensity variation with wavelength is required, and any measurement of this parameter assumes that the ratio of all the quantities in eqn (2.1) with the exception of M remains constant at all times and all wavelengths. This is approximately true for small changes at wavelengths which are closely spaced, but complex correction circuitry is sometimes required to compensate for changes in color-based transducers which use broadband light in the detection system.

Digital and quasi-digital modulation can be implemented using the following techniques.

Modulation frequency on a returned optical signal can be changed by causing the input light to interact with a mechanical oscillator which modulates the output light. The frequency of modulation in the output light is a direct measure of the frequency of the mechanical oscillator which in turn is related to the environmental parameter of interest.

On–off intensity modulation is used in limit switches, although usually with a slight transmission on the "off" position or sometimes a reference signal at another wavelength simply to serve as a check that the link is working whilst the switch is off. A wide variety of displacement-sensitive Gray-coded devices have been assembled and tested, some of which are very close to production. In these devices, multiple sources obtained either by differential delays or by color dispersion from a broadband source are used to illuminate a Gray-coded mask and the output observed through the mask is detected.

Doppler shifts are a means for the unambiguous determination of apparent speed as observed from the end of the fiber and sometimes, with more exotic processing, they can also be used to determine particle velocities. Doppler shifts are typically of the order of $1\,Hz\,\mu m^{-1}\,s^{-1}$. A number of commercial systems are available which either use modified laser Doppler velocimetry or, more simply, rely upon differential mixing between light reflected between the end of a probe fiber and light reflected from the sample volume. Such systems are typically used to measure flow.

Decay time or more generally pulse width modulation can also be used as a basis for measurement. Most of these methods rely upon decays in inorganic phosphors which are invariably temperature sensitive.

Hybrid systems represent a halfway house in which conventional transducers are interfaced to optically powered low consumption electronics. The output from the conventional transducer is digitally intensity modulated onto a light-emitting diode. As far as the external system is concerned this appears exactly like a fiber optic sensor. A number of commercial versions of such systems are already available.

2.2.2 The measurand interface

The modulator and the interface with the measurand are intimately connected and are totally interdependent. However, it is useful to categorize the types of measurands which can be interfaced with a fiber optic sensor and to outline the principal interaction mechanisms.

Mechanical parameters, e.g. pressure, temperature, flow, displacement etc., can be made to interact directly with light in the fiber causing direct modulation of the optical properties of the fiber itself for intrinsic sensors. However, more typically extrinsic modulators are used in which mechanical moving parts are caused to modulate the light transmitted along the fiber linking the modulator to the detector. Typical of these are reflections from moving diaphragms and the binary-coded modulators alluded to earlier. For these devices all the mechanical engineering problems associated with conventional transducers remain, and additionally it is necessary to ensure that the relative position of the illuminating and collection fibers and the mechanical assembly itself remain constant within the necessary tolerances determined by the system resolution.

Mechanical fields may also directly affect the optical properties of a material through which the light is propagating. Included in these are changes in delays as a result of photoelastic effects or simply stretching of the fiber and changes in optical fiber attenuation owing to variable microbend-induced loss. Other examples include changes in absorption with temperature based upon modifications to carefully chosen dopants within the fiber and, of course, differential delays between the two propagation directions in a single fiber loop in a fiber optic gyroscope. Temperature may also affect the optical properties of semiconductors owing to changes in bandgap and in free-carrier concentration. In addition mechanical fields can be caused to interact isotropically or anistropically with an optical delay path. The latter results in changes in birefringence, whilst the former simply affects straightforward delays. There are some related, although unusual, modulation mechanisms based upon the observation of phase transitions in specific materials such as liquid crystals.

Chemical quantities are typically measured using various forms of optical spectroscopy. The light used to illuminate the sample can be caused to interact with the sample either in a cell (i.e. an extrinsic device) or by coupling to the evanescent field in a waveguide. In both cases the normal spectroscopic techniques apply and the system will monitor changes in absorption lines, Raman shifts or fluorescence. Nonlinear spectroscopy has been postulated, although the power levels required are often so high that the concept becomes impracticable. Chemical properties of materials can sometimes be recognized via changes in refractive index, although index-sensitive devices will usually also be sensitive to temperature since the refractive index of all materials varies very quickly with temperature. The usual precautions requiring that reference channels are close to the appropriate observation wavelengths also apply here.

Biochemical parameters are generally detected in a similar way to chemical parameters. However, optical Doppler shifts have been used with fiber optic links to observe intravenous blood flow and sperm mobility.

This briefly covers most of the primary interactions between a measurand and an optical signal propagating or linked into an optical fiber. More detailed features are also often important, and in particular many of the interactions are wavelength sensitive. This can be exploited for monitoring two or more physical parameters simultaneously. For example, the relationships governing variations in optical delay with temperature through a fiber are different from those governing the variations in optical delay with mechanical strain along the fiber as a function of wavelength. Consequently a two-wavelength measurement can be utilized to measure both quantities at once in the same fiber. Again, this concept along with all the others mentioned will be discussed in more detail later in the book.

2.2.3 The optical fiber link

Typically, optical fibers are associated with long-haul telecommunication systems. The most popular fibers for this application at present are single-mode types designed for operation at wavelengths of 1.3 and/or 1.55 μm. These fibers are available very cheaply with a very high quality.

However, the range of fibers which can and indeed should be used in sensors is much wider. The greatest disadvantage with the 1.3 μm single-mode fiber is that optical sources which are compatible with it are very expensive and are outside the visible region of the spectrum. They also need fairly sophisticated detection equipment. For optical sensors it is often preferable to use optical sources (see below) in the visible or near-infrared where silicon detectors can be conveniently exploited and where either viewing equipment is unnecessary or viewing can be effected using an ordinary television camera whose red sensitivity extends beyond that of a human eye or a simple inexpensive infrared viewer. These sources are also considerably less expensive than the high performance equivalents in the 1.3 and 1.55 μm bands.

A wide and increasing variety of fibers can be used with these sources.

These include conventional silica-based single-mode and multimode fibers, the latter offering the additional convenience of a relatively large core size which substantially exceeds the few microns typical of single-mode fibers. Plastic fibers, which typically have diameters of the order of 1 mm, are also being used extensively in sensors. These are adequate for short-distance transmission (typically less than 20 m) and are particularly compatible with use in the visible region of the spectrum. They are very simple to handle mechanically since their ends can be prepared using a sharp blade and their connectors are often physically quite large.

Fibers can all be characterized by their loss as a function of wavelength (attenuation spectrum), their numerical aperture (the sine of the maximum acceptance angle at the input for the fiber) and the core diameter (i.e. the diameter of that section of the fiber in which the light is guided), their mechanical properties including the external diameter (typically 100 μm or more regardless of the core diameter), the coatings and the manner in which the fiber is finally cabled. The coating applied to the exterior surface of the fiber as it is drawn is extremely important in sensors. Its principal function in communication fibers is to prevent the ingress of moisture causing mechanical deterioration of the silica fiber characteristics. The coatings used in telecommunication fibers are typically polyurethanes and polysilicates. These coatings are only suitable for operation over a restricted (typically to 100 °C) temperature range, and extended temperature ranges are often desirable in sensors. For this reason a range of special coatings based upon metals (for instance, aluminum or gold) or higher temperature polymers (typically polyimides) have appeared.

The environmental influence of the fiber on the performance of the link between the sensor and the source and detector can be significant. In particular variations in loss and in the attenuation spectrum with the mechanical condition of the fiber are known to occur. Such variations can be introduced by, for example, changes in the temperature of the fiber which may result in changes in the longitudinal tension within the cabling structure. Additionally, if coherent light is used in a multimode fiber, the partial detection (which always occurs) of the light emerging from the far end of the fiber produces an environmentally sensitive total received signal as a result of changes in the speckle pattern observed at the end of the fiber as its pressure or temperature is varied. Under some circumstances the fiber can also fluoresce, and this is particularly true of plastic fibers. In silica fibers power densities are typically limited by stimulated Raman and stimulated Brillouin scattering; the latter, usually occurring at lower continuous wave (CW) power densities, has been observed for inputs of less than 100 mW in single-mode fibers.

In addition to fibers with special mechanical and thermal properties, there are a wide range of fibers with special optical properties which have been used with varying degrees of success in sensors. Perhaps the most important of these is the birefringent fiber which will be described in more detail later in the book. An emerging range of similar fibers with highly specific polarization properties or with special electro- or magneto-optic properties offer substantial promise for future systems.

Thus the fiber link has a much more important role to play in sensors than in telecommunications since its environmental characteristics are much more critical to sensor performance. This has resulted in a range of special sensor fibers, but since these are quite expensive owing to low production volumes it has also resulted in the judicious application of optical ingenuity in the use of standard fibers.

2.2.4 Fiber optic components and other micro-optics

A range of components is also necessary for use in sensors both to interface the fiber with the sensor itself and to perform spatial and temporal modulation functions.

Micro-optic devices are particularly useful for extrinsic sensors to form the means whereby the light in the fiber can be coupled to the modulating element. The most versatile of these is the graded index (GRIN) lens which can be obtained in half- or quarter-wave sections (or other sections to order) to perform collimation and one-to-one imaging functions respectively. These devices are also available with mounts for connection to optical fibers and form an extremely rugged well-engineered unit.

For extrinsic sensors or for occasions where fibers must be combined or divided, fiber optic couplers will permit such splitting operations entirely in the fiber optic domain. These can be designed with a wide range of splitting ratios between the two output arms and also to have tailored spectral characteristics enabling wavelength (de)multiplexing whereby two input wavelengths in the same fiber are caused to emerge from different fibers.

Optical modulation in fibers is also extremely important. To date, direct modulation has been very limited since the application of resonant piezoelectric stretching devices which induce phase modulation has been the only widely used technique. However, more recently liquid crystal evanescently coupled overlays have shown promise for a modulator which does not use acoustic components. Additionally, fiber optic overlay components in which the light in the fiber is caused to couple through the evanescent field to an external medium are essential features in many chemical and biochemical sensors.

Integrated optics also has an important part to play in the component catalog. It is currently the only established technology whereby broadband modulation can be imposed upon guided light and it is also the most competitive technique whereby a 1–16 or a 1–32 splitter, for example, can be fabricated in guided-wave form for either multimode or single-mode operation.

Both fiber and integrated optic devices are covered in more detail later in the book. The relative merits of the two technologies are usually simple to assess. Integrated optic devices require an interface to the fiber and the stability of this interface is often in question unless it is implemented using very expensive techniques. However, integrated optics is currently more flexible in the range of functions which can be performed. The situation is still changing, albeit slowly, but it is very likely that both technologies will have their part to play.

2.2.5 Optical sources for sensors

An optical source can be specified in terms of the following basic parameters: its central operating wavelength; the spread in this wavelength; the variation in optical power with wavelength; the variation in optical power with optical loading (reflections); the way in which these parameters vary with operating temperature, electrical bias conditions and time.

In addition, an optical source has important geometrical characteristics which include the following: a numerical aperture which is the sine of the half-angle of the radiation emitted by the source, also sometimes expressed in terms of a straightforward radiated angle; the luminance expressed in watts per square centimeter per steradian which is a measure of the intensity of the radiation which the source can generate (the luminance is a quantity which is preserved through a perfect lens, i.e. if the source is focused to a small spot the light radiating from that spot will do so over a wider solid angle such that the luminance remains constant or, owing to lens system aberrations, continues to decrease).

Optical sources also require some form of modulation, for example synchronous detection to assist in the signal processing in many optical fiber sensors. This can be effected in one of two ways: either internally within the source itself, typically by varying the electrical bias conditions, or in an external modulating element such as an integrated optical waveguide or a simple mechanical chopper. These modulation characteristics and the way in which the modulation process affects the basic parameters of the device mentioned are extremely important. For internal modulation, the modulation process invariably affects the wavelength, the output optical power and the wavelength distribution. In some cases it will also affect the numerical aperture of the radiation, and this can cause very curious secondary modulation phenomena in optical systems which are focused through some form of optical stop (which may in fact be an optical fiber—especially a single-mode fiber). These last phenomena are particularly prone to occur in semiconductor laser sources, although they can be eliminated with careful design of the laser and the modulation system.

Types of optical sources include surface- and edge-emitting light-emitting diodes, semiconductor lasers, gas lasers and solid state externally pumped lasers. All these have been used for sensor systems. Hot filament lamps have also proved to be useful, particularly for some chemical and/or chemically active sensor systems. An extremely wide range of sources are available, and indeed many different sources have been used in sensors.

2.2.6 Optical signal detection

Most, if not all, optical fiber sensors use some form of quantum optical detector, i.e. individual photons are converted into electronic carriers (electron–hole pairs in semiconductors or electrons in photomultipliers) which are detected as electric current. However, a very important class of photo-detectors is based upon observation of the thermal effects of radiation, and indeed there may be occasions when such devices may be useful especially for operation in the near- and mid-infrared. The major distinction between quantum-based and thermal detectors is that the former respond to the arrival of photons. Since the number of photons per unit of time depends upon both the optical incident power and the wavelength, these are intrinsically very sensitive to wavelength. Thermal detectors, however, can be made to be very insensitive to illuminating wavelength and to respond directly to optical power.

The chapter on detection concentrates on semiconductor devices, particularly PIN and avalanche photodiode (APD) detectors. For some applications, arrays of photodetectors are very important, and the charge-coupled device (CCD) is a particularly useful form of detector array since its output can be clocked using standard digital electronics. PIN arrays are also available. Perhaps the most important aspect of any photodetection system is its noise performance, and the major contributor to this is the input amplification stage. Details of design approaches to this particular problem are found later in the book.

2.2.7 Signal processing

The signal processing unit in the detection system is principally there to attempt to correct for any spurious elements detracting from Q in eqn (2.1). Its other principal function is to provide an interface to the remaining control electronics in the system which the sensor is monitoring.

Signal processing is most difficult for analog sensors and many attempts have been made to compensate for variations in the optical leads, i.e. changes in FT and FR in eqn (2.1), with the environmental condition of the sensor network. These processing systems all require information which somehow determines the state of the fiber transmission link through some form of reference which can be separated from the signal required in wavelength, time or space (i.e. in the routing systems). The success of these approaches has been relatively modest although much depends upon the distances over which the compensation process needs to be effected reliably. For distances exceeding a few tens of meters 1% compensation is probably all that is feasible. For shorter distances 0.1% may be approached.

The problem is obviously considerably simpler for "digital" or "quasi-digital" inputs, and the only one of the latter which is really difficult to measure is the decay time/pulse width modulation system since in both cases the time that an analog signal crosses a particular level must be determined. For modulation frequency systems the problem is a straightforward application of counting techniques.

Of course, the signal processing system can also be used to enhance sensitivity and selectivity, and the most important technique is the lock-in amplifier which by using some source modulation—often a chopper—enables very small alternating signals to be extracted from a very noisy background. The second important signal processing element is the boxcar integrator which permits the averaging of repeated pulsed signals in response to a predetermined time gate (often also used as an equivalent range gate). Such detection networks are very frequently used in optical fiber sensors.

There are very many more advanced signal processing concepts which are often applied. These may exploit the particular characteristics of frequency- or phase-modulated signals or may require multiplexing of different sensor signals in the frequency domain. There is no separate chapter on signal processing but its importance permeates the whole book.

2.3 System properties of optical fiber sensors

A particular feature of optical fiber sensors is that, in view of the very large information-carrying capacity of a typical optical fiber communications link, there is scope for incorporating very many sensors on a single optical fiber or, alternatively, using a single optical fiber as an extended distributed sensor and interrogating this sensor at different points along its length.

Such systems are very attractive and indeed are thought by many to be essential to the long-term exploitation of optical fiber sensors, particularly in aerospace and industrial applications. The reason centers upon the considerable simplification of the interconnection harness between a central control point and the sensor network and a sharing of the interrogation electronics between the various elements of the network. There is also an implied compatibility between sensors in such networks (especially for multiplexed point sensors) and similarly an implicit homogeneous approach to sensor design in networks.

There is again an incredible diversity of approaches to the design of fiber optic sensor networks and these will be discussed in substantial detail later in the book. Essentially, the sensor elements along the network are resolvable only in time (i.e. they are at different distances from the receiver and/or transmitter) or in frequency (i.e. they are addressed by different wavelengths from the transmitter spectrum and received at different wavelengths at the receiver). The latter approach is relatively straightforward since it implies that wavelength-selective components are simply used to join each sensor to the network. Incidentally, there is a limited readily available range of such components which tends to restrict their use. The former approach, i.e. time resolution, has much in common with radar systems, and several signal processing techniques used in radar have been adopted for use in optical fiber networks. The real difficulty—and this is very similar to radar—is to maintain the average power of the optical source, which in turn determines the eventual sensitivity of the system, whilst also maintaining and controlling the source bandwidth which determines the spatial resolution of the system. The simplest approach to the latter is to use very short optical pulses. These have very high bandwidths and will have a spatial resolution determined by the pulse rise time. However, the average optical power decreases rapidly since the duty cycle must be such that the total length of the network only has one pulse in it at any particular time. Many methods whereby these two conflicting requirements can be reconciled have been examined, of which frequency-modulated continuous wave (FMCW) and pseudorandom (m-sequence) codes appear the most promising.

Networking is one of the remaining major research areas in optical fiber sensors, and even though a wide variety of trial networks have been assembled and tested none as yet has begun to approach wide acceptance. Additionally the special features of the fiber optic network have not yet all been exploited; in particular its capacity to perform spatial and temporal processing in the optical domain has remained unused. This whole area is one which promises to spawn very interesting and important developments in the short and medium term.

2.4 Concluding comments

Optical fiber sensors have been in use for over 20 years. Since the first patents were taken out in the middle 1960s very little by way of product has actually emerged. This is probably a reflection of the fact that the initial devices using fiber sensors (particularly the Fotonic probe) have been designed for very specific applications. However, the situation is currently changing very rapidly and an ever-increasing range of fiber optic sensors is appearing on the market.

The peak research activity has taken place in the past 10 years and in this time much of the science and technology has been defined and characterized. Indeed the basic conceptual building blocks of optical fiber sensors are now well known so that the publication of this book at this time is particularly apt. The following chapters contain a succession of definitive statements of the science and technology by internationally recognized experts which should give this volume an authority as a future reference work.

Of course, now that the techniques are defined, the really basic questions have to be addressed and the most important of these is probably the eventual overall market acceptability of fiber optic sensors. This must follow the usual line, starting from new and hitherto inaccessible applications and branching out into a competing technology for the more conventional world. At present the principal areas of application appear to be in medical systems, aerospace and hydrospace and the electrical power supply industry, with some potential in specialist areas of the petrochemical and oil and gas industries.

The succeeding chapters address these questions in detail and describe the overall technology. The technical picture of fiber optic sensors is now very comprehensive. The same can also, of course, be said for optical fiber communication systems. However, there remains considerable scope for applications engineering and for the evolution of novel techniques to implement solutions to practical problems. The next decade will see far greater change in the use of fiber optic sensors than is likely in any other transducer technology. The remainder of this book paints a detailed picture of the beginning of this exciting era.

Bibliography

Conference Proceedings

International Conferences on Optical Fiber Sensors: London, 1983; Stuttgart, 1984; San Diego, 1985; Tokyo, 1986; New Orleans, 1988; Paris, 1989. *Proceedings* are all published by the professional electrical engineering body in the host country.
SPIE Proceedings. The SPIE, Bellingham, WA 98227-0010, has produced many conference proceedings on fiber optic sensors and related subjects.

Textbooks

Chester, A. N., Martellucci, S. and Scheggi, A. M. (eds) (1987). *Optical Fibre Sensors, Proc. NATO Summer School, 1986*, Nijhoff, Dordrecht.
Culshaw, B. (1984). *Optical Fibre Sensors and Signal Processing*, Peter Peregrinus, Stevenage.
Derniak, E. L. and Crowe, D. G. (1984). *Optical Radiation Detectors*, Wiley, New York.
Goodman, J. W. (1985). *Statistical Optics*, Wiley, New York.
Haus, H. (1984). *Waves and Fields in Optoelectronics*, Prentice-Hall, Englewood Cliffs, NJ.
Hecht, E. and Zajac, A. (1979). *Optics*, Addison-Wesley, Reading, MA.
Jones, B. K. (1986). *Electronics for Experimentation and Research*, Prentice-Hall, Englewood Cliffs, NJ.
Lee, D. L. (1986). *Electromagnetic Principles of Integrated Optics*, Wiley, New York.
Nye, R. F. (1986). *Physical Properties of Crystals* (reprint), Clarendon Press, Oxford.

Siegman, A. E. (1986). *Lasers*, University Science Books, Mill Valley, CA.
Skolnik, M. (1980). *Introduction to Radar Systems*, McGraw-Hill, New York.
Yariv, A. (1985). *Optical Electronics*, Holt, Rinehart and Winston, New York.
Yariv, A. and Yeh, P. (1984). *Optical Waves in Crystals*, Wiley, New York.

Handbooks

Electronic Materials Information Service (IEEE/Peter Peregrinus Ltd, Stevenage),
  Handbooks on the Properties of Silicon and Gallium Arsenide.
Lynch C. T. (ed.) (1974). *Handbook of Materials Science*, CRC Press, Boca Raton, FL.
Pallik, E. (ed.) (1985). *Handbook of Optical Constants of Solids*, Academic Press, New
  York.
Weast, R. C. and Astle, M. J. (eds). *Handbook of Chemistry and Physics*, CRC Press,
  Boca Raton, FL.
Kaye, G. W. C. and Laby, T. H. (1978). *Tables of Physical and Chemical Constants*,
  Longmans, London.

Chapter 3

Essential Optics

A. J. ROGERS

3.1 The nature of light

3.1.1 Historical sketch

Light has always occupied a central position in physics. The development of the understanding of the nature of light closely parallels the development of physics itself. The names associated with major advances in the understanding of light resound down the ages like a physics "roll of honor": Galileo, Newton, Huygens, Fresnel, Maxwell, Planck, Einstein—all were giants of their times. Galileo (1564–1642) heads this list because he was the first experimentalist of any real stature; before him experimentation was considered to be a rather messy inferior activity, unworthy of the highest intellects. Newton was born in the year that Galileo died, and between them they laid the basis for the great strides in understanding that were to be made over the following three centuries.

Newton believed that light was corpuscular in nature. He was not at all clear about the nature of the corpuscles themselves, but he was impressed by the fact that light appeared to travel in straight lines, a property possessed by projectiles. Although Newton recognized the difficulties that existed in reconciling some experimental data with this view, it was not until after his death (in 1727) that the views held by men such as Young, Fresnel and Fraunhöfer began to dominate. These men believed that light was a wave motion, and they adduced a wide range of evidence in support of this view.

The final blow in favor of the wave theory is usually considered to have been struck by Foucault (1819–1868) who performed an experiment to show that light traveled more slowly in water than in air. This result agreed with the wave theory and contradicted the corpuscular theory. The corpuscular theory was then effectively abandoned until 1900, when Planck (1858–1947) found it necessary to invoke the idea of "discrete packets of energy" or "quanta" in order to explain the way in which the light intensity emitted by a blackbody was known, from experiment, to vary with wavelength. Einstein (1879–1955) used this idea to explain the photoelectric effect, where light acts to emit electrons from matter. The explanation he offered was beautifully convincing.

Thus physics arrived (c 1920) at the position where light sometimes behaved like waves and sometimes like particles. We have since learned to understand that it consists neither of particles nor waves but is a phenomenon which cannot be modeled on the simple human level of understanding. (If the evolutionary survival processes had required an understanding of the subatomic world, then our abilities undoubtedly would be very different!)

However, by becoming aware of those (usually separate) situations where light will behave like waves and those where it will behave like particles, we have learned at least to *describe* the behavior of light to the extent of being able to control and use it for many practical purposes. It is this description, and the practical purposes of optical fiber sensors, to which this chapter is directed. The emphasis will be on the basic physical ideas. Most of the topics covered will be expounded in more formal detail in later chapters.

3.1.2 Electromagnetic waves

In 1864 Clerk Maxwell showed conclusively that light waves were electromagnetic in nature. He did this by expressing the laws of electromagnetism known then in such a way as to allow him to derive from them a wave equation (see Appendix). This wave equation permitted free-space solutions which corresponded to electromagnetic waves with a velocity equal to the known experimental value of the velocity of light. The consequent recognition of light as an electromagnetic phenomenon was probably the single most important advance in the progression of its understanding.

All the important features of light waves follow from a detailed examination of Maxwell's equations (see Appendix). If we take Cartesian axes Ox, Oy, Oz (Fig. 3.1), a typical sinusoidal solution is given by

$$E_x = E_0 \exp\{i(\omega t - kz)\}$$
$$H_y = H_0 \exp\{i(\omega t - kz)\} \tag{3.1}$$

which states that the electric field oscillates sinusoidally in the xz plane, the magnetic field oscillates in the yz plane (i.e. orthogonally to the electric field) and in phase with the electric field, and the wave propagates in the Oz direction (Fig. 3.1). The frequency and wavelength of the wave are given by

$$f = \omega/2\pi$$
$$\lambda = 2\pi/k$$

and $f\lambda = \omega/k = c$ where c is the wave velocity. The latter is related to the electromagnetic properties of the medium in which the wave propagates via the relation

$$c = (\varepsilon\mu)^{-1/2} \tag{3.2}$$

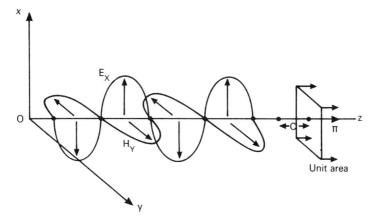

Fig. 3.1 Sinusoidal electromagnetic wave.

where ε is the electric permittivity of the medium and μ is its magnetic permeability. Relation (3.2) can also be written in the form

$$c = (\varepsilon_R \varepsilon_0 \mu_R \mu_0)^{-1/2}$$

where ε_R and μ_R are the permittivity and permeability factors of the medium relative to those for free space, ε_0 and μ_0. The electric displacement $\boldsymbol{D}$ and the magnetic flux density $\boldsymbol{B}$ are defined by the relations

$$\boldsymbol{D} = \varepsilon \boldsymbol{E}$$
$$\boldsymbol{B} = \mu \boldsymbol{H}$$

We can therefore also write

$$c = c_0/(\varepsilon_R \mu_R)^{1/2} \tag{3.3}$$

where c_0 is the velocity of the electromagnetic wave in free space and has the experimentally determined value $2.997925 \times 10^8 \, \text{m s}^{-1}$.

For most optical media of any importance we have $\mu_R \approx 1$ and $\varepsilon_R > 1$. These materials belong to the class known as dielectrics and are electrical insulators. Thus we can write (3.3) in the form

$$c \approx c_0/\varepsilon_R^{1/2}$$

and note that $c < c_0$. The ratio c_0/c is, by definition, the refractive index n of the medium, and we have

$$n \approx \varepsilon_R^{1/2} \tag{3.4}$$

Now ε_R is a measure of the ease with which the medium can be polarized electrically by the action of an external electric field. This polarization depends on the mobility of the electrons within the molecule in the face of resistance by molecular forces. Clearly then, ε_R will depend on the frequency of the applied electric field since it will depend on how quickly these forces respond. Thus eqn (3.4) will be true only if n and ε_R refer to the same wave frequency, and we also note that n is frequency dependent.

Let us now consider the energy content of the wave. For an electric field the energy per unit volume u_E is given by (Bleaney and Bleaney, 1959)

$$u_E = \tfrac{1}{2}\varepsilon E^2$$

and for a magnetic field

$$u_H = \tfrac{1}{2}\mu H^2$$

Maxwell's equations relate E and H for an electromagnetic wave according to (see Appendix)

$$H = (\varepsilon/\mu)^{1/2} E$$

Hence the total energy density in the wave is given by

$$u = u_E + u_H = \varepsilon E^2 = \mu H^2 \tag{3.5}$$

Consider now the plane wave propagating in the direction Oz (Fig. 3.1). The total energy flowing across unit area in unit time in the direction Oz will be that contained within a volume $c\,\mathrm{m}^3$, where c is the wave velocity. Hence the power flow across unit area is given by

$$I = \frac{\text{power}}{\text{area}} = c\varepsilon E^2 \tag{3.6}$$

This quantity is called the *intensity* of the wave and is proportional to the square of the electric field. Clearly, via (3.5), it will also be proportional to the square of the magnetic field.

More generally, the intensity is expressed in terms of the Poynting vector $\boldsymbol{\Pi}$ (see Appendix):

$$\boldsymbol{\Pi} = \boldsymbol{E} \times \boldsymbol{H}$$

where $\boldsymbol{E}$ and $\boldsymbol{H}$ are now vector quantities and $\boldsymbol{E} \times \boldsymbol{H}$ is their vector product. The intensity of the wave will be the value of $\boldsymbol{\Pi}$ averaged over one period of the wave. If E and H are spatially orthogonal and in phase, as in the case of a wave propagating in an isotropic dielectric medium,

$$I = \langle \boldsymbol{\Pi} \rangle = c\varepsilon E^2$$

as before ($\langle \boldsymbol{\Pi} \rangle$ denotes the average value of $\boldsymbol{\Pi}$).

If E and H were in phase quadrature we would have

$$I = \langle \boldsymbol{\Pi} \rangle = \langle E_0 \cos(\omega t)\, H_0 \sin(\omega t) \rangle = 0$$

3.1.3 Polarization

The "typical" sinusoidal solution of Maxwell's wave equation given by eqns (3.1) is, of course, only one of an infinite number of such sinusoidal solutions. The general solution for a sinusoid of angular frequency ω is given by

$$E(r, t) = E(r) \exp(i\omega t)$$

where $E(r, t) = E(r)$ are, in general, complex vectors and r is a real radius vector.

If, for simplicity, we consider only plane monochromatic (single frequency) waves propagating in free space in the direction Oz, we can write the general solution to the wave equation for the electric field in the form

$$E_x = e_x \cos(\omega t - kz + \delta_x)$$
$$E_y = e_y \cos(\omega t - kz + \delta_y)$$

where δ_x and δ_y are arbitrary phase angles. Thus we are able to describe this solution completely by means of two waves: one in which the electric field lies entirely in the xz plane, and the other in which it lies entirely in the yz plane (Fig. 3.2). If these waves are observed at a particular value of z, say z_0, they take the oscillatory form

$$E_x = e_x \cos(\omega t + \delta_x') \qquad \delta_x' = \delta_x - kz_0$$
$$E_y = e_y \cos(\omega t + \delta_y') \qquad \delta_y' = \delta_y - kz_0$$

and the tip of each vector appears to oscillate sinusoidally with time along a line. E_x is said to be linearly polarized in the direction Ox, and E_y is said to be linearly polarized in the direction Oy.

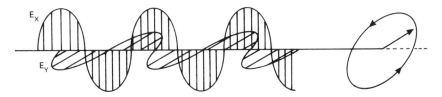

Fig. 3.2 Polarization components of the E wave.

The tip of the vector which is the sum of E_x and E_y will in general describe an ellipse whose Cartesian equation in the xy plane at the chosen z_0 will be given by

$$\frac{E_x^2}{e_x^2} + \frac{E_y^2}{e_y^2} + 2\frac{E_x E_y}{e_x e_y} \cos \delta = \sin^2 \delta$$

where

$$\delta = \delta_y' - \delta_x'$$

This ellipse will degenerate into a straight line (and the overall polarization state of the light will thus be linear) if

$$E_x \neq 0 \qquad\qquad E_y = 0$$

or

$$E_x = 0 \qquad\qquad E_y \neq 0$$

or

$$\delta = m\pi$$

where m is a positive or negative integer (this corresponds to the condition that E_x and E_y are either in phase or in antiphase).

The ellipse becomes a circle (and the light is thus circularly polarized) if

$$e_x = e_y$$

and

$$\delta = (2m+1)\frac{\pi}{2}$$

i.e. the waves are equal in amplitude and are in phase quadrature.

The polarization properties of light waves are particularly important for propagation within anisotropic media in which the physical properties are dependent on direction. In this case the propagation characteristics for the component E_x will in general differ from those for E_y, so that the values of e_1, e_2 and δ will vary along the propagation path. The polarization state of the light will now become dependent upon propagation distance and on the state of the medium. This topic will be dealt with in more detail in Section 3.6.

3.1.4 The electromagnetic spectrum

Up to now the discussion has been largely in terms of parameters whose physical values have not been specified. It will help to fix ideas if some numbers are quoted.

The electromagnetic spectrum is shown schematically in Fig. 3.3. It ranges from very low frequency radio waves (about 10^3 Hz) to very high frequency gamma radiation (about 10^{20} Hz). In principle, the range is from (almost) zero frequency to infinite frequency. However, since light sources must be comparable in size with the wavelength of the radiation, it is difficult to produce radiation below 1 kHz or so ($\lambda \approx 300$ km). On the other hand, the very high frequencies require very high energy phenomena for their production, and the most violent processes in the universe only allow up to about 10^{20} Hz. Visible radiation lies in the wavelength range 0.4–0.7 μm, corresponding to a frequency range of 7.5×10^{14}–4.3×10^{14} Hz. The infrared region lies just beyond 0.7 μm and is usually taken to extend to about 300 μm. The ultraviolet region lies below 0.4 μm and begins at about 0.003 μm. Clearly, these are arbitrary divisions. (Wavelengths will often be quoted in nanometers, and the visible range is then 400–700 nm.) The refractive index of silica in the visible range is about 1.47, so that the velocity of light at these wavelengths in this medium is close to 2×10^8 m s^{-1}. Correspondingly, at given optical

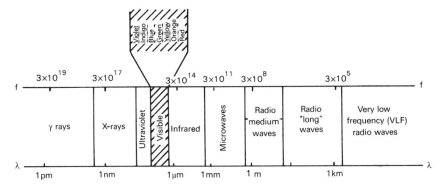

Fig. 3.3   The electromagnetic spectrum.

frequencies, wavelengths in the medium will be about 30% less than those in air in accordance with the relation $\lambda = c/f$.

3.2 Emission and absorption of light

3.2.1 The elementary processes

In considering the processes by which light is emitted and absorbed by atoms we must quickly come to terms with the corpuscular or, to use the more modern term, the "particulate" nature of light.

In classical (i.e. pre-quantum theory) physics the atom was held to possess natural resonant frequencies. These corresponded to the electromagnetic wave frequencies which the atom was able to emit when excited into oscillation. Conversely, when light radiation at any of these frequencies fell upon the atom, the atom was able to absorb energy from the radiation in the way of all classical resonant system–driving force interactions.

However, these ideas are incapable of explaining why, in a gas discharge, some frequencies which are emitted by the gas are not also absorbed by it under quiescent conditions; neither can it explain why, in the photoelectric effect (where electrons are ejected from atoms by the interaction with light radiation), the energy with which the electrons are ejected depends not on the intensity of the light but only on its frequency.

We know now that the explanation of these facts is that atoms and molecules can exist only in discrete energy levels. These energy levels can be listed in order of ascending value: E_0, E_1, E_2, ..., E_n. Under conditions of thermal equilibrium the number of atoms having energy E_i is related to the number having energy E_j by the Boltzmann relation

$$\frac{E_i}{E_j} = \exp\left(-\frac{E_i - E_j}{kT}\right) \tag{3.7}$$

where k is Boltzmann's constant and T is the absolute temperature. Light can only be absorbed by the atomic system when its frequency v corresponds to at least one of the values v_{ji} where

$$hv_{ji} = E_j - E_i \qquad j > i \qquad (3.8)$$

(The symbol v rather than $\omega/2\pi$ is used now for the frequency to emphasize that the light is exhibiting its particulate character.) Here, h is Planck's quantum constant, which has a value of 6.625×10^{-34} J s.

In this case the interpretation is that one quantum of light, or *photon*, with energy hv_{ji} has been absorbed by the atom, which in consequence has increased in energy from one of its allowed states E_i to another E_j. Correspondingly, a photon will be emitted when a downward transition occurs from E_j to E_i, and this photon will have the same frequency v_{ji}.

In this context we must think of the light radiation as a stream of photons. If there is a flux of q photons across unit area per unit time then we can write

$$I = qhv$$

where I is the light intensity defined in eqn (3.6). Similarly, any other quantity defined within the wave context also has its counterpart in the particulate context.

In attempting to reconcile the two views the electromagnetic wave should be regarded as a probability function whose intensity at any point in space defines the probability of finding a photon there. However, only in the specialized study of quantum optics are such concepts of real practical significance. For almost all other purposes (including the present one) either the wave or the particle representation is appropriate in any given practical situation without any mutual contradiction.

Each atom or molecule has a characteristic set of energy levels, so that the light frequencies emitted or absorbed by atoms and molecules are themselves characteristic of the material concerned. When an excited system returns to its lowest state, some return pathways are more probable than others, and these probabilities are also characteristic of the particular atoms or molecules in question. (They can be calculated from quantum principles.) Consequently, the emission and/or the absorption spectrum of a material can be used to identify it and to determine the quantity present. These ideas form the substance of the subject known as spectroscopy, which is a very extensive and powerful tool in materials analysis.

3.2.2 Elements of laser action

The laser is a very special source of light. Modern optics, of which the subject of optical fiber sensors forms a part, effectively dates from the invention of the laser in 1960 (Maiman, 1960). The word "laser" is an acronym for "light amplification by stimulated emission of radiation", and we will now proceed to determine the processes on which it depends.

It was noted in the previous section that a photon could cause an atomic system to change from one of its allowed states to another provided that eqn (3.8) was obeyed. This equation related to the action of the photon in raising the system from a lower to a higher energy state. However, if the system were already in the higher of the two states when the photon acted, then it is also true that its action would be to cause the transition down to the lower state, still in accordance with eqn (3.8) (but now with $j < i$). This process is called "stimulated emission" since the effect is to cause the system to emit a photon with energy $h\nu_{ij}$ corresponding to that lost by the system; thus we now have two photons—the "acting" photon and the emitted photon. This process is crucial to laser action. (A rough classical analogy is that where an a.c. driving force is "anti-resonant" with a naturally oscillating system, i.e. in negative phase quadrature. In this case the driving force will receive energy from the system.) We must also be aware of the fact that a system which is not in its lowest energy state is not in stable equilibrium. If it has any interaction with the outside world it will eventually fall to its lowest state. Thus an atomic system in a state E_i will fall spontaneously to the lower state E_j, even without the stimulus of $h\nu_{ij}$, in a time which depends on the exact nature of the equilibrium conditions; these can be broadly classed as unstable or metastable (a long-lived nonstable state). The photon which results from this type of transition is thus said to be due to spontaneous emission.

Let us now consider a two-level atomic system with energy levels E_0 and E_1 (Fig. 3.4(a)). Suppose that we illuminate this system with electromagnetic radiation of frequency $\nu_{10} = (E_1 - E_0)/h$. Initially, if the system is in thermal equilibrium at temperature T, the relative numbers of atoms in the two levels will be, according to (3.7),

$$\frac{N_1}{N_0} = \exp\left(-\frac{E_1 - E_0}{kT}\right) \tag{3.9}$$

so that if $E_1 > E_0$, $N_1 < N_0$. Suppose now that the intensity of the radiation at frequency ν_{10} is steadily increased from zero. At low levels, if it is assumed that the probability of transition is the same for the two transition directions, more atoms will be raised from the lower to the higher state than vice versa since, according to (3.9), there are more atoms in the lower state. As the intensity is increased the number of downward transitions (stimulated and spontaneous) will increase as the occupancy of the upper state rises, tending towards the saturation condition where the (dynamic) occupancies of the two states and the rates of transition in the two directions are equal.

Consider now the three-level system shown in Fig. 3.4(b). Here we have a lowest level E_0, a metastable level E_1 and an unstable level E_2. If this system (initially in thermal equilibrium) is irradiated with light of frequency $\nu_{20} = (E_2 - E_0)/h$, the effect is to raise a large number of atoms from E_0 to E_2. These then decay quickly to the state E_1 by spontaneous emission only (since the input light frequency does not correspond to this transition), and subsequently only

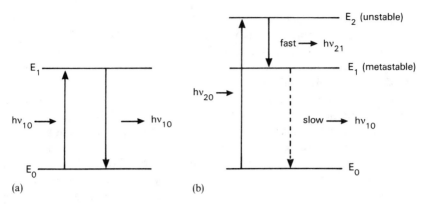

Fig. 3.4   Energy level diagram for laser action.

slowly from this metastable (i.e. long-lived) state back to the ground state. The consequence of this is that, under these circumstances, there can be a larger number of atoms in state E_1 than in state E_0. Since this does not correspond to a Boltzmann distribution (which requires fewer atoms in a state of increased energy), it is known as an "inverted" population (Yariv, 1976). Suppose that a second beam of light is incident on this inverted population at frequency $\nu_{10} = (E_1 - E_0)/h$. This light encounters a situation where it can more frequently produce downward transitions by stimulated emission from E_1 to E_0 than it can excite atoms from E_0 to E_1. Thus more stimulated photons are produced than are absorbed by excitation, and this beam receives "gain" from the medium, i.e. it is amplified. The medium is said to be "pumped" by the first beam to provide gain for the second. We have "light amplification by stimulated emission of radiation". If, now, the medium is enclosed in a tube with parallel mirrors at the ends (Fig. 3.5), the stimulated photons can be made to bounce back and forth between the mirrors and themselves act to stimulate

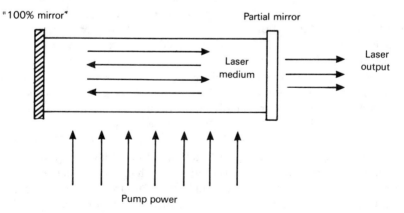

Fig. 3.5   Schematic diagram of laser action.

even more photons. We have provided the "amplifier" with positive feedback and have produced an "oscillator". If one of the two mirrors is only partially reflecting, some of the oscillator energy can emerge from the tube. This energy will be in the form of a light wave of frequency $v_{10} = (E_1 - E_0)/h$, which is accurately defined if the energy levels are sharp, is of relatively large intensity if the volume of the tube is large, the pump power is large and the cross-sectional area of the tube is small, is well collimated since the light will only receive amplification within the tube if it is able to bounce between the two parallel mirrors, and has an accurately defined phase since the phase of the stimulated photon is locked to that of the photon which stimulates it. Thus we have monochromatic (narrow frequency range), coherent (well-defined phase) and well-collimated light: we have laser light.

This simple description of laser action illustrates the main ideas involved. However, the excitation and de-excitation pathways for most commonly used lasers are quite complex, and it would be as well for the reader to be aware of this. In pursuit of this aim we can consider the action of what is, at present, probably the most commonly used visible light laser—the helium–neon (He–Ne) laser. The energy level structure for this laser system is shown in Fig. 3.6(a) and its basic physical construction is shown in Fig. 3.6(b).

An electrical discharge is struck in a mixture of, typically, helium at a pressure of 1 mmHg and neon at a pressure of 0.1 mmHg. The discharge electrons excite the atoms into a variety of excited states resulting, in

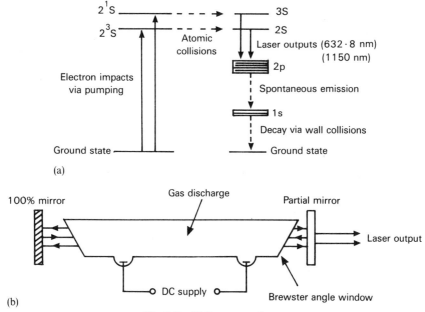

Fig. 3.6 Helium–neon laser.

equilibrium, in a relatively large number resting in the metastable states 2^1S and 2^3S, shown in Fig. 3.6(a). (These designations derive from a spectroscopic notation which is detailed in many books on atomic physics (e.g. Richtmeyer *et al.*, 1955) and which it is not necessary to understand fully for our present purposes.) These metastable levels happen to correspond to S levels in neon atoms which are not readily excited by the discharge (owing to the unfavorably acting quantum selection rules). There is a high probability of energy transfer from the metastable helium atoms to these neon atoms via direct atomic collisional exchange. Clearly, the excited neon atoms will now constitute an inverted population since there is no corresponding collisional tendency to depopulate them. The two excited neon levels decay quickly to the sparsely populated 2p levels shown, emitting optical wavelengths of 632.8 nm and 1150 nm respectively. Optical feedback is arranged for either one or other of these wavelengths via the wavelength selectivity of the end mirrors in the structure. Atoms in the 2p levels then decay spontaneously to 1s levels and subsequently, primarily via tube-wall collisions, to the ground state. (The last feature introduces a geometrical factor into the design of the laser and illustrates one of the many such considerations which must be taken into account in the optimization of laser design.) Typically, a He–Ne laser at 632.8 nm will provide 0.5–50 mW of laser light for 5–10 W of electrical excitation power. Thus it is not particularly efficient (about 0.05%).

3.2.3 Photon statistics

It has been noted already that light interacts with matter as a result of emission or absorption of photons by the individual atoms or molecules. When considering light incident upon matter it is thus useful to extrapolate these ideas and to assume that the incident light consists of a stream of photons which are guided by the electromagnetic wave. This view then raises the question of the statistics of the arrival rate since, by its very nature, a stream of individual particles cannot have an arrival rate which is constant in time.

Let us begin with the assumption that atoms in excited states emit photons at random when falling spontaneously to lower states: we cannot know which particular atoms will emit in any given time interval. For light of "normal" intensities a very small fraction of the total number of atoms in an emitting body will effect transitions in sensible detection times.

For example, for a He–Ne gas laser with an output power of 5 mW, only about 0.05% of the atoms will emit photons in 1 s. Thus we have the situation where an atom may randomly either emit or not emit a photon in a given time, and the probability that it will emit is very small. This is the prescription for Poisson statistics (Solkonikoff and Redheffer, 1958), i.e. the binomial distribution for very small event probability.

Suppose, then, that we have an assembly of n atoms and that the probability of any one of them emitting a photon in time τ is p. Clearly, the average number we would expect to detect in time τ would be np, but the actual number will vary statistically about this mean according to Poisson statistics which state that the probability of detecting r photons in this time is given by

$$P_r = \exp(-np)\frac{(np)^r}{r!}$$

Thus the probability of receiving zero photons is $\exp(-np)$, the probability of receiving two photons is $\exp(-np)(np)^2/2!$ etc.

We can relate np to the mean optical power received P_m, for np is just the mean number of photons received in time τ. Hence

$$P_m = np\frac{h\nu}{\tau}$$

and the mean of the distribution becomes

$$np = \frac{P_m\tau}{h\nu} = \frac{P_m}{Bh\nu}$$

where B is the detector bandwidth. We also need a measure of the spread of this distribution in order to quantify the extent of the expected deviation from the mean. This is given by a quantity called the variance, which is the mean value of the squares of all possible deviations from the mean (we take the squares because the mean value of all *deviations* from the mean must be zero by definition). For a Poisson distribution *the variance is equal to the mean*. The square root of the variance is called the standard deviation, and is the measure we require since it has the same dimensions as the mean. In light detection the standard deviation will thus be a measure of the variation of the received light power about its mean value—it will measure the "noise" on the signal. This noise is called quantum noise (or photon noise), and we see that it will have the value

$$N = \left(\frac{P_m}{Bh\nu}\right)^{1/2}$$

since it is the square root of the mean. Consequently the signal-to-noise ratio will be

$$\text{SNR} = \frac{P_m}{Bh\nu}\frac{1}{N} = \left(\frac{P_m}{Bh\nu}\right)^{1/2}$$

This is an important result. It provides the ultimate limit on the accuracy with which a light power level can be measured. We note that the measurement accuracy improves as $P_m^{1/2}$. For very low levels the accuracy is thus going to be poor. We would expect this since fewer photons are arriving and their "granular" nature is more evident. Correspondingly, if ν is larger for a given power, the accuracy is worse, since again there are fewer photons as a result of there being more energy per photon.

Finally, it must be remembered that these conclusions only apply when the probability of photon emission is very small. This assumption is no longer valid for the intense beams of light ($\gtrsim 10^6\,\mathrm{W\,m^{-2}}$) from powerful lasers because a substantial fraction of the atoms will emit in a typical detection time. Such light is sometimes said to be non-Poissonian (or sub-Poissonian) for reasons which the reader will now understand.

3.3 Propagation of light

3.3.1 Fresnel's equations

We have seen in Section 3.1.2 that Maxwell's equations allow a set of solutions of the form

$$E_x = E_0 \exp\{i(\omega t - kz)\}$$

$$E_y = E_0 \exp\{i(\omega t - kz)\}$$

where $\omega/k = (\varepsilon\mu)^{-1/2}$. These represent plane waves traveling in the Oz direction. We shall now investigate the behavior of such waves, with particular regard to the effects which occur at the boundaries between different optical media.

Of course, other types of solution are also possible. An important solution is that of a wave which spreads spherically from a point:

$$E_r = \frac{E_0}{r} \exp\{i(\omega t - \mathbf{k}\cdot\mathbf{r})\}$$

Here the $1/r$ factor in the amplitude is necessary to ensure conservation of energy (via the Poynting vector), for clearly the total area over which the energy flux occurs is $4\pi r^2$ so that the intensity falls as $1/r^2$ (remember that intensity is proportional to the square of the amplitude).

It is interesting and valuable to note that the propagation of a plane wave (such as that in Fig. 3.7) is equivalent to the propagation of spherical waves radiating from each point on the propagating wavefront of the plane wave. The waves at each point on a given wavefront begin in phase (this is the definition of a wavefront), so that they remain strictly in phase only in a direction at right angles to the front (Fig. 3.7). Hence the plane wave appears to propagate in that direction. This principle of equivalence, first enunciated by Huygens and later shown by Kirchhoff to be mathematically sound (Lipson and Lipson, 1969, Chapter 6), is very useful in the study of wave propagation phenomena generally.

3.3.2 Reflection and refraction

The laws of reflection and refraction were first formulated in terms of "rays" of light. It had been noticed (c 1600) that, when dealing with "point"

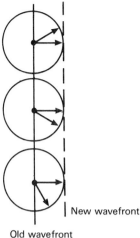

New wavefront

Old wavefront

Fig. 3.7 Huygens' principle.

sources, the light passed through apertures consistently with the view that it was composed of rays traveling in straight lines from the point. (It was primarily this observation which led to Newton's "corpuscular" theory.) The practical concept was legitimized by allowing such light to pass through a small hole so as to isolate a "ray". Such rays were produced and their behavior with respect to reflection and refraction at material boundaries was formulated as follows.

(i) On reflection at a boundary between two media, the reflected ray lies in the same plane as that of the incident ray and the normal to the boundary at the point of incidence (the plane of incidence); the angle of reflection equals the angle of incidence.

(ii) On refraction at a boundary the refracted ray also lies in the plane of incidence, and the sine of the angle of refraction bears a constant ratio to the sine of the angle of incidence (Snell's law).

These two laws form the basis of what is known as geometrical or "ray" optics. The majority of bulk optics (e.g. lens design, prismatics) can be formulated with its aid. However, it has severe limitations. For example, it cannot predict the intensities of the refracted and reflected rays.

If, in the attempt to isolate a ray of light of increasing fineness, the aperture is made too small, the ray divergence appears to increase rather than decrease in size. This occurs when the aperture size becomes comparable with the wavelength of the light, and it is under this condition that the geometrical theory breaks down. "Diffraction" has occurred, and this is quintessentially a wave phenomenon. The wave theory provides a more complete, but necessarily more complex, view of light propagation. We shall now deal with the phenomena of reflection and refraction using the wave theory, but we should remember that, under certain conditions (apertures much larger than the wavelength), the ray theory is useful for its simplicity: a wave can be replaced by a set of rays in the direction of propagation which are normal to surfaces of constant phase and obey simple geometrical rules.

Let us consider two nonconducting dielectric media with refractive indices n_1 and n_2 separated by a plane boundary which we take to be the xy plane at $z = 0$ (Fig. 3.8). Let us now consider a plane wave lying in the xz plane which is propagating in medium 1 and is incident on the boundary at angle θ_i, as shown in the figure. All the field components (E, H) will vary as

$$\exp\left\{i\omega\left(t - n_1 \frac{x \sin \theta_i + z \cos \theta_i}{c}\right)\right\}$$

After striking the boundary there will in general be a reflected and a transmitted (refracted) wave. This fact is a direct consequence of the boundary conditions that must be satisfied at the interface between the two media. The conditions follow from Maxwell's equations and essentially can be stated as follows.

(i) Tangential components of E and H are continuous across the boundary.

(ii) Normal components of B and D are continuous across the boundary.

The above conditions must be true at all times and at all places on the boundary. They can only be true at all times if the frequencies of all waves are the same. Further, since the phase of the incident wave is constant along any line for which x is constant (e.g. $x = 0$), this must also be true for the reflected and transmitted waves which must therefore also lie in the xz plane.

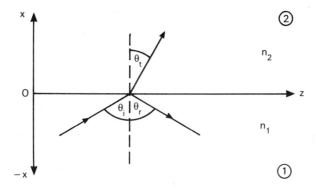

Fig. 3.8 Reflection and refraction.

Suppose that the reflected and transmitted waves make angles θ_r and θ_t respectively with the boundary in this plane. Then these waves will vary as follows:

reflected $\qquad \exp\left\{i\omega\left(t - n_1 \dfrac{x\sin\theta_r - z\cos\theta_r}{c}\right)\right\}$

transmitted $\qquad \exp\left\{i\omega\left(t - n_2 \dfrac{x\sin\theta_t + z\cos\theta_t}{c}\right)\right\}$

For reference, the incident wave was

incident $\qquad \exp\left\{i\omega\left(t - n_1 \dfrac{x\sin\theta_i + z\cos\theta_i}{c}\right)\right\}$

At the boundary ($z = 0$) these variations must be identical for any x, t; hence

$$n_1 x \sin\theta_i = n_1 x \sin\theta_r = n_2 x \sin\theta_t$$

Thus we have

$$\theta_i = \theta_r \qquad \text{(law of reflection)}$$

$$n_1 \sin\theta_i = n_2 \sin\theta_t \qquad \text{(Snell's law of refraction)}$$

We must now consider the relative amplitudes of the waves. To do this we match components of E, H, D and B separately. A further complication is that the values of these quantities at the boundary will depend on the direction of vibration of the E and H fields of the incident wave relative to the plane of incidence, i.e. the xz plane. In other words they will depend on the polarization of the wave. Therefore we need to consider these two polarization components separately. (Any other polarization state can be resolved into these two components, so that our solution will be complete.)

(a) E in the plane of incidence, H normal to the plane of incidence: the incident wave can now be written in the form

$$E_x = E_i \cos\theta_i \exp\left\{i\omega\left(t - n_1 \frac{x\sin\theta_i + z\cos\theta_i}{c}\right)\right\}$$

$$E_z = -E_i \sin\theta_i \exp\left\{i\omega\left(t - n_1 \frac{x\sin\theta_i + z\cos\theta_i}{c}\right)\right\}$$

$$H_y = H_i \exp\left\{i\omega\left(t - n_1 \frac{x\sin\theta_i + z\cos\theta_i}{c}\right)\right\}$$

We can again enlist the help of Maxwell's equations to relate H and E for a plane wave (see Appendix). We have

$$\frac{E}{H} = Z = \left(\frac{\mu}{\varepsilon}\right)^{1/2}$$

Z is known as the characteristic impedance of the medium. Since we are dealing with nonconducting dielectrics in this case, we have $\mu = 1$ and $n = \varepsilon^{1/2}$; hence

$$Z = 1/n$$

Thus

$$H_i = nE_i$$

and the expression for H_y becomes

$$H_y = n_1 E_i \exp\left\{i\omega\left(t - n_1 \frac{x \sin \theta_i + z \cos \theta_i}{c}\right)\right\}$$

Clearly we can construct similar sets of equations for the reflected and transmitted waves. Having done this we can impose the boundary conditions to obtain the required relationships between wave amplitudes:

$$\frac{E_r}{E_i} = \frac{n_1 \cos \theta_t - n_2 \cos \theta_i}{n_1 \cos \theta_t + n_2 \cos \theta_i} \tag{3.10a}$$

$$\frac{E_t}{E_i} = \frac{2n_1 \cos \theta_i}{n_1 \cos \theta_t + n_2 \cos \theta_i} \tag{3.10b}$$

We must now consider the wave with the other orthogonal polarization.

(b) E normal to the plane of incidence, H in the plane of incidence: using the same methods as before we obtain the relations

$$\frac{E_r'}{E_i'} = \frac{n_1 \cos \theta_i - n_2 \cos \theta_t}{n_1 \cos \theta_i + n_2 \cos \theta_t} \tag{3.10c}$$

$$\frac{E_t'}{E_i'} = \frac{2n_1 \cos \theta_i}{n_1 \cos \theta_i + n_2 \cos \theta_t} \tag{3.10d}$$

The four expressions (3.10) are known as Fresnel's equations. Fresnel derived them from the elastic–solid theory of light which prevailed at his time. They contain several points worthy of emphasis.

First we note that there is a possibility of eliminating the reflected wave. For E in the plane of incidence we find from eqn (3.10a) that this occurs when

$$n_1 \cos \theta_t = n_2 \cos \theta_i$$

However, from Snell's law we also have

$$n_1 \sin \theta_i = n_2 \sin \theta_t$$

so that, if we combine the two relations,

$$\sin 2\theta_i = \sin 2\theta_t = \frac{n_2}{n_1}$$

Of course, this equation has an infinite number of solutions, but the only one of interest is that for which $\theta_i \neq \theta_t$ ($\theta_i = \theta_t$ only if $n_1 = n_2$) and both θ_i and θ_t lie in the range of $0-\pi/2$. The required solution is

$$\theta_i + \theta_t = \pi/2$$

so that the reflected and refracted rays are normal to each other. Clearly, from Snell's law, this occurs when

$$\tan \theta_i = n_2/n_1$$

This particular value of θ_i is known as Brewster's angle θ_B. For example, for the glass–air boundary we find $\theta_B = 56.3°$.

If we consider the polarization which has E normal to the plane of incidence we find from eqn (3.10c) that

$$n_1 \cos \theta_i = n_2 \cos \theta_t$$

which, with Snell's law, gives

$$\tan \theta_i = \tan \theta_t$$

There is no solution of this equation which satisfies the required conditions, so that the reflected wave cannot be eliminated in this case. Therefore if a wave with arbitrary polarization is incident on the boundary at the Brewster angle, only the polarization with E normal to the plane of incidence is reflected. This is a useful way of polarizing a wave.

The second point worthy of emphasis is the condition at normal incidence. Here we have $\theta_i = \theta_r = \theta_t = 0$ and hence the relations, identical for both polarizations, become

$$\frac{E_r}{E_i} = \frac{E_r'}{E_i'} = \frac{n_1 - n_2}{n_1 + n_2}$$

$$\frac{E_t}{E_i} = \frac{E_t'}{E_i'} = \frac{2n_1}{n_1 + n_2}$$

We know that the wave intensities are proportional to the square of the electric field amplitudes, and so we can also write

$$\frac{I_r}{I_i} = \frac{(n_1 - n_2)^2}{(n_1 + n_2)^2} \tag{3.11a}$$

$$\frac{I_t}{I_i} = \frac{4n_1{}^2}{(n_1 + n_2)^2} \tag{3.11b}$$

These are useful expressions, for they tell us how much light is lost by normal reflection when transmitting from one medium (say air) to another (say glass). For example, when passing through a glass lens (air → glass → air), taking the refractive index of the glass as 1.5, we find from (3.11) that the fractional loss at the front face of the lens (assumed to be approximately normal) is

$$\frac{I_r}{I_i} = \frac{(0.5)^2}{2.5} = 0.04$$

Another 4% will be lost at the back face, giving a total "Fresnel" loss of the order of 8%.

Finally we should notice that all the expressions for the ratios of amplitudes are real, and thus any change of phase which occurs at the boundary must be either zero or π. We shall now look at a rather different type of reflection where this is not the case.

3.3.3 Total internal reflection

We return to Snell's law

$$n_1 \sin \theta_i = n_2 \sin \theta_t$$

or

$$\sin \theta_t = \frac{n_1}{n_2} \sin \theta_i$$

The factor $\sin \theta_i$ is, of course, always less than unity. However, if $n_2 < n_1$ (i.e. the second medium is less optically dense than the first, which contains the incident ray), it may be that

$$\sin \theta_i > n_2/n_1$$

i.e.

$$\frac{n_1}{n_2} \sin \theta_i > 1$$

If this is so, we have

$$\sin \theta_t > 1 \tag{3.12}$$

Clearly, eqn (3.12) is not satisfied for any real value of θ_t and there can be no real refracted ray. The explanation of this is that, under these conditions of passage from a less dense to a more dense medium, the refracted ray angle θ_t is always greater than the incident angle θ_i. Consequently θ_t will reach a value of 90° (i.e. parallel to the boundary) before θ_i, and any greater value of θ_i cannot yield a refracted ray. The value of θ_i for which (3.12) becomes true is known as the critical angle θ_c:

$$\sin \theta_c = n_2/n_1$$

For all values of $\theta_i > \theta_c$ the light is totally reflected at the boundary: this phenomenon is called total internal reflection (TIR).

However, Fresnel's equations must still apply, for we made no limitations on the values of the quantities when imposing the boundary conditions.

Furthermore, if the fields are to be continuous across the boundary, as required by Maxwell's equations, there must be a field disturbance of some kind in the second medium. We can use Fresnel's equations to investigate this disturbance. We write

$$\cos \theta_t = (1 - \sin^2\theta_t)^{1/2}$$

Since $\sin \theta_t > 1$ for $\theta_t > \theta_c$ and since also the function $\cosh \gamma > 1$ for all γ, we can, for convenience, use the substitution

$$\sin \theta_t = \cosh \gamma \qquad \theta_t > \theta_i$$

Then $\cos \theta_t = i(\cosh^2 \gamma - 1)^{1/2} = \pm i \sinh \gamma$. Hence we can write the field components in the second medium to vary as

$$\exp\left\{i\omega\left(t - n_2 \frac{x \cosh \gamma - iz \sinh \gamma}{c}\right)\right\}$$

or

$$\exp\left(-\frac{\omega n_2 z \sinh \gamma}{c}\right) \exp\left(i\omega \frac{t - n_2 x \cosh \gamma}{c}\right)$$

This represents a wave traveling in the Ox direction in the second medium (i.e. parallel to the boundary) with amplitude decreasing exponentially in the Oz direction (at right angles to the boundary). The rate at which the amplitude decreases with z can be written

$$\exp\left(-\frac{2\pi z \sinh \gamma}{\lambda_2}\right)$$

where λ_2 is the wavelength of the light in the second medium. This shows that the wave is attenuated significantly over distances of about λ_2. For example, at the glass–air interface, the critical angle will be $\sin^{-1}(1/1.5)$, i.e. 41.8°. For a wave in the glass incident on the glass–air boundary at 60° we find that $\sin \gamma = 1.64$. Hence the amplitude of the wave in the second medium is reduced by a factor of 5.4×10^{-3} in a distance of only one wavelength, which is of the order of 1 μm.

Even though the wave is propagating in the second medium, it transports no light energy in a direction normal to the boundary. All the light is totally internally reflected at the boundary. The fields which exist in the second medium give a Poynting vector which averages zero in this direction over one oscillation period of the light wave.

The totally internally reflected wave now undergoes a phase change which depends on both the angle of incidence and the polarization. This can readily be derived from Fresnel's equations. From eqn (3.10a) we have for the $E_\parallel$ polarization

$$\frac{E_r}{E_i} = \frac{in_1 \sinh \gamma - n_2 \cos \theta_i}{in_1 \sinh \gamma + n_2 \cos \theta_i}$$

This complex number provides the phase change on TIR as δ_p where for $E_{\parallel}$ polarization

$$\tan\left(\frac{\delta_p}{2}\right) = \frac{n_1(n_1{}^2 \sin^2 \theta_i - n_2{}^2)^{1/2}}{n_2{}^2 \cos \theta_i}$$

and for $E_{\perp}$ polarization

$$\tan\left(\frac{\delta_s}{2}\right) = \frac{(n_1{}^2 \sin^2 \theta_i - n_2{}^2)^{1/2}}{n_1 \cos \theta_i}$$

We note also that

$$\tan\left(\frac{\delta_p}{2}\right) = n_1{}^2 \tan\left(\frac{\delta_s}{2}\right)$$

and that

$$\tan\left(\frac{\delta_p - \delta_s}{2}\right) = \frac{\cos \theta_i (n_1{}^2 \sin^2 \theta_i - n_2{}^2)^{1/2}}{n_1 \sin^2 \theta_i}$$

The variations in δ_p, δ_s and $\delta_p - \delta_s$ as a function of θ_i are shown in Fig. 3.9. It is clear that the polarization state of light undergoing TIR will be changed as a result of the differential phase change $\delta_p - \delta_s$. By choosing θ_i appropriately and perhaps using two TIRs, it is possible to produce any required final polarization state from any given initial state.

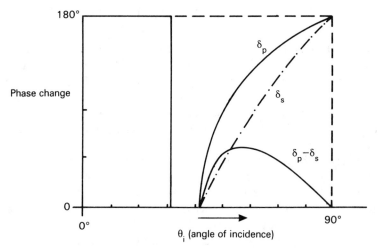

Fig. 3.9   Phase changes on total internal reflection.

It is interesting to note that the reflected ray in TIR appears to originate from a point which is displaced along the boundary from the point of incidence. This is consistent with the incident ray's being reflected from a parallel plane which lies a short distance within the second boundary (Fig. 3.10). This view is also consistent with the observed phase shift, which is now regarded as being due to the extra optical path traveled by the ray. The displacement is known as the Goos–Hänchen effect and provides an entirely consistent alternative explanation of TIR (Kapany and Burke, 1972).

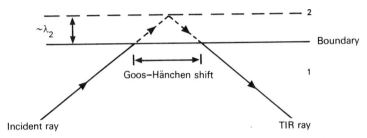

Fig. 3.10   The Goos–Hänchen shift for total internal reflection.

3.3.4 Interference of light

We have seen that light consists of oscillating electric and magnetic fields. We know that these are vector fields because they represent forces (on unit charge and unit magnetic pole respectively). The fields will thus add vectorially. Consequently, when two light waves are superimposed on each other we obtain the resultant by constructing their vector sum at each point in time and space, and this fact has already been used in consideration of the polarization of light (Section 3.6).

If two sinusoids are added, the result is another sinusoid. Suppose that two light waves given via their electric fields as

$$e_1 = E_1 \cos(\omega t + \varphi_1)$$

$$e_2 = E_2 \cos(\omega t + \varphi_2)$$

have the same polarization and are superimposed at a point in space. The resultant field at the point will be given, using elementary trigonometry, by

$$e_T = E_T \cos(\omega t + \varphi_T)$$

where

$$E_T{}^2 = E_1{}^2 + E_2{}^3 + 2E_1E_2 \cos(\varphi_2 - \varphi_1)$$

and

$$\tan \varphi_T = \frac{E_1 \sin \varphi_1 + E_2 \sin \varphi_2}{E_1 \cos \varphi_1 + E_2 \cos \varphi_2}$$

For the important case where $E_1 = E_2 = E$, say, we have

$$E_T{}^2 = 4E^2 \cos^2\left(\frac{\varphi_2 - \varphi_1}{2}\right) \tag{3.13}$$

and

$$\tan \varphi_T = \tan\left(\frac{\varphi_1 + \varphi_2}{2}\right)$$

The intensity of the wave will be proportional to E_T^2 so that, from (3.13), it can be seen to vary from $4E^2$ to zero as $(\varphi_2 - \varphi_1)/2$ varies from zero to $\pi/2$.

Consider now the arrangement shown in Fig. 3.11. Here two slits, separated by a distance p, are illuminated by a plane wave. The portions of the wave which pass through the slits will interfere on the screen S, a distance d away. Now, from Huygens' principle, each of the slits will act as a source of cylindrical waves. Moreover, since they originate from the same plane wave, they will start in phase. On a line displaced a distance s from the line of symmetry on the screen the waves from the two slits will differ in phase by

$$\delta = \frac{2\pi}{\lambda} \frac{sp}{d} \qquad d \gg s, p$$

Thus, as s increases, the intensity will vary between a maximum and zero in accordance with eqn (3.13). These variations will be viewed as fringes, i.e. lines of constant intensity parallel with the slits. They are known as Young's fringes, after their discoverer, and are the simplest example of light interference. We shall be considering some more complex (and more interesting) examples later.

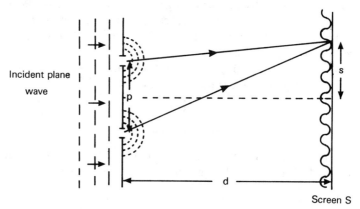

Fig. 3.11 "Young's slits" interference pattern.

3.3.5 Light waveguiding

Consider now the symmetrical dielectric structure shown in Fig. 3.12. Here we have an infinite (in width and length) dielectric slab of refractive index n_1, sandwiched between two other infinite slabs, each of refractive index n_2.

Using the Cartesian axes defined in the figure let us consider a light ray starting at the origin of the axes and propagating within the first medium at an

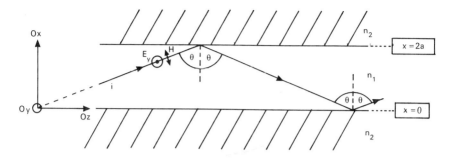

Fig. 3.12   Slab-guided wave.

angle θ. If θ is greater than the critical angle θ_c, the light will bounce down the first medium by means of a series of TIRs at the boundaries with the other media. Since the wave is thus confined to the first medium it is said to be "guided" by the structure, which is consequently called a "waveguide". Let us firstly consider guided light which is linearly polarized normal to the plane of incidence. The electric field of the wave represented by ray i (see Fig. 3.12) can be written

$$E_i = E_0 \exp(-i\omega t - ikn_1 x \cos\theta - ikn_1 z \sin\theta)$$

and that represented by the ray r reflected from the first boundary can be written

$$E_r = E_0 \exp(-i\omega t + ikn_1 x \cos\theta - ikn_1 z \sin\theta + i\delta_s)$$

where δ_s is the phase change at TIR for this polarization. These two waves will be superimposed on each other and will thus interfere. The interference pattern is obtained by adding them:

$$\begin{aligned} E_T &= E_i + E_r \\ &= E_0 \exp(-i\omega t - ikn_1 z \sin\theta + i\delta_s/2) \times 2\cos(kn_1 x \cos\theta + \delta_s/2) \end{aligned} \qquad (3.14)$$

This is a wave propagating in the direction Oz with wavenumber $kn_1 \sin\theta$, and it is amplitude modulated in the Ox direction according to

$$\cos(kn_1 x \cos\theta + \delta_s/2)$$

Now symmetry tells us that the intensity of the wave must be the same at each of the two boundaries. This requires that it is the same for $x = 0$ and $x = 2a$, i.e.

$$\cos^2(\delta_s/2) = \cos^2(kn_1 2a \cos\theta + \delta_s/2)$$

or

$$2akn_1 \cos\theta + \delta_s = m\pi$$

where m is an integer. (This is sometimes known as the transverse resonance condition.) Since δ_s depends only on θ (Fresnel's equations!) this tells us that θ can have only certain discrete values if the interference pattern is to remain constant along the length of the fiber. Each interference pattern is characterized by a value of m which provides a corresponding value for θ. The allowed interference patterns are called the "modes" of the waveguide.

If we now turn to the progression of the wave along the guide (i.e. down the Oz axis), we see from (3.14) that this is characterized by a wavenumber $n_1 k \sin \theta = \beta$, say. Furthermore, since the TIR condition requires that $\sin \theta \geqslant n_2/n_1$, it follows that

$$n_1 k \geqslant \beta \geqslant n_2 k$$

so that the longitudinal wavenumber always lies between those of the two media.

We can also define a "transverse" wave number

$$q = n_1 k \cos \theta$$

If, for convenience, we also define a parameter p where

$$p^2 = \beta^2 - n_2^2 k^2$$

we discover that we can cast our "transverse resonance" condition into the form

$$\tan\left(aq - m\frac{\pi}{2}\right) = \frac{p}{q} \tag{3.15a}$$

for the perpendicular polarization $E_\perp$ and

$$\tan\left(aq - m\frac{\pi}{2}\right) = \frac{n_1^2 p}{n_2^2 q} \tag{3.15b}$$

for the parallel polarization $E_\parallel$. The conventional waveguide notation designates these two cases as "transverse electrical" (TE) for $E_\perp$ and "transverse magnetic" (TM) for $E_\parallel$. The terms refer, of course, to the direction of the stated fields with respect to the plane of incidence of the ray.

We can use eqns (3.15) to characterize the modes for any given slab geometry. The solutions of the equations can be separated into odd and even types depending on whether m is odd or even. For odd m we have

$$\tan\left(aq - m_{\text{odd}}\frac{\pi}{2}\right) = -\cot(aq) \tag{3.16a}$$

and for even m

$$\tan\left(aq - m_{\text{even}}\frac{\pi}{2}\right) = \tan(aq) \tag{3.16b}$$

If we take m to be even we can then write eqn (3.15a), for example, in the form

$$aq \tan(aq) = ap \tag{3.17}$$

Now from the definitions of p and q it is clear that

$$a^2p^2 + a^2q^2 = a^2k^2(n_1{}^2 - n_2{}^2) \qquad (3.18)$$

If we take rectangular axes ap, aq, the latter relation between p and q translates into a circle of radius $ak(n_1{}^2 - n_2{}^2)^{1/2}$ (Fig. 3.13). If, on the same axes, we also plot the function $aq \tan(aq)$, eqn (3.17) is satisfied at all points of intersection between the two functions (Fig. 3.13). (Clearly, a similar set of solutions can be found for odd m.) Therefore these points provide the values of θ which correspond to the allowed modes of the guide. Having determined a value of θ for a given k, we can obtain β from

$$\beta = n_1 k \sin \theta$$

and hence β can be determined as a function of k (for a given m). The resulting curves are called "dispersion" curves and are important determinants of waveguide behavior (for reasons which will become clearer in Section 3.7).

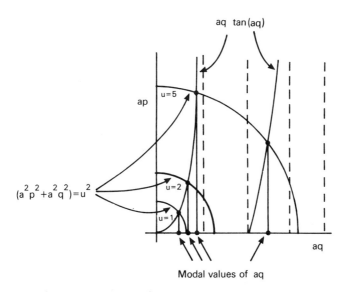

Fig. 3.13   Graphical solution of the modal equation for the slab waveguide.

A final point of importance should be made. Clearly the number of possible modes depends upon the values of the waveguide parameters. There will always be at least one mode solution, since the circle will always intersect the tangent curve even for a vanishingly small circle radius. If there is to be just one solution then Fig. 3.13 shows that the radius of the circle must be less than $\pi/2$, i.e.

$$ak(n_1{}^2 - n_2{}^2)^{1/2} < \pi/2$$

or

$$\frac{2\pi a}{\lambda}(n_1{}^2 - n_2{}^2)^{1/2} < 1.57$$

The last equation is the single-mode condition for this symmetrical slab waveguide. It represents an important case, since the existence of just one mode in a waveguide considerably simplifies the behavior of the radiation within it.

Let us now consider the cylindrical dielectric structure shown in Fig. 3.14. This is just the geometry of the optical fiber, where the central region is known as the "core" and the outer region as the "cladding". In this case the same basic principles apply as for the dielectric slab, but the circular rather than planar symmetry complicates the mathematics. For convenience, we use cylindrical coordinates (r, φ, z) as defined in Fig. 3.14. This allows us to cast Maxwell's wave equation for the dielectric structure into the form

$$\nabla^2 E = \frac{1}{r}\frac{\partial}{\partial r}\left(r\frac{\partial E}{\partial r}\right) + \frac{1}{r^2}\frac{\partial^2 E}{\partial\varphi^2} + \frac{\partial^2 E}{\partial z^2} = \mu\varepsilon\frac{\partial^2 E}{\partial t^2} \qquad (3.19)$$

If we try a solution for E in which all variables are separable, we write

$$E = E_r(r)\,E_\varphi(\varphi)\,E_z(z)\,E_t(t)$$

and, from the known physics, we can immediately take

$$E_z(z)E_t(t) = \exp\{i(\beta z - \omega t)\}$$

This allows us to rewrite the wave equation (3.19) in the form

$$\frac{\partial}{\partial r}\left\{r\frac{\partial(E_rE_\varphi)}{\partial r}\right\} + \frac{1}{r^2}\frac{\partial^2(E_rE_\varphi)}{\partial\varphi^2} - \beta^2 E_rE_\varphi + \mu\varepsilon\omega^2 E_rE_\varphi = 0$$

Now, if we suggest a periodic function for E_φ of the form

$$E_\varphi = \exp(\pm il\varphi)$$

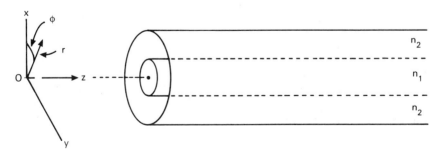

Fig. 3.14   Cylindrical waveguide.

where l is an integer, we can further reduce the equation to

$$\frac{\partial^2 E_r}{\partial r^2} + \frac{1}{r}\frac{\partial E_r}{\partial r} + \left(n^2 k^2 - \beta^2 - \frac{l^2}{r^2}\right)E_r = 0$$

This is a form of Bessel's equation and its solutions are Bessel functions. If we use the same substitutions as for the previous planar case, i.e.

$$n_1^2 k^2 - \beta^2 = q^2$$

$$\beta^2 - n_2^2 k^2 = p^2$$

we find

$$\frac{\partial^2 E_r}{\partial r^2} + \frac{1}{r}\frac{\partial E_r}{\partial r} + \left(q^2 - \frac{l^2}{r^2}\right)E_r = 0 \qquad \text{for } r \leqslant a \text{ (core)}$$

and

$$\frac{\partial^2 E_r}{\partial r^2} + \frac{1}{r}\frac{\partial E_r}{\partial r} - \left(p^2 + \frac{l^2}{r^2}\right)E_r = 0 \qquad \text{for } r > a \text{ (cladding)}$$

Solutions of these equations are

$$E_r = E_c J_l(qr) \qquad\qquad r \leqslant a$$

$$E_r = E_{cl} K_l(pr) \qquad\qquad r > a$$

J_l is a "Bessel function of the first kind". K_l is a "modified Bessel function of the second kind" (sometimes known as a "modified Hankel function"). The two functions must clearly be continuous at $r = a$, and we have for our full "trial" solution in the core

$$E = E_c J_l(qr) \exp(\pm il\varphi) \exp\{i(\beta z - \omega t)\}$$

and a similar solution for the cladding:

$$E = E_{cl} K_l(pr) \exp(\pm il\varphi) \exp\{i(\beta z - \omega t)\}$$

Again, we can determine the allowable values for p, q and β by imposing the boundary conditions at $r = a$ (Adams, 1981). The result is a relationship which provides the β versus k or "dispersion" curves shown in Fig. 3.15. The mathematical manipulations are tedious but are somewhat eased by using the so-called "weakly guiding" approximation. This makes use of the fact that if $n_1 \approx n_2$ the ray's angle of incidence on the boundary must be very large if TIR is to occur. The ray must bounce down the core almost at grazing incidence. This means that the wave is very nearly a transverse wave, with very small z components. By neglecting the longitudinal components H_z, E_z, a considerable simplification of the mathematics results.

Since the wave is transverse to a first approximation, it can be resolved conveniently into two linearly polarized components, just as for free-space

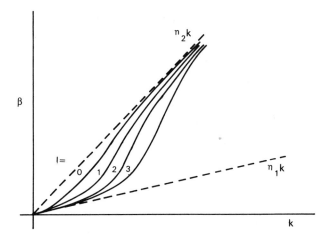

Fig. 3.15   Dispersion curves for a cylindrical waveguide.

propagation. The modes are thus dubbed "linearly polarized" (LP) modes, and the notation describing the profile's intensity distribution is known as the LP notation.

Of course, the cylindrical geometry relates directly to the optical fiber. The latter has just the geometry we have been considering and, for a typical fiber,

$$\frac{n_1 - n_2}{n_1} \approx 0.01$$

so that the weakly guiding approximation is valid. Some of the low order "LP modes" of intensity distribution are shown in Fig. 3.16 together with their polarizations and values for the azimuthal integer l. There are two possible LP optical fiber modes. For cylindrical geometry the "single-mode condition" is (Adams, 1981)

$$\frac{2\pi a}{\lambda}(n_1{}^2 - n_2{}^2)^{1/2} < 2.404$$

Some important practical features of optical fiber design can be appreciated by reversion to geometrical (ray) optics. Let us consider firstly the problem of launching light into the fiber. Referring to Fig. 3.17(a), we have for a ray incident on the front face of the fiber at angle θ_0 and with refracted angle θ_1

$$n_0 \sin \theta_0 = n_1 \sin \theta_1$$

where n_0 and n_1 are the refractive indices of air and the fiber core material respectively. If the angle at which the ray then strikes the core–cladding boundary is θ_T, for TIR we must have

$$\sin \theta_T > n_2/n_1$$

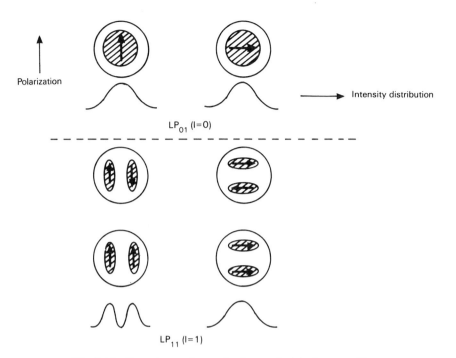

Polarization

Intensity distribution

LP_{01} $(l=0)$

LP_{11} $(l=1)$

Fig. 3.16   Some low order modes for a cylindrical waveguide.

where n_2 is the cladding index. Since

$$\theta_T = \pi/2 - \theta_1$$

the inequality is equivalent to

$$\cos\theta_1 > n_2/n_1$$

so that, from Snell's law,

$$\cos\theta_1 = \left(1 - \frac{n_0^2 \sin^2\theta_0}{n_1^2}\right)^{1/2} > \frac{n_2}{n_1}$$

or

$$n_0 \sin\theta_0 < (n_1^2 - n_2^2)^{1/2}$$

The quantity on the right-hand side of this inequality is known as the numerical aperture (NA) of the fiber. It is a specification of the "acceptance" cone of light, which is a cone of apex half-angle θ_0. Clearly, a large difference in refractive index between core and cladding is necessary for a large acceptance angle; for a typical fiber $\theta_0 \approx 10°$.

The discrete values of reflection angle which are allowed by the transverse resonance condition (within the TIR condition) can be represented by the ray propagations shown in Fig. 3.17(b). This makes it clear that for a large number

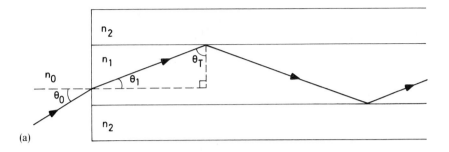

(a)

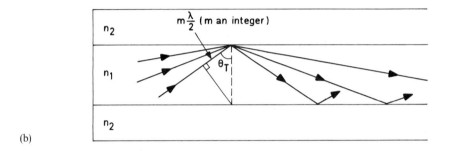

(b)

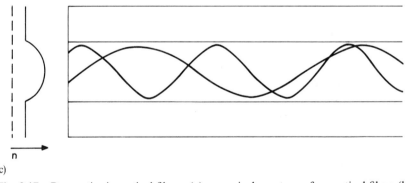

(c)

Fig. 3.17   Ray optics in optical fibers: (a) numerical aperture of an optical fiber; (b) modal rays within the total internal reflection condition for multimode fiber; (c) ray propagations in graded-index fiber.

of allowable rays (i.e. modes) the TIR angle should be large, implying a large NA.

However, it is also clear geometrically that the rays will progress down the guide at a velocity which depends on their angles of reflection: the smaller the angle, the smaller the velocity. This leads to large "modal dispersion" at large NA since, if the launched light energy is distributed amongst many modes, the differing velocities will lead to varying times of arrival of the energy components at the far end of the fiber. This is undesirable in, for example, communications applications, since it will lead to a limitation on the communications bandwidth. In a digital system a pulse cannot be allowed to spread into the pulses before or after it. For greatest bandwidth only one mode should be allowed, and this requires a small NA. Thus a balance must be struck between good signal level (large NA) and large signal bandwidth (small NA).

A fiber design which attempts to attain a better balance position between these is shown in Fig. 3.17(c). This fiber is known as graded index (GRIN) fiber and possesses a core refractive index profile which falls off parabolically (approximately) from its peak value on the axis. The profile effectively constitutes a continuous convex lens which allows a large acceptance angle whilst limiting the number of allowable modes to a relatively small value. GRIN fiber is used widely in short and medium distance communications systems. For trunk systems, single-mode fiber is invariably used, however.

3.4 Interference and diffraction

3.4.1 Introduction

In Section 3.3.1 it was noted that each point on a wavefront could be regarded formally and rigorously as a source of spherical waves. In Section 3.3.5 it was noted that any two waves will interfere when superimposed. Consequently wavefronts can interfere with themselves and with other separate wavefronts. The former phenomenon is usually known as "diffraction" and the latter as "interference", but the distinction is somewhat arbitrary and in several cases is far from clear-cut. However, we shall deal with them under separate headings, beginning with interference.

3.4.2 Interference

The essentials of dual-beam interference were stated in Section 3.3.5. Although very simple in concept the phenomenon is extremely useful in practice. The reason for this is that the maxima of the resulting fringe pattern appear where the phase difference between the interfering light beams is a multiple of 2π. Any quite small perturbation in the phase of one of the beams will thus cause a transverse shift in the position of the fringe pattern, which can be readily observed using optoelectronic techniques to about 10^{-4} of the fringe spacing. Such a shift is caused by, for example, an increase in path length of one of the beams by one-hundredth of a wavelength, or about 5×10^{-9} m for visible light. This means that differential distances of this order can be measured, leading to obvious applications in, for example, strain monitoring on mechanical structures. An example is shown in Fig. 3.18. Here the two beams are rendered parallel, but spatially separate, by a slit–lens arrangement. One of the two paths (A) passes through a chamber which contains a gas whose pressure can be varied, whilst the other (B) enjoys constant conditions and acts as a reference. The fringe pattern now depends on the change in refractive index, which in turn results from the pressure change in the gas chamber in path A. Thus the (very small) change in refractive index can be measured, accurately, as a function of pressure. Lord Rayleigh used just such an arrangement precisely for this purpose, developing an instrument known as a Rayleigh refractometer.

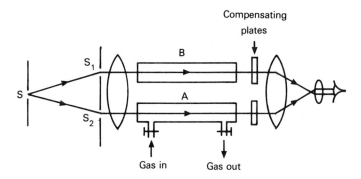

Fig. 3.18   Rayleigh refractometer.

A variation on Rayleigh's instrument is shown in Fig. 3.19. Here the beams are produced from the partial reflection and transmission at a dielectric or partially silvered mirror M_1. Another such mirror M_4 recombines the two beams after their separate passages. Such an arrangement is known as a Mach–Zehnder interferometer and is used extensively to monitor changing

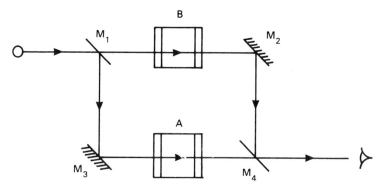

Fig. 3.19   Mach–Zehnder interferometer.

phase differences between two optical paths. An optical fiber version of a Mach–Zehnder interferometer is shown in Fig. 3.20. In this case the "mirrors" are optical couplings between the cores of the two fibers. The "fringe pattern" consists effectively of just one fringe, since the fiber core acts as an efficient spatial filter. However, the light which emerges from the fiber end E will clearly depend on the phase relationship between the two optical paths when the light beams recombine at R, and thus it will depend critically on propagation conditions within the two arms. If one of the arms varies in temperature, strain, density etc. compared with the other, the light output will also vary. Hence the latter can be used as a sensitive measure of any physical parameters which are capable of modifying the propagation properties of the fiber.

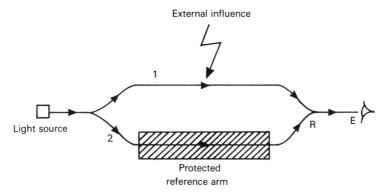

Fig. 3.20 Optical fiber Mach–Zehnder interferometer.

Finally, Fig. 3.21(a) shows another rather more sophisticated variation of the Rayleigh idea. In this case the beams are again separated by means of a beam-splitting mirror but are returned to the same point by fully silvered mirrors placed at the ends of the two optical paths. (The compensating plate is

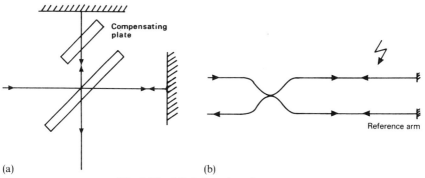

Fig. 3.21 Michelson interferometers.

necessary to provide equal optical paths for the two beams in the absence of any perturbation.) This arrangement is called the Michelson interferometer after the experimenter who in the late nineteenth century used optical interferometry with great skill to make many physical advances. His interferometer (not to be confused with his "stellar" interferometer, of which more later) allows for a greater accuracy of fine adjustment via control of the reflecting mirrors but uses, of course, just the same basic interferometric principles as before. The optical fiber version of this device is shown in Fig. 3.21(b) (Jones *et al.*, 1986).

For completeness, mention must be made of the use of Michelson's interferometer in the famous Michelson–Morley experiment of 1887. This demonstrated that light traveled with the same velocity in each of two orthogonal paths, no matter what the orientation of the interferometer with respect to the Earth's "proper" motion through space. This result was crucial to Einstein's formulation of special relativity in 1905, and thus is certainly one of the most important results in the history of experimental physics.

Valuable as dual-beam interferometry is, it suffers from the limitation that its accuracy depends upon the location of the maxima (or minima) of a sinusoidal variation. For very accurate work, such as precision spectroscopy, this limitation is severe. By using the interference between many beams, rather than just two, we find that we can improve the accuracy very considerably. We can see this by considering the arrangement shown in Fig. 3.22. Light from a single source gives a large number of phase-related separate beams by means of multiple reflections and transmissions within a dielectric (e.g. glass) plate.

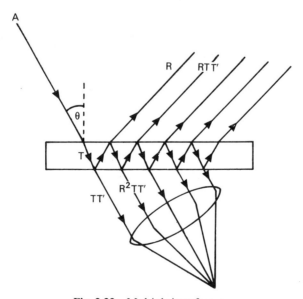

Fig. 3.22 Multiple interference.

For a given angle of incidence θ there will be fixed values for the transmission coefficients T and T' and the reflection coefficient R as shown. If we start with a wave of amplitude A, the waves on successive reflections will suffer attenuation by a constant factor and will increase in phase by a constant amount. If we consider the transmitted light only, the total amplitude which arrives at the focus of the lens is given by the sum

$$A_T = aTT' \exp(i\omega t) + aTT'R^2 \exp(i\omega t - iks) + aTT'R^4 \exp(i\omega t - 2iks) + \ldots$$

where s is the optical path difference between successive reflections at the lower surface (including the phase changes on reflection and transmission). This sum can be expressed as

$$A_T = aTT' \sum_{p=0}^{\infty} R^{2p} \exp(i\omega t - ipks)$$

which is a geometric series whose sum is

$$A_T = aTT' \frac{\exp(i\omega t)}{1 - R^2 \exp(-iks)}$$

Hence the intensity of the light is proportional to

$$A_T A_T^* (\propto I) = \frac{(aTT')^2}{1 + R^4 - 2R^2 \cos(ks)} \tag{3.20}$$

We note from this equation that

$$\frac{I_{max}}{I_{min}} = \frac{(1+R^2)^2}{(1-R^2)^2}$$

so that the fringe contrast increases with R. However, as R increases so does the attenuation between the successive reflections. Hence the total transmitted light power will fall.

Figure 3.23 shows how I varies with ks for different values of R. We note that the fringes become very sharp for large values of R. Hence the position of the maxima can now be accurately determined. Further, since the spacing of the maxima specifies ks, this information can be used to determine either k or s if the other is known. Consequently, multiple interference can be used either to select (or measure) a very specific wavelength or to measure very small changes in optical path length.

The physical reason for the sharpening of the fringes as the reflectivity increases is indicated in Fig. 3.24. The addition of the multiplicity of waves is equivalent to the addition of vectors with progressively decreasing amplitude and increasing relative phase. For small reflectivity (Fig. 3.24(a)) the wave amplitudes decrease rapidly so that the phase increase has a relatively small effect on the resultant wave amplitude. In the case of high reflectivity (Fig. 3.24(b)) the reverse is the case and each small successive phase change rapidly reduces the resultant.

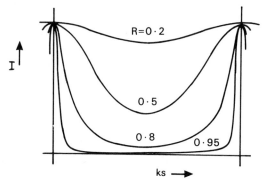

Fig. 3.23   Variation in intensity with optical path, for various reflectivities, in a multiple interference plate.

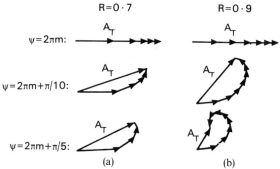

Fig. 3.24   Graphical illustration of the dependence of fringe sharpness on reflectivity.

Two important devices based on these ideas of multiple reflection are the Fabry–Pérot interferometer and the Fabry–Pérot etalon. In the former case the distance between the two surfaces is finely variable for fringe control; in the case of the etalon the surfaces are fixed. In both cases the flatness and parallelism of the surfaces must be accurate to approximately $\lambda/100$ for good quality fringes. This is difficult to achieve in a variable device, and the etalon is preferred for most practical purposes.

The performance of a Fabry-Pérot etalon is specified by three important parameters. As is to be expected, these parameters relate to the instrument's ability to separate closely spaced optical wavelengths. The first is a measure of the sharpness of the fringes. This measure is normalized to the separation of the fringes for a single wavelength, since there is clearly no advantage in having narrow fringes if they are all crowded together so that the orders of different wavelengths overlap. Therefore we define a quantity

$$\Phi = \frac{\text{separation of successive fringes}}{\text{width at half-maximum of a single fringe}}$$

which is called the finesse. It is easy to derive its value from eqn (3.20). The equation can be written in the form

$$I = \frac{I_{max}}{1 + F \sin^2(\psi/2)} \qquad (3.21)$$

where

$$F = \frac{4R^2}{(1-R^2)^2} \qquad \text{and} \qquad \psi = ks$$

From this it is clear that $I = I_{max}/2$ when $\psi_h = 2/F^{1/2}$. Hence the width at half-maximum, which is equal to $2\psi_h$, is $4/F^{1/2}$. The "ψ distance" between successive maxima is just 2π, and thus the finesse is given by

$$\Phi = \frac{\pi F^{1/2}}{2} = \frac{\pi R}{1 - R^2}$$

This quantity has a value of 2 for a dual-beam interferometer. For a Fabry–Pérot etalon with $R = 0.9$ its value is 15.

The next quantity we need to look at is the resolving power. This is a measure of the smallest detectable wavelength separation $\delta\lambda$ at a given wavelength λ and is defined as

$$\rho = \frac{\lambda}{\delta\lambda}$$

If we take λ to be the wavelength which corresponds to a ψ difference equal to the width of the half-maximum, we have

$$\rho = \frac{\lambda}{\delta\lambda} = \frac{\psi}{2\psi_h} = \frac{2\pi p}{4/F^{1/2}} = \frac{\pi p}{2} F^{1/2} = p \times \text{finesse}$$

where p is the "order" of the maximum. If the etalon is being viewed close to normal incidence, p will effectively be just the number of wavelengths in a double passage across the etalon. If the etalon has optical thickness t we have

$$\rho = \frac{\pi t F^{1/2}}{\lambda}$$

This is typically of order 10^6, compared with a figure of about 10^4 for a dual-beam interferometer such as the Michelson. The ratio of these figures thus represents the improvement in accuracy afforded by multiple-beam interferometry over dual-beam techniques.

Finally, we define a quantity concerned with the overlapping of orders. If the wavelength range $\Delta\lambda$ under investigation is such that the $(p+1)$th maximum of λ is to coincide with the pth maximum of $\lambda + \Delta\lambda$, there is clearly an unresolvable confusion. For this just to be so,

$$(p+1)k = p(k + \Delta k)$$

so that

$$\frac{\Delta k}{k} = \frac{\Delta \lambda}{\lambda} = \frac{1}{p}$$

Again, close to normal incidence we can write

$$\Delta \lambda = \frac{\lambda^2}{2t}$$

$\Delta \lambda$ is called the "free spectral range" of the etalon and represents the maximum wavelength range which can be used without recourse to prior separation of the confusable wavelengths.

3.4.3 Diffraction

Diffraction of light can be regarded as the limiting case of multiple interference as the source spacings become infinitesimally small. Consider the slit aperture in Fig. 3.25. This slit is illuminated with a uniform plane wave and the light which passes through it is observed on a screen which is sufficiently distant from the slit for the light which falls upon it to be effectively a plane wave once more. These are the conditions for Fraunhöfer diffraction. If source

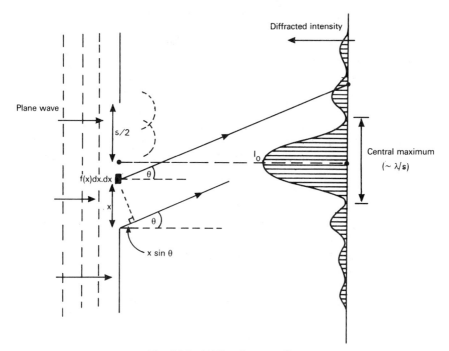

Fig. 3.25   Diffraction at a slit.

and screen are close enough to the slit for the waves not to be plane we have a more complex situation known as Fresnel diffraction (e.g. Jenkins and White, 1953, Chapter 18). Fraunhöfer diffraction is by far the more important of the two and is the only form of diffraction we shall deal with here.

Suppose that the amplitude of the wave at distances between x and $x + dx$ along the slit is given by the complex quantity $f(x)dx$ and consider the effect of this at angle θ, as shown in Fig. 3.25. (Since each point on the wavefront acts as a source of spherical waves, all angles will, of course, be illuminated by the strip.) The screen, which is effectively infinitely distant from the slit, will be illuminated at one point by the light leaving the slit at angles between θ and $\theta + d\theta$. If the bottom of the slit is taken as the phase reference, the light, on arriving at the screen, will lead by a phase

$$\varphi = kx \sin \theta$$

and hence the total amplitude in directions θ to $\theta + d\theta$ will be given by

$$A(\theta) = \int_{-\infty}^{\infty} f(x) \exp(-ikx \sin \theta) \, dx$$

We can also write

$$A(\alpha) = \int_{-\infty}^{\infty} f(x) \exp(-i\alpha x) \, dx$$

where

$$\alpha = k \sin \theta$$

Hence $A(\alpha)$ and $f(x)$ constitute a reciprocal Fourier transform pair, i.e. each is the Fourier transform of the other. This is an important result. For small values of θ it implies that the angular distribution of the diffracted light is the Fourier transform of the aperture's amplitude distribution. Let us see how this works for some simple cases.

Take first a uniformly illuminated slit of width s. The angular distribution of diffracted light will now be

$$A(k \sin \theta) = \int_{-s/2}^{s/2} a \exp(-ikx \sin \theta) \, dx$$

where a is the (uniform) amplitude at the slit per unit of slit width. Hence

$$A(k \sin \theta) = \frac{a \sin\{(ks \sin \theta)/2\}}{(k \sin \theta)/2} \tag{3.22}$$

Writing, for convenience, $\beta = (ks \sin \theta)/2$, we have that intensity in a direction θ is given by

$$I(\theta) = a^2 s^2 \frac{\sin^2 \beta}{\beta^2} = I_0 \frac{\sin^2 \beta}{\beta^2}$$

where I_0 is intensity at the center of the diffraction pattern. This variation is shown in Fig. 3.25 and, as in the case of multiple interference between discrete sources, its shape is a result of the addition of wavevectors with phase increasing steadily with θ. An important feature of this variation is the scale of the angular divergence. The two minima immediately on each side of the principal maximum (at $\theta = 0$) occur when

$$ks\frac{\sin\theta}{2} = \pm\pi$$

giving

$$\sin\theta = \pm\lambda/s$$

so that, if θ is small, the width of the central maximum is given by

$$\theta_w = 2\theta = \frac{2\lambda}{s}$$

Thus the smaller s is for a given wavelength the more quickly does the light energy diverge, and vice versa. This is an important determinant of general behavior in optical systems.

As a second example consider a sinusoidal variation in amplitude over the aperture. The Fourier transform of a sinusoid consists of one positive and one negative "frequency" equally spaced around the origin. Thus the diffraction pattern consists of just two lines of intensity equally spaced about the center position of the observing screen (Fig. 3.26). These two lines of intensity could themselves be photographed to provide a "two-slit" aperture plate which would provide a sinusoidal diffraction (interference?) pattern. The

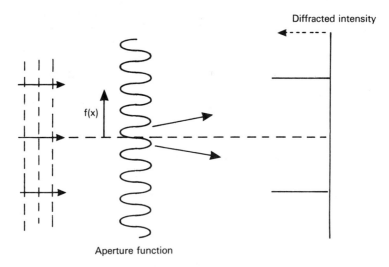

Fig. 3.26   Sinusoidal diffraction grating.

latter pattern will be viewed as an "intensity" pattern, however, and not an "amplitude" pattern. Consequently, it will not comprise the original aperture which must have positive and negative amplitude in order to yield just two lines in its diffraction pattern. Thus, whereas this example illustrates well the strong relationship which exists between the two functions, it also serves to emphasize that the relationship is between the *amplitude* functions while the observed diffraction pattern is (in the absence of special arrangements) the *intensity* function.

Finally, we consider one of the most important examples of all: a rectangular wave aperture amplitude function. The function is shown in Fig. 3.27. This is equivalent to a set of narrow slits, i.e. a diffraction grating. The Fourier transform (and hence the Fraunhöfer diffraction pattern) will be a set of discrete lines of intensity spaced uniformly to accord with the "fundamental" frequency of the aperture function and enveloped by the Fourier transform of one slit. If the aperture function extended to infinity in each direction then the individual lines would be infinitely narrow (δ functions) but, since it cannot do so in practice, the width is inversely proportional to the total width of the grating (i.e. the intensity distribution across one line is essentially the Fourier transform of the envelope function for the square wave).

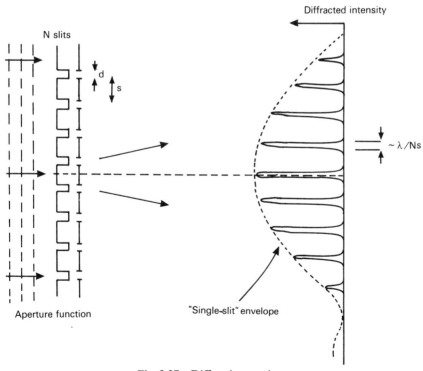

Fig. 3.27 Diffraction grating.

To illustrate these ideas consider a grating of N slits, each of width d and separated by distance s. The diffracted intensity pattern is now given by

$$I(\theta) = I_0 \frac{\sin^2 \beta}{\beta^2} \frac{\sin^2(N\gamma)}{\sin^2\gamma}$$

where

$$\beta = kd\frac{\sin \theta}{2} \qquad \gamma = ks\frac{\sin \theta}{2}$$

The pattern is shown in Fig. 3.27. It is similar in many ways to that of the Fabry–Pérot etalon, as we would expect. Clearly each wavelength present in the light incident on a diffraction grating will produce its own separate diffraction pattern. This fact is used to analyze the spectrum of incident light and also to select and measure specific component wavelengths. Its ability to perform these tasks is most readily characterized by means of its resolving power, which is defined as it was for the Fabry–Pérot etalon, i.e.

$$\rho = \frac{\lambda}{\delta\lambda}$$

where $\delta\lambda$ is the smallest resolvable wavelength difference. If we take $\delta\lambda$ to be that wavelength difference which causes the pattern from $\lambda + \delta\lambda$ to produce a maximum of order p which falls on the first minimum of λ at that same order, we have

$$pN\lambda + \lambda = pN(\lambda + \delta\lambda)$$

and thus

$$\rho = \frac{\lambda}{\delta\lambda} = pN$$

Gratings are ruled on either glass (transmission) or mirrors (reflection) with about 10^5 "lines" (slits) in a distance of about 150 mm. The first-order resolving power is thus about 10^5, which is an order down on that for a Fabry–Pérot etalon. However, the grating is less demanding of optical and mechanical tolerances in production and use, and is thus cheaper and less prone to degradation with time.

3.4.4 Gaussian beams and stable optical resonators

In the discussions of Fabry–Pérot etalons the reflecting surfaces were assumed to be parallel and plane. It was noted in Section 3.2.2 that this was also the structure required for providing positive optical feedback for laser action: in fact we now recognize the parallel-mirror configuration introduced in Section 3.2.2 as just a Fabry–Pérot cavity whose resonator modes will be enveloped by the gain spectrum of the laser medium between them (Siegman, 1971).

The more recent discussions of diffraction now provide further insights into the detailed behavior of such an arrangement. We have assumed that the light incident on the mirrors is a plane wave with uniform amplitude and phase across its aperture. For a circular mirror of diameter d our considerations of Fraunhöfer diffraction have indicated that such an aperture will yield a reflected beam which diverges at an angle of about λ/d. Hence, if the mirrors are separated by a distance $D \gg d$, only a fraction of about $\lambda^2 D^2/d^4$ of the light power will be interrupted by the second mirror, and this loss will be sustained for each mirror-to-mirror passage. How can this loss be reduced? To answer this question it is reasonable to look first for a stable solution to the problem, i.e. a solution which does not involve an additional loss for each pass between mirrors. To find this we can employ our knowledge of diffraction theory to ask the subsidiary question: what aperture distribution is stable in the face of aperture diffraction effects? Since we know that the far-field diffraction pattern is the Fourier transform of the aperture distribution function, it is clear that we are effectively asking which function Fourier transforms into itself or, in more mathematical language, which function is invariant under Fourier transformation. There is only one such function—the Gaussian function, of the form

$$f(r) = A \exp\left(-\frac{r^2}{\sigma^2}\right)$$

where r is the radial dimension in the aperture plane and σ is a constant known in this context as the "spot size".

Suppose, then, that we consider a wave with uniform phase in the plane (x_0, y_0) at P_0 as shown in Fig. 3.28 and that this wave has a Gaussian amplitude distribution

$$f(x, y) = A \exp\left(-\frac{x^2 + y^2}{\sigma^2}\right)$$

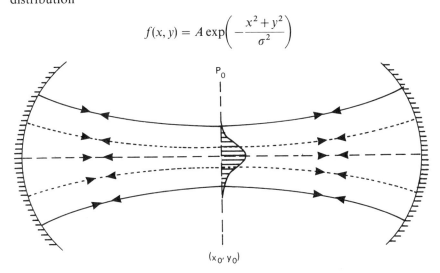

Fig. 3.28 Gaussian stable resonator.

In the far field this will diffract into a spherical wave with the same form of amplitude distribution and thus, if we place in that field a perfectly reflecting spherical mirror whose diameter is much greater than the spot size at that distance from P_0, essentially all the light will be returned along its incident path (Fig. 3.28) (99% of the light will be reflected for a mirror diameter three times the spot size). If another such mirror is placed on the opposite side of P_0, the light continues to bounce between the spherical mirrors with very little loss. Such an arrangement is known as a "stable resonator", and it is clear that the light within it is in the form of a "Gaussian beam". Such arrangements are preferred for laser structures since the losses are minimized. It also follows that the light which emerges from the partially silvered mirror of the laser source will possess a Gaussian intensity distribution. The condition on the size of the mirror will be satisfied automatically since the settling position for the resonance will be that which minimizes the losses (Siegman, 1971). We can also readily see that if a plane mirror is placed at the central plane which contains (x_0, y_0) the optical situation is essentially unchanged, so that a spherical mirror can also be used with a plane mirror to create a stable resonator. Indeed, this configuration is sometimes used in laser design.

As the radii of curvature of the mirrors increase, so their diameters must also increase, for a given spacing, in order to obtain a stable Gaussian resonator mode. In the limit as the radius tends to infinity and the two mirrors thus become plane, the configuration is right on the limit of stability. In fact, the diffraction approximations break down and other methods must be used to obtain the aperture intensity distribution (Siegman, 1971), which is now critically dependent on mirror alignment and surface finish.

3.5 Coherence

3.5.1 Introduction

In dealing with the subjects of interference and diffraction the assumption was made that each of the interfering waves had a constant phase relationship with the others in both time and space. Such an assumption cannot be valid for all time and space intervals since, as we saw in Section 3.2, the atomic emission processes which give rise to light are largely uncorrelated, except for the special case of laser emission. In this section the topic of "coherence" will be dealt with.

The coherence of a wave describes the extent to which it can be represented by a pure sine wave. A pure sine wave has infinite extension and hence cannot exist in reality. Perfect coherence is thus unachievable, but it is nevertheless a valuable concept.

Waves which can be quite accurately represented by sine waves for a limited period of time or in a limited region of space are called partially

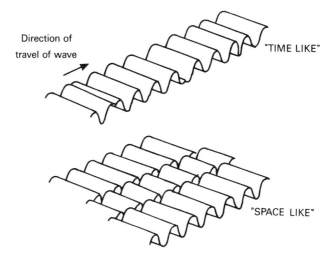

Fig. 3.29 Partial coherence (from Lipson and Lipson, 1969).

coherent waves. Figure 3.29 shows examples of time-like and space-like partial coherence.

A normal light source emits quanta of energy at random. Each quantum can be regarded as a finite wave train having angular frequency ω_0, say, and duration $2\tau_c$ (Fig. 3.30). Fourier theory tells us that this wave train can be described in the frequency domain as a set of waves lying in the frequency range $\omega_0 \pm 1/\tau_c$. For a large number of randomly emitted wave packets all the components at a given frequency will possess random relative phases. Spatial and temporal coherence will thus only exist for, respectively, a distance of the order of the length of one packet ($2c\tau_c$) and a time of the order of its duration ($2\tau_c$). If the wave packets were of infinitely short duration (δ function pulses) then Fourier theory tells us that all frequencies would be present in equal amounts and they would be completely uncorrelated in relative phase. This is

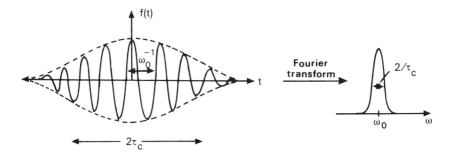

Fig. 3.30 Optical wave packet.

the condition that we call white light. Its spatial and temporary coherence are zero and, again, it is an unachievable fiction. Between the two fictions of perfect coherence and perfect incoherence lies the real world.

3.5.2 Measure of coherence

If we are to determine the measurable effect which the degree of coherence is to have on optical systems, particularly those which involve interference and diffraction effects, we need a quantitative measure of coherence. This must measure the extent to which, knowing the (complex) amplitude of a periodic disturbance at one place and/or time, we can predict its magnitude at another place and/or time. We know that this measure can be expected to have its maximum value for a pure sine wave and its minimum value for white light. A convenient definition will render these values unity and zero respectively. To fix ideas and to simplify matters, let us first consider just temporal coherence.

We can sensibly postulate that a knowledge of the value of a time function $f(t)$ at t will provide us with some knowledge of its value up to say t' when it becomes completely independent of its value at t. If two time functions are completely independent, we expect the average value of their product over a time which is long compared with the timescale of their variations (i.e. reciprocal of the bandwidth) to be equal to the product of their individual average values, i.e.

$$\langle f(t)f(t')\rangle = \langle f(t)\rangle\langle f(t')\rangle$$

and if, as is the case for the vast majority of optical disturbances, the functions oscillate about a zero mean, i.e.

$$\langle f(t)\rangle = \langle f(t')\rangle = 0$$

it follows that

$$\langle f(t)f(t')\rangle = 0$$

However, if we set $t = t'$, our "delay average" above must have its maximum possible value, since a knowledge of the value of $f(t)$ at t enables us to predict its value at t with absolute certainty! Hence we have

$$\langle f(t)f(t)\rangle = \langle f^2(t)\rangle$$

and this must be the maximum value of the quantity. From this we can conclude that a convenient measure of the coherence may well be the parameter which characterizes the decay of the "delay average" in either time or space.

Suppose that we consider a pure temporal sine wave in this context. We know in advance that this is a perfectly coherent disturbance, and conveniently we would thus require our coherence measure to be unity. Let us write it as

$$f(t) = a\sin(\omega t)$$

If we now multiply this by a replica of itself displaced by time τ (Fig. 3.31), we have

$$f(t)f(t+\tau) = a\sin(\omega t)\, a\sin\{\omega(t+\tau)\}$$

$$= \frac{a^2}{2}\{\cos(\omega\tau) - \cos(2\omega t + \omega\tau)\}$$

We now average this over all time and, since $\langle\cos(2\omega t + \omega\tau)\rangle = 0$, we have

$$\langle f(t)f(t+\tau)\rangle = \frac{a^2}{2}\cos(\omega\tau)$$

This quantity is called the self-correlation function $c(\tau)$ of the disturbance. In more formal mathematical terms we would calculate it as follows:

$$c(\tau) = \lim_{T\to\infty}\frac{1}{T}\int_0^T f(t)f(t+\tau)\,\mathrm{d}t$$

i.e.

$$c(\tau) = \lim_{T\to\infty}\frac{1}{T}\int_0^T \frac{a^2}{2}\{\cos(\omega\tau) - \cos(2\omega t + \tau)\}\,\mathrm{d}t$$

and thus, again,

$$c(\tau) = \frac{a^2}{2}\cos(\omega\tau)$$

This function does not decay, but oscillates with frequency ω and constant amplitude $a^2/2$. It is the latter amplitude which we take as our measure of coherence of the light wave, since the sinusoidal term in $\omega\tau$ will always be present for an oscillatory field and provides no useful information on the coherence. Since we require, for convenience, that this measure is unity for the sine wave, we choose to normalize it to its value at $\tau = 0$ (i.e. $c(0) = a^2/2$ in this case). This normalized function is called the coherence function $\gamma(\tau)$.

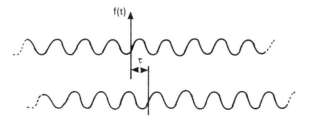

Fig. 3.31 Self-correlation.

Now let us consider white light. We have noted that this is equivalent to a series of randomly spaced δ functions. Clearly this series must have a mean amplitude of zero if it is to represent a spread of optical sinusoids over an infinite frequency range, each with a mean amplitude of zero. If we now multiply this set of δ functions by a displaced replica of itself, only a fraction of the total will overlap. The probability of an overlap between two δ functions of the same sign is equal to that of an overlap between two of opposite signs. Consequently, the mean value of the overlap function will also be zero, regardless of the time delay. Hence, for this case, $c(\tau) = 0$ for all τ and $\gamma(\tau) = 0$ also.

Finally, let us consider a random stream of quanta or wave packets (Fig. 3.32). The packets run into each other, but each packet is largely coherent within itself. If this waveform is multiplied by a displaced replica of itself the result will be of the form shown in Fig. 3.33. Only when the displacement exceeds the duration of one packet does the correlation fall essentially to zero. Thus, in this case, we have an exponentially decaying sine wave, and the decay rate of its amplitude will be our measure of coherence.

The coherence function $\gamma(\tau)$ for $f(t)$ can be written in the general form

$$\gamma(\tau) = \frac{\left| \int_0^\infty f(t)f^*(t+\tau)\,\mathrm{d}t \right|}{\int_0^\infty f(t)f^*(t)\,\mathrm{d}t} = \frac{|c(\tau)|}{|c(0)|}$$

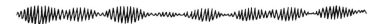

Fig. 3.32   A stream of quanta.

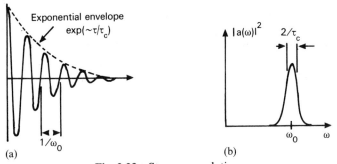

Fig. 3.33   Stream correlation.

The coherence functions for the three cases we have been considering are shown in Fig. 3.34: the sine wave's function does not decay and therefore its coherence time is infinite; the white light's function decays in zero time and thus its coherence time is zero; the "stream of wave packets" function decays in time τ_c and thus it is partially coherent with coherence time τ_c. All other temporal functions can have their coherence time quantified in this way. It is also clear that the quantity $c\tau_c$, where c is the velocity of light, will specify a coherence length.

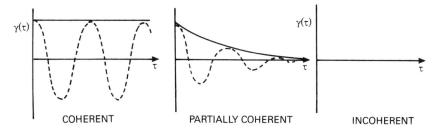

Fig. 3.34 Coherence function.

Fairly obviously, the same ideas can also be used for spatial coherence, with τ replaced by the spatial delay σ. Specifically, in this case

$$\gamma(\sigma) = \frac{\left| \int_0^\infty f(s)f^*(s+\sigma)\,ds \right|}{\int_0^\infty f(s)f^*(s)\,ds} = \frac{|c(\sigma)|}{|c(0)|}$$

and the coherence length will be defined by a "decay parameter" σ_c.

Finally, the mutual coherence of two separate functions $f_1(t)$ and $f_2(t)$ can

$$\gamma_{12}(\tau) = \frac{\left| \int_0^\infty f_1(t)f_2(t+\tau)\,dt \right|}{\int_0^\infty f_1(t)f_2^*(t)\,dt}$$

$$= \frac{|c_{12}(\tau)|}{|c_{12}(0)|}$$

where t and τ are again replaceable by s and σ respectively for the mutual spatial coherence case.

3.5.3 Wiener–Khinchin theorem

The Wiener–Khinchin theorem states that the Fourier transform of the self-correlation function $c(\tau)$ for a function $f(t)$ provides the power spectrum of $f(t)$. This follows directly from the convolution theorem in Fourier analysis, which states that the Fourier transform of the convolution of two functions is the product of their individual Fourier transforms (see any text on Fourier theory, e.g. Panter, 1965). "Convolution" is essentially just the "delayed average" process we have been considering.

Thus we have

$$\text{FT} \int_0^\infty f(t)f^*(t+\tau)\,dt = \text{FT}\,c(\tau) = \text{FT}f(t).\,\text{FT}f^*(t)$$

where FT denotes the Fourier transform operator. If we now write $f(t)$ in the form

$$f(t) = \int_0^\infty a(\omega)\exp(i\omega t)\,d\omega$$

we have

$$\text{FT}f(t).\,\text{FT}f^*(t) = |a(\omega)|^2$$

which is the "power spectrum" of $f(t)$. Hence the power spectrum of a light source can be determined from its self-correlation function. This is a useful result.

3.5.4 Dual-beam interference

We shall now consider in more detail the conditions for interference between two light beams (Fig. 3.35). It is clear, from our previous look at this topic, that interference fringes will be formed if the two waves bear a constant phase relationship to each other, but we must now consider the form of the interference pattern for varying degrees of mutual coherence. In particular, we must consider the "visibility" of the pattern, i.e. the extent to which it contains measurable structure.

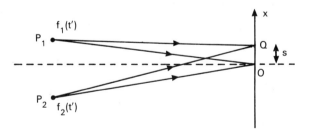

Fig. 3.35 Two-source interference.

At point O the amplitude resulting from the two sources P_1 and P_2 is given by

$$A = f_1(t'') + f_2(t'')$$

where $t'' = t' + \tau_0$ and τ_0 is the time taken for light to travel from P_1 or P_2 to O. If f_1 and f_2 represent the electric field amplitudes of the waves, the observed intensity at O will be given by

$$I_O = \langle AA^* \rangle = \langle \{f_1(t'') + f_2(t'')\}\{f_1^*(t'') + f_2^*(t'')\} \rangle$$

where the angular brackets indicate an average taken over the response time of the detector (e.g. the human eye).

At point Q the amplitudes will be

$$f_1(t'' - \tau/2) \qquad\qquad f_2(t'' + \tau/2)$$

where τ is the time difference between paths P_2Q and P_1Q. Writing $t = t'' - \tau/2$ we have the intensity at Q:

$$I_Q = \langle \{f_1(t) + f_2(t + \tau)\}\{f_1^*(t) + f_2^*(t + \tau)\} \rangle$$

or

$$I_Q = \langle f_1(t)f_1^*(t) \rangle + \langle f_2(t)f_2^*(t) \rangle + \langle f_2(t + \tau)f_1^*(t) \rangle + \langle f_1(t)f_2^*(t + \tau) \rangle$$

The first two terms are clearly the independent intensities of the two sources at Q. The second two terms have the form of our previously defined mutual correlation function; in fact

$$\langle f_1(t)f_2^*(t + \tau) \rangle = c_{12}(\tau)$$

$$\langle f_1^*(t)f_2(t + \tau) \rangle = c_{12}^*(\tau)$$

We may note, in passing, that each of these terms will be zero if f_1 and f_2 have orthogonal polarizations, since in that case neither field amplitude has a component in the direction of the other and the two cannot interfere. Hence the average value of their product is again just the product of their averages, each of which is zero as they are sinusoids.

If $c_{12}(\tau)$ is now written in the form

$$c_{12}(\tau) = |c_{12}(\tau)| \exp(i\omega\tau)$$

(which is valid provided that f_1 and f_2 are sinusoids in ωt), we have

$$c_{12}(\tau) + c_{12}^*(\tau) = 2|c_{12}(\tau)| \cos(\omega\tau)$$

Hence, provided that we observe the light intensity at Q with a detector which has a response time very much greater than the coherence times (self and mutual) of the sources (so that the time averages are valid), we can write the intensity at Q as

$$I_Q = I_1 + I_2 + 2|c_{12}(\tau)| \cos(\omega\tau)$$

As we move along x we shall effectively increase τ, so that we shall see a variation in intensity whose amplitude will be $2c_{12}(r)$, i.e. twice the modulus of the mutual coherence function, and which will vary about a mean value equal to the sum of the two intensities. Thus we have an experimental method by which the mutual coherence of the sources can be measured.

If we now define a fringe *visibility* for this interference pattern by

$$V = \frac{I_{max} - I_{min}}{I_{max} + I_{min}}$$

then

$$V(\tau) = \frac{2|c_{12}(\tau)|}{|c_{12}(0)|}$$

and with, as previously defined,

$$\gamma(\tau) = \frac{|c_{12}(\tau)|}{|c_{12}(0)|}$$

we note that

$$|c_{12}(0)| = \left| \int_0^\infty f_1(t) f_2^*(t) \, dt \right|$$
$$= \langle E_1 \rangle \langle E_2 \rangle$$
$$= (I_1 I_2)^{1/2}$$

and thus

$$\gamma(\tau) = \frac{c_{12}(\tau)}{(I_1 I_2)^{1/2}}$$

Hence the visibility function $V(\tau)$ is related to the coherence function $\gamma(\tau)$ by

$$V(\tau) = \frac{2(I_1 I_2)^{1/2}}{I_1 + I_2} \gamma(\tau)$$

and if the two intensities are equal we have

$$V(\tau) = \gamma(\tau)$$

i.e. the functions are identical. From this we can conclude that for equal-intensity coherent sources the visibility is 100% ($\gamma = 1$), for incoherent sources it is zero and for partially coherent sources it gives a direct measure of the actual coherence.

If we arrange that the points P_1 and P_2 are pinholes equidistant from and illuminated by a single source S, the visibility function clearly measures the self-coherence of S. Moreover, the Fourier transform of the function will yield the power spectrum via the Wiener–Khinchin theorem.

Suppose now that the two holes are placed in front of an extended source S, as shown in Fig. 3.36, and that their separation is variable. The interference pattern produced by these sources of light now measures the correlation between the two corresponding points on the extended source. If the separation is initially zero and is increased until the visibility first falls again to zero, the value of the separation at which this occurs defines a spatial coherence length for the extended source. If the source has uniform properties, a coherence area is correspondingly defined. In other words, any given source point has no phase correlation with any point which lies outside the circular area of which it is the center point.

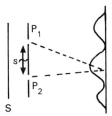

Fig. 3.36 Extended-source interference.

An extension of this idea is used in Michelson's stellar interferometer to measure the angular diameters of stars (Fig. 3.37). If the star subtends an angle α at two mirrors, spaced at distance d, the two monochromatic (with the aid of an optical filter) rays A, A' (essentially parallel owing to the very large distance of the star) will be coherent and will produce an interference pattern with visibility unity. Similarly, so also will the two rays B, B' from the other edge of the star. If the distance d between the mirrors is such that the ray B' is just one wavelength closer to M_2 than B is to M_1, the second interference pattern, from BB', coincides with the first from AA'. All the intermediate points across the star produce interference patterns between these two to give a total resultant visibility of zero. Hence the value of d for which the fringe visibility first disappears provides the angular diameter of the star as λ/d (in fact, owing to

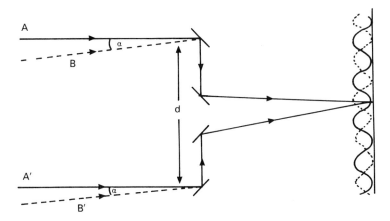

Fig. 3.37 Michelson's stellar interferometer.

the circular rather than rectangular area, it is $1.22\lambda/d$). This method was first used by Michelson in 1920 to determine the angular diameter of the star Betelgeuse as 0.047 arcsec. Distances d between mirrors of up to 10 m have been used.

Finally, consider again the Mach–Zehnder arrangement of Fig. 3.20. The measurand M in a Mach–Zehnder interferometer causes a phase change in arm 1 which is detected by means of a change in the position on the interference pattern resulting from the recombination at point R. Interference can only occur if the recombining beams have components of the same polarization and if the difference in path length between the two arms is less than the source coherence length. This is not practicable with a light-emitting diode, which has a coherence length of about 0.02 mm, but even a modest semiconductor laser has a coherence length of about 1 m (time, 5 ns) and can easily be used in this application. A single-mode He–Ne laser has a coherence length of several kilometers.

3.6 Polarization optics

3.6.1 The polarization ellipse

In Section 3.1.3 the most general form of polarized light wave propagating in the Oz direction was derived from the two linearly polarized components in the Ox and Oy directions:

$$E_x = e_x \cos(\omega t - kz + \delta_x)$$

$$E_y = e_y \cos(\omega t - kz + \delta_y)$$

If we eliminate $\omega t - kz$ from these equations we obtain the expression

$$\frac{E_x^2}{e_x^2} + \frac{E_y^2}{e_y^2} + 2\frac{E_x E_y}{e_x e_y}\cos(\delta_y - \delta_x) = \sin^2(\delta_y - \delta_x)$$

which is the ellipse circumscribed by the tip of the electric vector at any one point in space over one period of the combined wave. This can only be true, however, if $\delta_y - \delta_x$ is constant in time or, at least, is changing only very slowly in a time of the order of the response time of the detector. In other words the two waves must have a large mutual coherence. If this were not so then relative phases and hence resultant field vectors would vary randomly in the detector response time, giving no ordered pattern to the behavior of the resultant field and thus presenting to the detector what would be, essentially, unpolarized light.

Assuming that the mutual coherence is good, we can investigate further the properties of the polarization ellipse. Note firstly that the ellipse always lies in the rectangle shown in Fig. 3.38 but that the axes of the ellipse are not

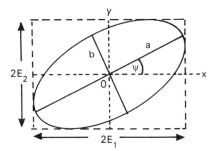

Fig. 3.38 Polarization ellipse.

parallel to the original x, y directions. The ellipse is specified as follows: with e_x, e_y and $\delta (= \delta_y - \delta_x)$ known, we define $\tan \alpha = e_y/e_x$. The orientation ψ of the ellipse is given by

$$\tan \psi = \tan(2\alpha) \cos \delta$$

The semimajor and semiminor axes a and b are given by

$$e_x{}^2 + e_y{}^2 = a^2 + b^2 (= I)$$

$$e = \tan \chi = \pm b/a$$

(the sign determines the sense of the rotation) where $\sin 2\chi = -\sin 2\alpha \sin \delta$.

Control over the polarization state of light can be effected by utilizing the polarization properties of crystals. Most crystals exhibit polarization anisotropy, i.e. a different refractive index for differing polarization states. This is the result of differing electron vibrational frequencies in the molecules depending on the direction with respect to the crystal axes.

For crystals without optical activity (i.e. crystals which do not rotate the polarization direction for linearly polarized light), in any given direction of propagation there will be two orthogonal directions of linear polarization which will propagate without change of form (i.e. will remain linear). In general they will propagate at different velocities, thus exhibiting two refractive indices; the crystal is said to be doubly refracting or "birefringent". In this case it is *linearly* birefringent. There will be either one or two directions where the velocity is independent of polarization direction (i.e. the linear birefringence vanishes). These are the optic axes of the crystal. A linearly birefringent crystal can thus be either uniaxial or biaxial.

In a crystal which possesses optical activity, a spiral structure in the crystal causes the polarization direction of a linearly polarized wave to rotate as it propagates. In this case only a circularly polarized wave propagates without change of form, and the right-hand and left-hand circularly polarized waves propagate with differing velocities. The crystal now exhibits circular birefringence.

When both circular and linear birefringence are present, the normal modes (or "eigenmodes"—polarization states which propagate without change of form) are elliptical states, and the crystal shows elliptical birefringence. All states other than the normal modes will be changed by the propagation through the crystal. In general one elliptical state will be translated into a different elliptical state, and we need firstly a measurement method for determining the state of polarization for any polarized beam of light.

A convenient method for practical determination of the polarization ellipse is to measure the Stokes parameters (Born and Wolf, 1975). These can be measured with the aid of a linear polarizer (e.g. Polaroid) and a 90° retarder (quarter-wave plate), which is a device for imposing 90° phase retardation on one linear optical polarization component compared with its orthogonal component. If $I(\theta, \varepsilon)$ denotes the intensity of the light passed by the linear polarizer at angle θ to Ox after the Oy component has been retarded by angle ε as a result of insertion of the retardation element, the Stokes parameters are defined as follows:

$$S_0 = I(0°, 0) + I(90°, 0) = e_x^2 + e_y^2$$

$$S_1 = I(0°, 0) - I(90°, 0) = e_x^2 + e_y^2$$

$$S_2 = I(45°, 0) - I(135°, 0) = 2e_x e_y \cos \delta$$

$$S_3 = I(45°, \pi/2) - I(135°, \pi/2) = 2e_x e_y \sin \delta$$

Only three of these parameters are independent, since

$$S_0^2 = S_1^2 + S_2^2 + S_3^2$$

where S_0 is the total light intensity. Measurement of the S_n provides the ellipticity e and the orientation ψ of the polarization ellipse via the relations

$$e = \tan \chi$$

$$\sin(2\chi) = S_3/S_0$$

$$\tan(2\psi) = S_2/S_1$$

Now, the above relations suggest a geometrical construction which provides a powerful and elegant means for description and analysis of optical polarization phenomena. The Stokes parameters S_1, S_2, S_3 can be regarded as the Cartesian coordinates of a point referred to axes Ox_1, Ox_2, Ox_3. Thus every elliptical polarization state corresponds to a unique point in three-dimensional space. For a constant S_0 (lossless medium) it follows that all such points lie on a sphere of radius S_0—the Poincaré sphere (Fig. 3.39). The properties of the sphere are quite well known (Jerrard, 1954). We can see that the equator will comprise the continuum of linearly polarized states whilst the two poles will correspond to the two oppositely handed states of circular polarization.

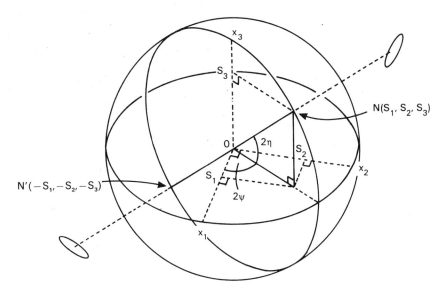

Fig. 3.39 The Poincaré sphere.

It is clear that any change within a lossless element from one polarization state to another corresponds to a rotation of the sphere about a diameter. Now any such rotation of the sphere can be expressed as a unitary 2×2 matrix M. Thus the conversion from one polarization state E to another E' can also be expressed in the form

$$E' = ME$$

or

$$\begin{pmatrix} E_x' \\ E_y' \end{pmatrix} = \begin{pmatrix} m_1 & m_4 \\ m_3 & m_2 \end{pmatrix} \begin{pmatrix} E_x \\ E_y \end{pmatrix}$$

i.e.

$$E_x' = m_1 E_x + m_4 E_y$$
$$E_y' = m_3 E_x + m_2 E_y$$

where

$$M = \begin{pmatrix} m_1 & m_4 \\ m_3 & m_2 \end{pmatrix}$$

is a unitary Jones matrix (Jones, 1941 to 1956) which completely characterizes the optical element effecting the polarization change. The two eigenvectors of the matrix correspond to the normal modes or eigenstates of the element (i.e. those polarization states which can propagate through the element without change of form). These two polarization eigenstates lie at opposite ends of a diameter of the Poincaré sphere, and the effect of the element is to rotate the sphere about this diameter (Fig. 3.39).

The polarization action of the element can thus be regarded as that of resolving the input polarization state into two eigenstates with appropriate amplitudes and then inserting a phase difference between them before recombining to obtain the emergent state. Thus a pure rotator is equivalent to a rotation about the polar axis with the two oppositely handed circular polarizations as eigenstates. The phase velocity difference between these two eigenstates is a measure of the circular birefringence. Analogously, a pure linear retarder (such as a wave plate) inserts a phase difference between orthogonal linear polarizations and measures the linear birefringence. The linear retarder's eigenstates lie at opposite ends of an equatorial diameter. It is useful for many purposes to resolve the polarization action of any given element into its linear and circular birefringence components. The Poincaré sphere makes it clear that this can always be done since any rotation of the sphere can always be resolved into two subrotations, one about the polar diameter and the other about an equatorial diameter.

Figure 3.40 illustrates simple methods of control over the polarization state of light. In Fig. 3.40(a) a Polaroid plate allows just one linear direction to be transmitted as a result of an anisotropy in its structure which absorbs one linear polarization much more strongly than it absorbs the orthogonal linear polarization. In Fig. 3.40(b) a $\lambda/4$ phase plate (quarter-wave plate) is being used to generate an ellipse of varying ellipticity by varying the direction of the input linear polarization; a phase shift of $\pi/2$ is inserted between the two crystal axis components, and thus the major axes of the ellipse will always be parallel with the crystal axes whereas the ellipticity will vary continuously with input polarization direction. In Fig. 3.40(c) the direction of polarization of a linearly

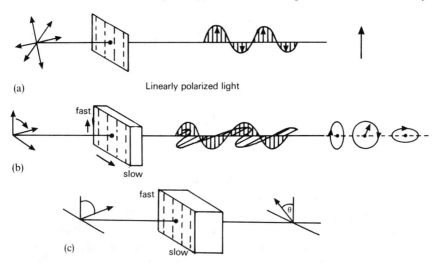

Fig. 3.40   Polarization controllers: (a) linear polarizer; (b) quarter-wave plate; (c) half-wave plate.

polarized output beam can be varied by altering the direction of the crystal axes of a $\lambda/2$ phase plate (half-wave plate) with respect to the polarization direction of a linearly polarized input beam. Combinations of these three elements can effect most of the polarization transformations required in practice.

3.6.2 Applications of polarization optics

3.6.2.1 Passive optical fiber effects
The ray picture of optical fiber propagation indicates the polarization dependence of any particular mode since, as we saw in Section 3.3.5, the phase change on TIR is polarization dependent. Each mode will have its own polarization properties and hence the light in a multimode fiber will be of mixed polarization. A monomode fiber must be used to retain the light in a definable polarization state.

A truly symmetrical monomode fiber exhibits no anisotropy and is polarization degenerate, i.e. all elliptical states propagate without change of form. However, as soon as any cross-sectional asymmetry is introduced, the degeneracy is lifted. All real fibers possess some asymmetry owing to one or more of the following: noncircularity of the core (Fig. 3.41(a)); linear strain in the core (Fig. 3.41(b)); twist strain in the core (Fig. 3.41(c)). Bending will introduce linear strain, and twisting will introduce circular strain.

In telecommunications, a strained fiber will introduce a polarization dispersion but, for available fiber, it is only of the order of $1–10\,\mathrm{ps\,km^{-1}}$. The dispersion can be reduced still further, to about $0.01\,\mathrm{ps\,km^{-1}}$, by using the "spun preform" technique (Barlow *et al.*, 1981). In order to introduce birefringence into the fiber deliberately, either the core can be made elliptical or stress can be introduced into the core by asymmetric doping of the cladding (Varnham *et al.*, 1983) (Fig. 3.41(d)).

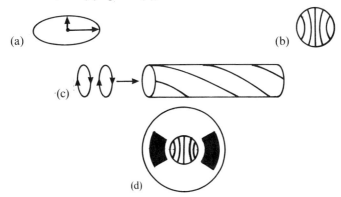

Fig. 3.41 Birefringence in optical fibers: (a) linearly birefringent fiber (form); (b) linearly birefringent fiber (strain); (c) twist–strain circularly birefringent fiber; (d) doped linearly birefringent fiber ("bow tie").

With large birefringence the phase velocity differences are also large and coupling between eigenmodes is difficult. Fiber with a phase velocity difference of the order of 10^{-3} of the light velocity is known as "hi-bi" (high birefringence) fiber, or "polarization-holding" fiber, since light launched into one eigenstate will tend to stay there. Such fiber has many applications, some of which will be dealt with in later chapters.

3.6.2.2 Active polarization effects

The optical polarization properties of material media can be influenced by the action of external electric and magnetic fields. Fundamentally, this results from the fact that the fields will exert forces on the atomic electrons in the media and thus will constrain their motions. When an electromagnetic wave passes through a medium it interacts with these electrons and is thus itself constrained in its oscillations to some extent (this topic is dealt with in more detail in Section 3.7.2). We shall consider just three such active effects to illustrate the general phenomenon.

Electro-optic effect When an electric field is applied to an optical medium the electrons suffer restricted motion in the direction of the field when compared with that orthogonal to it. Thus the material becomes linearly birefringent in response to the field.

Consider the arrangement of Fig. 3.42(a). Here we have incident light which is linearly polarized at 45° to an electric field which acts on a medium transversely to the propagation direction of the light. The field-induced linear birefringence will cause a phase displacement between components of the incident light which lie respectively parallel and orthogonal to the field; hence the light will emerge elliptically polarized.

A (perfect) polarizer placed with its acceptance direction parallel to the input polarization direction will pass all the light in the absence of a field. When the field is applied the fraction of light power which is passed will depend upon the form of the ellipse, which in turn depends upon the phase delay introduced by the field. Consequently, the field can be used to modulate

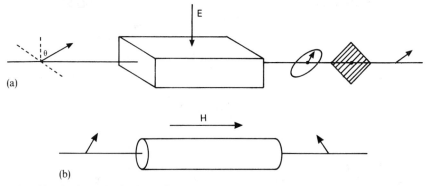

Fig. 3.42 Active polarization effects: (a) electro-optic effect; (b) magneto-optic effect.

the intensity of the light, and the electro-optic effect is, indeed, very useful for the modulation of light.

The phase delay introduced is proportional either to the field (Pockels effect) or to the square of the field (Kerr effect). All materials manifest a transverse Kerr effect. Only crystalline materials can manifest any kind of Pockels effect or a longitudinal Kerr effect (E field parallel to the propagation direction). In addition to light modulation, it is clear that the effect could be used to measure an electric field or the voltage which gives rise to it. Sensors of this type will be discussed in later chapters.

Magneto-optic effect   The polarization effect of a longitudinal magnetic field is to rotate the polarization direction of an input linearly polarized light wave (Fig. 3.42(b)). The reason for this is that the atomic electrons can more easily rotate in one direction about the field direction than in the other (Lorentz force) and thus a field-dependent circular birefringence is introduced. This is known as the Faraday magneto-optic effect, and the polarization rotation is proportional to the line integral of the magnetic field along the propagation path, i.e.

$$\rho = V \int_0^L \boldsymbol{H} \cdot \mathrm{d}\boldsymbol{l}$$

where V is known as the Verdet constant and is a constant for a given material.

This effect has a number of uses. It can be used to modulate light, although it is less convenient for this than is the electro-optic effect in view of the increased difficulties in manipulating magnetic fields compared with electric fields. It can be used to measure magnetic fields and the electric currents which give rise to them. It can also be used (and often is) in optical isolators for it is a nonreciprocal effect. This means that if the rotation through an optical element is 45°, then on passing back through the element the light is rotated another 45° in the same direction. (If the effect were reciprocal, the two rotations would cancel.) Consequently, in this case the back-reflected light emerges with a linear polarization direction which is orthogonal to the original direction, and a linear polarizer at the input end will block it. Hence the input end is effectively "isolated" from the output end of the element. This is particularly useful when using laser sources which are sensitive to back-reflected light.

Electrogyration effect   An electric field will induce circular birefringence in some materials (e.g. quartz, bismuth germanium oxide). This effect is thus the electric field analog of the Faraday magneto-optic effect. This effect occurs only when the material possesses a spirality in the crystal structure and thus an intrinsic circular birefringence. The electric field effectively alters the pitch of the spiral and hence the magnitude of the circular birefringence. The effect is known as the electrogyration effect (Rogers, 1977), and it can be used to measure electric field/voltage and also as a source of reciprocal (rather than nonreciprocal, as in the Faraday effect) polarization rotation.

3.7 Interaction of light with matter

3.7.1 General

The basic atomic processes involved in the absorption and emission of light were discussed in Section 3.2. In this section the subject will be dealt with in more detail. When considering the propagation of light in optical media there is much advantage in using the wave rather than the particle approach. It is with this that we shall begin.

3.7.2 Classical theory of propagation in uniform dielectric media

Consider the standard electric field component of an electromagnetic wave propagating in the Oz direction in an optical medium of refractive index n, i.e.

$$E = E_0 \exp\{i(\omega t - kz)\}$$

We know that

$$\frac{\omega}{k} = c = \frac{c_0}{n}$$

and hence we can write

$$E = E_0 \exp\left\{i\omega\left(t - \frac{nz}{c_0}\right)\right\}$$

We can conveniently include both the attenuation and the phase behavior of the wave in this expression by defining a complex refractive index

$$n = n' - in''$$

so that

$$E = E_0 \exp\left(-\frac{\omega n'' z}{c_0}\right) \exp\left\{i\omega\left(t - \frac{n' z}{c_0}\right)\right\} \qquad (3.23)$$

The first exponential clearly represents an attenuation factor and the second represents the propagating wave.

When electromagnetic radiation propagates through a material medium it stimulates the atomic electrons to oscillate, and thus to radiate, in the manner of elementary electric dipoles. The resulting intensity distribution of the radiation will depend upon the interference between the original wave and the scattered radiation from these elementary dipoles; it will thus depend upon the distribution of the dipoles.

Whatever the dipole distribution, however, the secondary wavelets in the forward direction will retain coherence with each other and with the original primary wave. The resultant forward wave will thus suffer a phase displacement (with respect to the undisturbed primary) leading to a different phase velocity and hence to a refractive index different from unity. Since the elementary dipole oscillators will also be damped to some extent by the loss of radiation, by atomic collisions etc., some absorption of the primary wave will also occur, leading to attenuation (and giving rise to a heating of the medium). The refractive index for this forward scatter will thus be complex in form to allow for the two effects.

The intensity distribution for radiation scattered in directions other than forward will depend upon the dipole distribution. For a regular crystalline structure, for example, when the wavelength is of the same order as the molecular spacing, we obtain the sharp intensity peaks typical of diffraction gratings and well known in X-ray diffractometry. For random distributions of the scattering centers we obtain the uniform intensity distribution associated with Rayleigh scattering (Jenkins and White, 1953, Chapter 22). We can therefore conveniently separate the refractive index function into two components, one due to forward scatter (n_f) and the other to nonforward scatter (n_s). We now have

$$n = n_f + n_s = n' - in''$$

Consider a material through which is propagating an electromagnetic wave whose electric field is given by

$$E = E_0 \exp(i\omega t)$$

and let us assume that the wavelength of the propagating radiation is large compared with the interatomic spacing. An electron within an atom or molecule of the medium will be displaced by an amount s, say, and as a result of this displacement will experience a restoring force $-m\omega_r^2 s$, where m is the electron mass and ω_r is its natural frequency of oscillation. Additionally there will be a damping of the oscillation, and we can represent this by a term of the form $-m\gamma s$. The damping results from losses due to radiation by the electron, collisions which occur during the oscillation etc., and γ will always be positive. Now the force acting to displace the electrons will be that due to the electric field of the original wave plus that due to the electric polarization of the surrounding medium.

For an electron displacement s the electric dipole moment of an elementary dipole is

$$p = es$$

where e is the electronic charge. For N dipoles per unit volume the total polarization of the medium is

$$P = Nes \tag{3.24}$$

The effective electric field acting on a dipole in an isotropic medium is then given by

$$E_e = E + \frac{P}{3\varepsilon_0}$$

The term $P/3\varepsilon_0$ is known as the Lorentz correction (Bleaney and Bleaney, 1959).

We can now write the equation of motion for a displaced electron:

$$\ddot{s} + \gamma \dot{s} + \omega_r{}^2 s = \frac{e}{m}\left(E + \frac{P}{3\varepsilon_0}\right) \tag{3.25}$$

Substituting for s from (3.24) we obtain

$$\ddot{P} + \gamma \dot{P} + P\left(\omega_r{}^2 - \frac{Ne^2}{\varepsilon_0 m}\right) = \frac{Ne^2}{m} E_0 \exp(i\omega t)$$

Solving for P (and ignoring transients) we obtain an expression for the volume susceptibility (polarizability) of the medium:

$$\chi = \frac{P}{E_0} = \frac{Ne^2}{m} \frac{1}{(\omega_r{}^2 - Ne^2/\varepsilon_0 m) - \omega^2 + i\gamma\omega}$$

or

$$\chi = \frac{Ne^2}{m} \frac{1}{(\omega_e{}^2 - \omega^2) + i\gamma\omega}$$

where

$$\omega_e{}^2 = \omega_r{}^2 - \frac{Ne^2}{\varepsilon_0 m}$$

It is important to note that $\omega_e{}^2$ will always be positive, for, if it were negative, the electron's restoring force would also be negative and the atom would ionize under the influence of the electric field; normal linear propagation could not occur under such conditions.

Finally, we can generalize the expression for χ to include electrons with various natural frequencies of oscillation and hence obtain a total effective volume susceptibility:

$$\chi_e = \sum_j \frac{C_j}{(\omega_j{}^2 - \omega^2) + i\gamma_j\omega}$$

and all the C_j, $\omega_j{}^2$, γ_j will always be positive.

Using the well-known relations

$$\varepsilon = 1 + \chi_e$$

and

$$n_f{}^2 = \varepsilon$$

for the dielectric constant and the refractive index of the medium respectively we have that

$$n_f{}^2 = 1 + \chi_e = 1 + \sum_j \frac{C_j}{(\omega_j{}^2 - \omega^2) + i\gamma_j\omega} \tag{3.26}$$

To find the nonforward scatter component we first note that for an oscillating electron with an electric dipole moment of amplitude p_0, the total radiated power is

$$W_s = \frac{\mu_0}{12\pi c}\omega^4 p_0{}^2$$

where μ_0 is the permeability and c is the velocity of light in free space. If there are N dipoles per unit volume,

$$P = Np_0$$

where P is the polarization of the medium. We have that the volume susceptibility is

$$\chi_e = \frac{P}{E_0}$$

and thus

$$p_0 = \frac{\chi_e E_0}{N}$$

giving

$$W_s = \frac{KE_0{}^2}{N^2}\omega^4 \chi_e{}^2$$

where $K = \mu_0/12\pi c$. Now from (3.26) it is noted that, if $\omega_j \gg \omega$, χ_e is approximately independent of ω. Under this condition W_s is proportional to ω^4. This is the well-known Rayleigh scattering condition and it occurs for frequencies well removed from any molecular resonances. In the region of the resonances the dependence of the scattering on frequency is more complex; the scattering itself is much stronger (resonance scattering).

W_s can be interpreted as an imaginary component of the refractive index which will take the form

$$n_s = -iK''\omega^3\chi_e$$

so that we have for the full complex refractive index

$$n = (1+\chi_e)^{1/2} - iK''\omega^3\chi_e$$

where

$$\chi_e = \sum_j \frac{C_j}{(\omega_j{}^2 - \omega^2) + i\gamma_j\omega}$$

Schematic variations in the real and imaginary components of the refractive index of doped silica (of which optical fibers are made) with frequency are shown in Fig. 3.43. The effects of molecular absorption are clearly seen on both

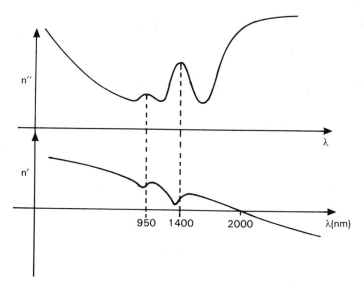

Fig. 3.43   Refractive index components for doped silica.

components. In fact, it is possible to relate the real and imaginary components mathematically. This is due to the fact that they each rely on the same fact of resonant absorption. The relevant mathematical expressions are known as the Kramers–Krönig relations (Rogers, 1984).

3.7.3 Dispersion

The fact that the real part of the refractive index varies with frequency has some important implications for the propagation of the wave, for it means that the wave velocity varies with frequency. All real sources of light provide their radiation over a range of frequencies. This range is large for an incandescent radiator such as a light bulb and very small for a gas laser, but it can never be zero. Consequently, in the case of a medium whose refractive index varies with frequency, different portions of the source spectrum will travel at different velocities. This causes "dispersion" of the light energy, and the medium is thus said to be "dispersive".

In order to understand some of the consequences of dispersion, suppose that just two closely spaced frequency components of equal amplitude are present in the source spectrum, i.e.

$$E = E_0 \cos(\omega t - kz) + E_0 \cos \overline{(\omega + \delta\omega}\, t - \overline{k + \delta k}z)$$

Hence, using elementary trigonometry,

$$E = 2E_0 \cos\left(\frac{\delta\omega}{2} t - \frac{\delta k}{2} z\right) \cos\left(\overline{\omega + \frac{\delta\omega}{2}}\, t - \overline{k + \frac{\delta k}{2}}z\right)$$

This represents a sinusoidal wave (second factor) whose amplitude is modulated by another sinusoid (first factor). The wave itself travels at a velocity

$$\frac{\omega + \delta\omega/2}{k + \delta k/2} \approx \frac{\omega}{k} = c$$

which is the mean velocity of the two waves. However, the point of maximum amplitude of the wave will always occur when

$$\frac{\delta\omega}{2}t - \frac{\delta k}{2}z = 0$$

i.e.

$$\frac{\delta\omega}{\delta k} = \frac{z}{t} = c_g$$

Now we also know that

$$\frac{\omega}{k} = \frac{c_0}{n} = c$$

where n is the refractive index. Hence we have, in the limit as $\delta\omega, \delta k \to 0$,

$$\frac{d\omega}{dk} = \frac{c_0}{n}\left(1 - \frac{k}{n}\frac{dn}{dk}\right)$$

If n does not vary with frequency (or wavelength) then $dn/dk = 0$ and

$$\frac{d\omega}{dk} = c_g = \frac{c_0}{n} = c$$

However, if $dn/dk \neq 0$ (i.e. the medium is dispersive), $c_g \neq c$ and the maximum of the disturbance travels at a different velocity from the "carrier" optical wave. These ideas can readily be generalized to include the complete spectrum of a practical source. Provided that dn/dk is sensibly constant over the spectrum of wavelengths, it follows that a pulse of light from the source will effectively travel at a velocity c_g rather than c. c_g is called the group velocity of the pulse. For convenience, a "group refractive index" N_g is defined by

$$N_g = \frac{c_0}{c_g}$$

Some simple algebra shows that

$$N_g = n - \lambda\frac{dn}{d\lambda}$$

Another important consequence of dispersion is that the pulse might increase in width as it propagates. This can be seen by examining the expression for the propagation time of the pulse over a given distance l:

$$t = \frac{l}{c_g} = \frac{l}{c_0}\left(n - \lambda\frac{dn}{d\lambda}\right)$$

This time is a constant provided that $dn/d\lambda$ is a constant for all wavelengths present. However, if $dn/d\lambda$ varies over the source spectrum, it is not possible to assign a single group velocity to all parts of the pulse and they will thus traverse l in different times. Hence the pulse shape must change. To quantify this we consider a range of wavelengths $\delta\lambda$ and write

$$\tau = \frac{dt}{d\lambda}\delta\lambda = -\frac{l}{c_0}\lambda\frac{d^2n}{d\lambda^2}\delta\lambda$$

where τ is the spread of pulse arrival times. Clearly, to minimize this we must choose our spectral range to ensure that $d^2n/d\lambda^2 \approx 0$.

To set these ideas into practical context we may note that for silica at a wavelength of 850 nm the pulse spreading for a light-emitting diode (spectral width of about 30 nm) is about 2.5 ns km^{-1}, whereas for a semiconductor laser at the same wavelength (width about 3 nm) the spread is only about 0.25 ns km^{-1}. The condition for minimum dispersion, i.e. $d^2n/d\lambda^2 = 0$, is usually achieved at a wavelength of around 1.3 μm in silica, and this wavelength is therefore the choice for large bandwidth optical fiber communications systems.

3.7.4 Luminescence

So far in this chapter the study of the interaction of light with matter has proceeded on the assumption that the material medium consists of natural oscillators which are stimulated by the propagating light wave to oscillate at the wave frequency.

We shall now consider oscillations at other than the stimulating frequency and, since the classical theory of interactions is inadequate to deal with such processes, we must return to the quantum theory for assistance.

Quantum emission processes from atoms were discussed in Section 3.2, and it was noted that an atom, when raised to an excited state by an incoming photon, could return to the ground state via various intermediate levels. Indeed, this was seen to be the basis for laser action. Whenever energy is absorbed by a substance, a fraction of the energy may be re-emitted in the form of visible or near-visible light radiation via such processes. This phenomenon is given the name "luminescence". Thus we may have photoluminescence (excitation by photons), cathodoluminescence (excitation by electrons), thermoluminescence (excitation by heat), chemiluminescence (excitation by chemical reaction), electroluminescence (excitation by electric field) etc.

If the light is emitted during the excitation process the phenomenon is often called "fluorescence" whilst in the case of emission after the excitation has ceased it is called "phosphorescence". Clearly both are aspects of luminescence, and the distinction between them must be arbitrary since there must always be *some* delay between emission and absorption. A delay of 10^{-8} s is usually taken as the upper limit for fluorescence; beyond this lies phosphorescence.

Phosphorescence is usually due to metastable (i.e. long-lived) excited states. These, in turn, are usually due to impurity "activators" in solids, which, by distorting the host lattice in some way, lead to "traps" in which excited atomic electrons can "rest" for a relatively long time before returning to their ground state.

One consequence of this is that phosphorescence is often temperature sensitive. This can readily be seen by reference to Fig. 3.44. Here we have the situation where a substance absorbs sufficient energy to excite atoms to an excited state E from their ground state E_0. The atoms find that they can then do one of two things: either return to the ground state directly or drop into the metastable state E_m. Let us suppose that the first probability is very much greater than the second, so that most of the light at frequency $(E - E_0)/h$ is emitted rapidly as fluorescence. There will then follow a much longer period of phosphorescence which is a result of the atoms being excited thermally from E_m to E and then quickly decaying again to E_0 (see Fig. 3.44). The latter process is thus controlled by the thermal $E_m \rightarrow E$ excitation, which has a probability of the form $p_0 \exp\{-(E - E_m)/kT\}$ and is thus strongly temperature dependent. The decay time can thus be used to measure temperature by purely optical means (both excitation and detection), and this has already proved useful in some application areas.

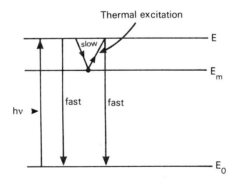

Fig. 3.44   Temperature-dependent phosphorescence.

Another device in which luminescence features strongly is the light-emitting diode. In this case (Fig. 3.45) a junction is constructed from a p-type and an n-type semiconductor. The p–n junction comes to equilibrium by

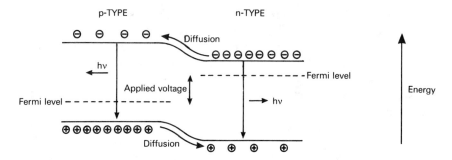

Fig. 3.45   Energy diagram for light-emitting diode.

diffusion of majority carriers (i.e. holes and electrons) across the physical junction until an equilibrium is established between the force exerted by the field (which results from the polarization of charge) and the tendency to diffuse. If an external electric field is now imposed on the junction, in opposition to the equilibrium field ("forward bias"), the result is to cause electrons and holes with differing energy levels to annihilate each other and thus give rise to photons equal in energy to the bandgap of the material. This is thus an example of electroluminescence. The efficiency with which this process occurs (i.e. the fraction of injected electrons which gives rise to photons) depends significantly on the difference in *momentum* between the combining electron–hole pairs. Any momentum difference must be lost or gained in order to conserve momentum overall. The greater is this momentum difference the more difficult is the compensation process (it is usually lost or gained via "phonons", i.e. lattice vibrational energy) and the less efficient will be the conversion process. Substances for which the two momenta are the same are called "direct-bandgap" semiconductors, and two of the best known of these are gallium arsenide (GaAs) and gallium phosphide (GaP). Doping these substances with impurities can give some control over the emission wavelengths, which lie in the near infrared for GaAs and in the visible range for GaP. The two substances can also be combined into ternary alloys with the general formula $GaAs_{1-x}P_x$ which, by varying x, give a useful range of devices. These materials are widely used in optical devices because of their robustness, ease of activation, compactness and range of possible emitted wavelengths. If a crystal of, say, GaAs has two opposite facets polished accurately parallel to each other, these form a Fabry–Pérot laser cavity which allows laser action when "pumped" by injecting electrons from a current source. This is the basis for the semiconductor laser diode which is very widely used in both optical fiber sensors and optical fiber telecommunications.

3.7.5 Nonlinear optics

In Section 3.7.2 we assumed a linear relationship between the electric polarization of a medium and the electric field of an optical wave propagating in it by taking

$$\chi = \frac{P}{E}$$

where χ is the volume susceptibility of the medium and is assumed to be constant. The underlying assumption for this is that the separation of atomic positive and negative charges is proportional to the imposed field, leading to a dipole moment P per unit volume which is proportional to the field.

However, it is clear that the linearity of this relationship cannot persist for ever-increasing field strengths. Any resonant physical system must eventually be torn apart by a sufficiently strong perturbing force and, well before such a catastrophe occurs, we might expect the separation of oscillating components to increase nonlinearly with the force. In the case of an atomic system under the influence of the electric field of an optical wave, we can allow for this nonlinear behavior by writing the electric polarization of the medium in the more general form

$$P(E) = \chi_1 E + \chi_2 E^2 + \chi_3 E^3 + \ldots \chi_j E^j + \ldots \qquad (3.27)$$

The value of χ_j decreases rapidly with increasing j for most materials. Also the importance of the jth term, compared with the first, varies as $(\chi_j/\chi_1)E^{j-1}$ and so depends strongly on E. In practice, only the first three terms are of any great importance, and only for laser-like intensities with their large electric fields. It is not until we are dealing with power densities of about 10^9 W m^{-2} and fields of about 10^6 V m^{-1} that $\chi_2 E^2$ becomes comparable with $\chi_1 E$.

Another important practical conclusion can be drawn immediately from eqn (3.27). In a medium which has an identifiable center of symmetry (this includes all isotropic and many crystalline media) all terms with even j must be zero. This follows from the fact that the electric polarization must have the same magnitude but must reverse in sign, as the electric field E reverses in sign for such media. This is only true if only odd powers of E exist in the expression for $P(E)$.

Let us now consider the refractive index of the medium. In Section 3.7 it was noted that

$$n = (1+\chi)^{1/2} = \left(1+\frac{P}{E}\right)^{1/2}$$

i.e.

$$n = (1+\chi_1+\chi_2 E+\ldots\chi_j E^{j-1}+\ldots)^{1/2}$$

Hence we note that the refractive index has become dependent on E. The optical wave is altering its own propagation conditions as it travels. This leads to many interesting "nonlinear" effects.

3.7.5.1 Second-harmonic generation

The first effect we shall consider is that whereby harmonics of the input optical wave frequency can be generated in a medium.

Let us take a crystal medium with no center of symmetry and consider just the first two terms of (3.27). For a wave $E_0 \cos(\omega t)$ we then have

$$P(E) = \chi_1 E_0 \cos(\omega t) + \chi_2 E_0{}^2 \cos^2(\omega t)$$

i.e.

$$P(E) = \chi_1 E_0 \cos(\omega t) + \frac{\chi_2 E_0{}^2}{2} + \frac{\chi_2 E_0{}^2}{2} \cos(2\omega t)$$

The last term, which is the second harmonic term at twice the original frequency, is clearly in evidence. Fundamentally, it is due to the fact that, as a result of the crystal asymmetry, it is easier to polarize the medium in one direction than in the opposite direction.

Now the propagation of the wave through the crystal is the result of adding the original wave to the secondary wavelets from the oscillating dipoles which it induces. These oscillating dipoles are represented by P, as we saw in Section 3.7. Thus $\partial^2 P/\partial t^2$ leads to electromagnetic waves, and waves at all the frequencies of P will propagate through the crystal.

Suppose now that an attempt is made to generate a second harmonic over a length l of crystal. At each point along the path of the input wave a second harmonic component will be generated. However, since the crystal medium will almost certainly be dispersive, the fundamental and second harmonic components will travel at different velocities. Hence the successive portions of the second harmonic component generated by the fundamental will not, in general, be in phase with each other and thus will not interfere constructively. Hence the efficiency of the generation will depend upon the velocity difference between the waves. This effect can be quantified as follows.

Suppose that the amplitude of the fundamental between distances z and $z + dz$ along the optical path is $e \cos(\omega t - kz)$. Then there is a component of the electric polarization of the form $\chi_2 e^2 \cos^2(\omega t - kx)$. This represents an electric dipole moment per unit volume, so that for unit cross-sectional area and path between z and $z + dz$ the electric moment is $\chi_2 e^2 \cos^2(\omega t - kz)\,dz$. The propagating component due to this is obtained from its second derivative $\partial^2 P/\partial t^2$, and thus we have a component of the form $C\omega^2 \chi_2 e^2 \cos(2\omega t - 2kz)\,dz$ where C is a constant. However, this second harmonic component propagates with wavenumber k_s, say, so that when it emerges from the crystal after a further distance $L - z$ it will have become

$$C\omega^2 \chi_2 e^2 \cos\{2\omega t - 2kz - k_s(L - z)\}\,dz$$

Thus the total amplitude on emergence will be

$$E(2\omega, L) = \int_0^L C\omega^2 \chi_2 e^2 \cos\{2\omega t - 2kz - k_s(L - z)\}\,dz$$

Performing this integration we obtain

$$E(2\omega, L) = C\chi_2 e^2 L\omega^2 \frac{\sin(k - k_s/2)}{k - k_s/2} \cos\{2\omega t - (2k + k_s)L\}$$

and hence the intensity of the emerging second harmonic will be

$$I(2\omega, L) = C^2\chi_2{}^2 e^4 L^2 \omega^4 \left\{\frac{\sin(k - k_s/2)L}{(k - k_s/2)L}\right\}^2$$

For maximum intensity we therefore require that

$$k_s = 2k_f$$

This is known as the *phase-matching condition* for second harmonic generation. Since the velocity of the fundamental is ω/k_f and the velocity of the second harmonic is $2\omega/k_s$, the condition is equivalent to requiring that the two velocities are equal, as we would expect from the basic physics. This can, in fact, be achieved by choosing a direction in the anisotropic (and hence birefringent) crystal (without which there would be no second harmonic generation in any case!) such that the two orthogonal eigenmodes have equal velocities. There will always be one such direction in a crystal, and for most crystal classes there are two (Nye, 1976). These directions are known as the optic axes of the crystal. Provided that the input light propagates along one such axis, the conversion efficiency can be maximized for any given length of crystal. However, care must be taken to minimize the divergence of the beam (so that most of the energy travels in the chosen direction) and to ensure that the temperature is constant (since the directions of the axes are temperature dependent).

In the particle picture of the process it is viewed as an annihilation of two photons at the fundamental frequency and the creation of one photon at the second harmonic. This must be so in order to conserve energy, i.e.

$$2h\nu_f = h(2\nu_f) = h\nu_s$$

The phase-matching condition is then equivalent to conservation of momentum. The momentum of a photon of wavenumber k is given by

$$p = \frac{hk}{2\pi}$$

and thus conservation requires that

$$k_s = 2k_f$$

as in the wave treatment. Quantum processes which have no need to dispose of excess momentum are again the most probable, and thus this represents the condition for maximum conversion efficiency.

The primary practical importance of second harmonic generation is that it allows laser light to be produced at the higher frequencies, into the blue and ultraviolet, where conditions are not intrinsically favorable for laser action.

3.7.5.2 Optical mixing

Optical mixing is a process closely related to second harmonic generation. If, instead of propagating just one laser wave through the nonlinear crystal, we superimpose two (at different optical frequencies) simultaneously along the same direction, we will generate sum and difference frequencies, i.e.

$$E = E_1 \cos(\omega_1 t) + E_2 \cos(\omega_2 t)$$

and thus from (3.27)

$$P(E) = \chi_1\{E_1 \cos(\omega_1 t) + E_2 \cos(\omega_2 t)\} + \chi_2\{E_1 \cos(\omega_1 t) + E_2 \cos(\omega_2 t)\}^2$$

This expression for $P(E)$ is seen to contain the term

$$2\chi_2 E_1 E_2 \cos(\omega_1 t)\cos(\omega_2 t) = \chi_2 E_1 E_2 \cos\{(\omega_1 + \omega_2)t\} + \chi_2 E_1 E_2 \cos\{(\omega_1 - \omega_2)t\}$$

giving the required sum and difference frequency terms. Again, for efficient generation of these components, we must ensure that they are phase matched. For example, to generate the sum frequency efficiently we require that

$$k_1 + k_2 = k_{(1+2)}$$

which is equivalent to

$$\omega_1 n_1 + \omega_2 n_2 = (\omega_1 + \omega_2)n_{(1+2)}$$

where the ns are the refractive indices at the subscript frequencies. Again, this condition is satisfied by choosing an appropriate direction relative to the crystal axes.

This mixing process is particularly useful in the reverse sense. If a suitable crystal is placed in a Fabry–Pérot cavity which possesses a resonance at ω_1, say, and is "pumped" by laser radiation at $\omega_{(1+2)}$, the latter generates both ω_1 and ω_2. This process is called parametric oscillation: ω_1 is called the signal frequency and ω_2 the idler frequency. It is a useful method for "down conversion" of an optical frequency, i.e. conversion from a higher to a lower value.

3.8 Photodetection

The processes which enable light powers to be measured accurately depend directly upon the interaction between photons and matter. In most cases of quantitative measurement the processes rely on the photon to raise an electron in an atom to a state where it can be observed directly as an electric current.

Consider, again, the p–n junction of Fig. 3.45. When considering luminescence it was noted that the physical contact between these two types of semiconductor (i.e. p and n) led to a diffusion of majority carriers across the junction in an attempt to equalize their concentrations on either side. The result, however, was to establish an electric field across the junction as a consequence of the charge polarization. Suppose now that a photon is incident upon the region of the semiconductor exposed to this field. If this photon has sufficient energy to create an electron–hole pair, these two new charge carriers will be swept quickly in opposite directions across the junction to give rise to an electric current which can then be measured. The process is assisted by application of an external "reverse bias" electric field. This simple picture of the process enables us to establish two important relationships appropriate to such devices (which are called photodiodes).

Firstly, for the photon to yield an electron–hole pair its energy must satisfy $h\nu > E_g$, where E_g is the bandgap energy of the material. If ν is too high, however, all the photons will be absorbed in a thin surface layer and the charge pairs will not be collected efficiently by the junction. Thus there is a frequency "responsivity" spectrum for each type of photodiode, which, consequently, must be matched to the spectrum of the light which is to be detected.

Secondly, suppose that we are seeking to detect a light power of P at an optical frequency ν. This means that $P/h\nu$ photons are arriving every second. Suppose now that a fraction η of these produce electron–hole pairs. Then there are $\eta p/h\nu$ charge carriers of each sign produced every second so that, if all are collected, the observed electric current is given by

$$i = \frac{e\eta P}{h\nu}$$

Thus the current is proportional to the optical power. This means that the electrical power is proportional to the square of the optical power. It is important, therefore, when specifying the signal-to-noise ratio for a detection process, to be sure about whether the ratio is stated in terms of electrical or optical power. (This is a fairly common source of confusion in the specification of detector noise performance.)

Photodetector diodes, like photo-emitter diodes, have the advantages of compactness, ruggedness, good temperature stability and low operating voltage (10–20 V). They are not very sensitive devices, however, and if high sensitivities are required we might turn to a device known as a photomultiplier. This is shown schematically in Fig. 3.46. Photons impinging on a suitably chosen sensitive photocathode material S have sufficient energy to eject electrons from the material into a surrounding vacuum. They are then accelerated to another electrode (dynode) by the electric field which exists between the two. On arriving at the second dynode they eject a large number of secondary electrons by energy of impact. This process continues for up to about 10 more stages, providing an electron multiplication factor of 10^6–10^9 depending on the materials and the voltages employed. Hence quite large

$(V_{n+1} > V_n)$

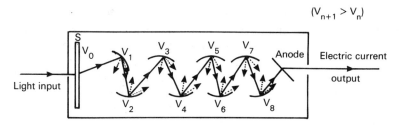

Fig. 3.46   Principle of the photomultiplier.

electric currents can result from very small optical power inputs. Powers as low as 10^{-15} W can be measured with these devices, the limitation being, as in all detection devices, the inherent noise level generated within the detection bandwidth. Although they are very sensitive, photomultipliers have the disadvantages of requiring several kilovolts for their operation and of using bulky vacuum tubes, which are vulnerable to damage and suffer from aging problems.

A good compromise between the photodiode and the photomultiplier is the avalanche photodiode. In this case a p–n junction photodiode is operated with high reverse bias voltage across the junction. When an electron–hole pair is created by the incoming photon, the charge carriers can acquire sufficient energy from the field across the junction to create further electron–hole pairs themselves, leading to an "avalanche" multiplication process similar to that in the photomultiplier. An increase in sensitivity is thus obtained at the expense of a higher operating voltage. The multiplication process is also quite electrically noisy, thus adding to the noise level of the photodetection.

The reason for this lies in the statistically random nature of the multiplication process. If each photogenerated charge carrier produced a constant number of secondary carriers, the only noise present would be the multiplied-up shot noise of the photogenerated current, i.e.

$$\Delta i_s = M(2ei_p\Delta f)^{1/2}$$

where M is the multiplication factor, e is the electronic charge, i_p is the photogenerated current and Δf is the bandwidth. Since the final detected current i_d is given by

$$i_d = Mi_p$$

we have

$$\Delta i_s = (2eMi_d\Delta f)^{1/2}$$

However, there is excess noise associated with the multiplication process since the number of secondaries produced by a given photogenerated carrier will vary statistically. The noise actually observed is expressed as

$$\Delta i_s' = F^{1/2}(2eMi_d\Delta f)^{1/2}$$

where F is the excess noise factor. F is a function of M, but typically lies in the range 2–20.

On speed of response, we can say broadly that all types of photodetection work quite readily up to optical modulation frequencies of about 1 GHz. To exceed this figure requires special attention to materials and design, but bandwidths of up to 30 GHz have been reported.

3.9 Conclusion

In this chapter we have attempted to provide a basis of essential optics which will underpin the rest of the book. The subject of optical fiber sensors calls upon a wide range of optical techniques.

Firstly it calls upon the techniques whereby the measurand (quantity to be measured) impresses its value on the optical wave, secondly it requires optical techniques to produce and control the light which will be impressed by the measurand and thirdly it utilizes a range of optical techniques to extract the information optimally from the emerging impressed light waves.

In this chapter we have concentrated on the basic physical ideas and the interrelationships which exist between them. It is hoped that this information will facilitate the understanding of the later chapters and also provide the reader with an appreciation of the wealth of future possibilities which lies beyond them.

Appendix

Maxwell's equations

Maxwell's equations can be expressed in vectorial form:

$$\operatorname{div} \boldsymbol{D} = \rho \qquad \text{Gauss's theorem} \tag{3.A1}$$

$$\operatorname{div} \boldsymbol{B} = 0 \qquad \text{no free magnetic poles} \tag{3.A2}$$

$$\operatorname{curl} \boldsymbol{E} = -\frac{\partial \boldsymbol{B}}{\partial t} \qquad \text{Faraday's law of induction plus Lenz's law} \tag{3.A3}$$

$$\operatorname{curl} \boldsymbol{H} = \frac{\partial \boldsymbol{D}}{\partial t} + \boldsymbol{j} \qquad \begin{array}{l} \text{Ampère's circuital theorem plus Maxwell's} \\ \text{displacement current} \end{array} \tag{3.A4}$$

where ρ is the density of electric charge, $\boldsymbol{j}$ is the current density and

$$\boldsymbol{B} = \mu \boldsymbol{H}$$
$$\boldsymbol{D} = \varepsilon \boldsymbol{E}$$

In free space we have $\mu = \mu_0$, $\varepsilon = \varepsilon_0$, $\rho = 0$ and $j = 0$, and thus the equations become

$$\text{div } E = 0 \tag{3.A5}$$

$$\text{div } H = 0 \tag{3.A6}$$

$$\text{curl } E = \mu_0 \frac{\partial H}{\partial t} \tag{3.A7}$$

$$\text{curl } H = \varepsilon_0 \frac{\partial E}{\partial t} \tag{3.A8}$$

Taking the curl of eqn (3.A7) we have

$$\text{curl curl } E = \text{grad div } E - \nabla^2 E \qquad \text{(mathematical identity)}$$

$$= -\mu_0 \text{ curl} \left(\frac{\partial H}{\partial t} \right)$$

$$= -\mu_0 \frac{\partial}{\partial t} (\text{curl } H)$$

and thus

$$\nabla^2 E = \varepsilon_0 \mu_0 \frac{\partial^2 E}{\partial t^2} \tag{3.A9}$$

This is a wave equation for E with wave velocity

$$c_0 = \frac{1}{(\varepsilon_0 \mu_0)^{1/2}}$$

From symmetry, there will clearly be a similar solution for H. A sinusoidal solution for E is

$$E_x = E_0 \exp\{i(\omega t - kz)\}$$

where $\omega/k = c_0$. In this case we have from (3.A7), with the resolution

$$E = iE_x + jE_y + kE_z$$

$$\text{curl } E = \begin{vmatrix} i & j & k \\ \dfrac{\partial}{\partial x} & \dfrac{\partial}{\partial y} & \dfrac{\partial}{\partial z} \\ E_x & E_y & E_z \end{vmatrix}$$

$$= j \frac{\partial E_x}{\partial z} = -\mu_0 \frac{\partial H}{\partial t} \tag{3.A10}$$

(since $E_y = E_z = 0$ and $\partial E_x/\partial y = 0$). Thus H can only have a y component (j

vector) and we have

$$H_y = H_0 \exp\{i(\omega t - kz)\}$$

as the corresponding value for H_y. Moreover, using (3.A10), we have

$$\frac{E_0}{H_0} = \left(\frac{\mu_0}{\varepsilon_0}\right)^{1/2} = Z_0$$

Z_0 is called the electromagnetic impedance of free space in this case.
Quite generally

$$\frac{E}{H} = \left(\frac{\mu}{\varepsilon}\right)^{1/2} = Z \qquad (3.A11)$$

From elementary electromagnetics the energy stored per unit volume in an electromagnetic wave is given by

$$U = \tfrac{1}{2}(\mathbf{D}\cdot\mathbf{E} + \mathbf{B}\cdot\mathbf{H})$$

$$= \tfrac{1}{2}(\varepsilon E^2 + \mu H^2)$$

From (3.A11) we have

$$\tfrac{1}{2}\varepsilon E^2 = \tfrac{1}{2}\mu H^2$$

so that the energy stored in each of the two fields is the same. The energy crossing unit area per second in the Oz direction for components E_x and H_y will be

$$cU = \frac{1}{(\varepsilon\mu)^{1/2}} \frac{1}{2}(\varepsilon E_x{}^2 + \mu H_y{}^2)$$

$$= \left(\frac{\varepsilon}{\mu}\right)^{1/2} E_x{}^2 = \left(\frac{\mu}{\varepsilon}\right)^{1/2} H_y{}^2 = E_x H_y = \mathbf{E} \times \mathbf{H}$$

This quantity, the vector product of $\mathbf{E}$ and $\mathbf{H}$, is the Poynting vector, i.e.

$$\mathbf{\Pi} = \mathbf{E} \times \mathbf{H}$$

and represents the flux of energy through unit area in the direction of wave propagation.

References and bibliography

Adams, M. J. (1981). *An Introduction to Optical Waveguides*, Chapter 7, Wiley, New York.

Barlow, A. J., Payne, D. N., Hadley, M. R. and Mansfield, R. J. (1981). Production of single-mode fibres with negligible intrinsic birefringence and polarisation mode dispersion, *Electron. Lett.*, **17**, 725–726.

Bleaney, P. I. and Bleaney, B. (1959). *Electricity and Magnetism*, pp. 243–245, Clarendon Press, Oxford.

Born, M. and Wolf, E. (1975). *Principles of Optics*, Section 1.4, Pergamon Press, Oxford.

Dekker, A. J. (1958). *Solid State Physics*, Macmillan, London.

Hecht, E. (1987). *Optics*, Addison–Wesley, Reading, MA.

Jenkins, F. A. and White, H. E. (1953). *Fundamentals of Optics*, McGraw-Hill, New York.

Jerrard, H. G. (1954). Transmission of light through birefringent and optically active media, *J. Opt. Soc. Am.*, **44** (8), 634–640.

Jones, J. D. C., Leilabady, P. A. and Jackson, D. A. (1986). Monomode fibre-optic sensors, *Int. J. Opt. Sensors*, **1** (2), 123–134.

Jones, R. C. (1941 to 1956). A new calculus for the treatment of optical systems, *J. Opt. Soc. Am.*, **31**, 488–493, 1941; **46**, 234–241, 1956.

Kapany, N. S. and Burke, J. J. (1972). *Optical Waveguides*, Chapter 3, Academic Press, New York.

Lipson, S. G. and Lipson, H. (1969). *Optical Physics*, Cambridge University Press, Cambridge.

Maiman, T. H. (1960). Stimulated optical radiation in ruby masers, *Nature, London*, **187**, 493.

Marcuse, O. (1972). *Light Transmission Optics*, Van Nostrand-Reinhold, New York.

Midwinter, J. E. (1979). *Optical Fibers for Transmission*, Wiley, New York.

Nye, J. F. (1957). *Physical Properties of Crystals*, Part 4, Clarendon Press, Oxford.

Panter, P. F. (1965). *Modulation, Noise and Spectral Analysis*, McGraw-Hill, New York.

Reitz, J. R., Milford, F. J. and Christy, R. W. (1979). *Foundations of Electromagnetic Theory*, Addison–Wesley, Reading, MA.

Richtmeyer, F. K., Kennard, E. H. and Lauritsen, T. (1955). *An Introduction to Modern Physics*, Chapter 7, McGraw-Hill, New York.

Rogers, A. J. (1977). The electrogyration effect in crystalline quartz, *Proc. R. Soc. London, Ser. A*, **353**, 177–192.

Rogers, A. J. (1984). Phase–amplitude relationships for the frequency response of a single-mode optical fibre, *J. Phys. D*, **17**, 253–271.

Siegman, A. E. (1971). *An Introduction to Lasers and Masers*, McGraw-Hill, New York.

Siegman, A. E. (1986). *Lasers*, University Science Books, Mill Valley, CA.

Solkonikoff, I. S. and Redheffer, R. M. (1958). *Mathematics of Physics and Modern Engineering*, Chapter 8, McGraw-Hill, New York.

Varnham, M. P. *et al.* (1983). Single polarization operation of highly birefringent bow-tie optical fibres, *Electron. Lett.*, **19**, 246–247.

Yariv, A. (1976). *Introduction to Optical Electronics*, Chapter 5, Holt, Rinehart and Winston, New York.

Chapter 4

Optical Detectors and Receivers

B. T. DEBNEY AND A. C. CARTER

4.1 Introduction

The requirements of optical detection systems for sensors are diverse. They range from the relatively cheap and simple circuits required for low frequency (or even d.c.) sensing of slowly varying signals from discrete sensors to the very high frequency circuits required for obtaining high spatial resolution in distributed and multiplexed sensor networks which commonly use an optical radar (or lidar) concept to determine the precise location of the zone that the sensor is addressing. All these sensors will be discussed in more detail in later parts of the book and therefore it will be convenient simply to state here the range of requirements for optical receivers in a short list of categories:

(a) low frequency or d.c. detection for low cost discrete sensors (typically 0–100 kHz frequency range);

(b) radiofrequency detection for heterodyne (or frequency-modulated carrier wave) sensor systems (typically 100 kHz to 40 MHz range);

(c) very high and ultrahigh frequency detection for fiber-based optical lidar systems, such as optical time domain reflectometry (OTDR) in various distributed sensors, and also rather specialist requirements for sensors in high speed event monitoring (typically 40 MHz to several gigahertz).

It can be seen, therefore, that optical receiver requirements for optical sensors cover the whole range from d.c. to several gigahertz. The tendency toward greater use of distributed and multiplexed sensors (Chapters 14 and 15) in recent years is increasing the requirement for the high frequency end of the scale, whereas previously most sensors had used relatively low frequency circuitry. The signals from point-multiplexed sensors involve serial pulse trains not unlike the pulse-coded modulation schemes used for high bandwidth communications. In addition, in all the interferometric sensor schemes, the concept of coherent detection, in which optical "mixing" takes place at the detector, is applicable. In some circumstances, for example in coherent OTDR systems, the latter may also require very high bandwidth receiver circuitry.

Perhaps the greatest difference between the sensor field and the communications field at present is the fact that most sensors use "first fiber window" operation (i.e. 750–950 nm) whereas telecommunications makes increasing use of 1300 and 1500 nm devices. As sensor developments have often followed communications device development, significant discussion of the longer wavelength devices will be included in this chapter.

Section 4.2 is a short introduction to the concepts of direct detection and coherent detection, and is followed by sections on materials technology, detector types and optical receiver circuits (i.e. detector–amplifier combinations). Finally a more comprehensive discussion of coherent technology is given.

4.2 Basic detection principles

4.2.1 Intensity modulation and direct detection

Intensity modulation and direct detection (IM–DD) is the basic principle of most present-day fiber optic sensing and data transmission systems. A laser or light-emitting diode (LED) source is intensity modulated, by modulating

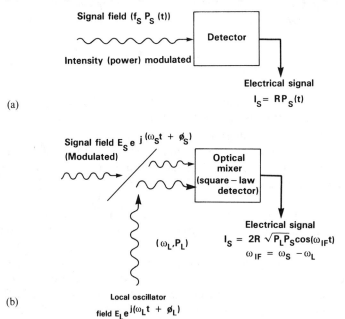

Fig. 4.1 (a) The principle of intensity modulation and direct detection; (b) the principle of coherent detection.

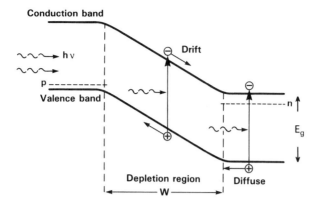

Fig. 4.2 Energy band diagram for a reverse-biased PIN junction photodiode illustrating electron–hole pair generation via photon absorption.

the drive current, and a photocurrent which is directly proportional to the received power is generated at the detector (Fig. 4.1(a)). The detector is essentially a power detector and the basic principles can be illustrated by considering the simplest form of semiconductor detector—the PIN diode. The detection process is illustrated in Fig. 4.2.

Photons with energy hv greater than the bandgap E_g enter the semiconductor and are able to excite electrons from the valence band to the conduction band. If the electrons and holes produced reach the junction or are created within the depletion region, they can be swept through the device and so generate a photocurrent. The depth over which optical absorption occurs is characterized through the absorption coefficient $\alpha(hv)$. If $\Phi(x)$ is the optical intensity within the material at a depth x,

$$\Phi(x) = \Phi(0) \exp(-\alpha x) \tag{4.1}$$

α is important because it is a measure of the thickness of material required to absorb the radiation. For example, if $x = 2/\alpha$, 86% absorption is achieved, and if $x = 3/\alpha$ this rises to 95%. The absorption coefficient depends on wavelength and the band structure of the material (see Fig. 4.3). Direct-gap semiconductors (e.g. GaAs, InP) have absorption coefficients which rise steeply at the absorption edge. Indirect-gap materials (e.g. silicon) require phonons to mediate the absorption process and hence the absorption is not as strong.

An important detector parameter is the quantum efficiency η. This is defined as the ratio of the number of photogenerated electrons which are collected (traverse the depletion region and contribute to the photocurrent) to the number of photons which are incident on the detector. The definition strictly refers to the external quantum efficiency of the device which takes into account losses due to reflection at the detector surface. The internal quantum efficiency is defined so as to consider only the loss processes inside the detector,

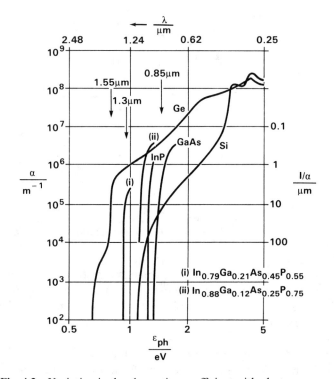

Fig. 4.3　Variation in the absorption coefficient with photon energy.

but this quantity will not be used in the following discussion. If Φ is the photon intensity and J_{ph} is the photocurrent density,

$$\eta = \frac{J_{ph}}{e\Phi} \qquad (4.2)$$

where e is the electronic charge. Denoting the optical power incident on the detector surface, of area A, as P_r we can write

$$\eta = \frac{I_{ph} \, hv}{e P_r} \qquad (4.3)$$

This leads to the definition of detector responsivity R as

$$R = \frac{e\eta}{hv} \quad A \, W^{-1} \qquad (4.4)$$

so that the detector photocurrent is given by

$$I_{ph} = R P_r \qquad (4.5)$$

This is the basic result for direct detection.

A high value of external quantum efficiency depends on the following:

(a) reducing reflections from the detector surface (achieved through the use of an antireflection coating);

(b) maximizing absorption within the depletion region (this is a function of device design and requires $W \approx 2/\alpha - 3/\alpha$);

(c) avoiding carrier recombination (achieved through device designs which are aimed at minimizing photon absorption outside the depletion region).

For a PIN diode detector reverse bias is normally applied so that a wide depletion zone is created; carrier generation predominantly takes place there. Carriers are swept through by the drift field with little or no recombination. Generation of electron–hole pairs outside the depletion zone relies upon the process of diffusion to drive carriers toward the junction and hence contribute to the photocurrent. In the event that photogenerated electrons and holes recombine before reaching the junction they do not contribute. Hence carrier generation outside the depletion region can lead to recombination losses and in addition affect the rise and fall time of the detector, thus influencing the speed and bandwidth.

If the reverse bias is increased, a point is reached when the electrons and holes can acquire sufficient energy from the field to be able to impact ionize and create additional electron–hole pairs (Fig. 4.4). This carrier multiplication process gives rise to avalanche gain and is the principle behind the avalanche photodiode (APD). In this case

$$I_{ph} = MRP_r \qquad (4.6)$$

where M is the current gain or multiplication factor.

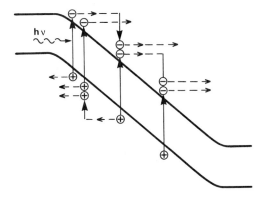

Fig. 4.4   The principle of avalanche multiplication in an avalanche photodiode.

4.2.2 Coherent detection

The principle of coherent detection in optical systems is precisely that utilized in the superheterodyne radio receiver invented by E. H. Armstrong in 1920. The differences are really to be found in the implementation which follows from the fact that the oscillator frequencies are optical rather than radiofrequency or microwave. The principle is illustrated in Fig. 4.1(b). At the detector the field from a modulated signal laser (frequency ω_S) is combined with the field from a local oscillator (LO) laser (frequency ω_L). Because the basic detector is a power detector and the optical power is proportional to the square modulus of the combined optical field, the photocurrent produced is proportional to

$$|E_S \exp\{j(\omega_S t + \varphi_S)\} + E_L \exp\{j(\omega_L t + \varphi_L)\}|^2 \tag{4.7}$$

When time averaged, this yields

$$\frac{E_S{}^2}{2} + \frac{E_L{}^2}{2} + E_L E_S \cos(\omega_{IF} t + \Delta\varphi) \tag{4.8}$$

where $\omega_{IF} = \omega_S - \omega_L$ is referred to as the intermediate frequency (IF). The resulting photocurrent is then

$$I_{ph} = RP_S + RP_L + 2R(P_L P_S)^{1/2} \cos(\omega_{IF} t + \Delta\varphi) \tag{4.9}$$

Because the detector is a power detector, or a "square-law" detector from the point of view of the laser field, it behaves as a mixer and produces an output electrical signal at an IF which carries the signal information. The above expression illustrates the basic principle of coherent detection. The signal modulation appears in the amplitude (P_S modulated), frequency (ω_S modulated) or phase (φ_S modulated), unlike direct detection systems where only amplitude modulation is possible. The IF signal can be made large by increasing the LO power P_L, thus improving the receiver signal-to-noise ratio (SNR). The process of detecting the combined signal field and LO laser field at the receiver therefore acts as a mixer and provides gain. The SNR cannot be improved indefinitely by increasing the LO power. This will be discussed more fully in Section 4.7. For the present we will simply indicate that in the limit of large LO power the detector shot noise which arises from the detector photocurrent associated with the LO laser dominates over all other noise sources and the SNR approaches a limiting value, independent of the LO power P_L.

4.3 Materials for detectors

The choice of detector needs to be related to the source wavelength used in any given sensor system. Today, the most common semiconductor laser and

LED sources are based on either the GaAs–GaAlAs system or the InP–GaInAsP system. LEDs or lasers based on GaAlAs as the active material can produce sources with wavelengths typically in the range 0.7–0.9 μm. The largest market for semiconductor lasers at the present time is represented by the compact disk (CD) player which has led to the development of low cost lasers operating in the region of 0.8 μm. Such lasers are often suitable for many sensor applications. Lasers and LEDs based on the GaInAsP material system can in principle produce source wavelengths in the range 1.1–1.65 μm. However, the manufacture of lasers in this range has in the main been driven by telecommunications requirements, which have limited the lasers produced to wavelengths in the neighborhood of 1.3 and 1.55 μm, representing the low attenuation windows of silica fiber.

Detection of light at a wavelength λ, or equivalently photons of energy $hv = hc/\lambda$, requires a material with bandgap E_g which is less than the energy hv. Figure 4.5 can be used to investigate the range of materials which are available to perform the detection process in the wavelength region 0.8–1.55 μm. Silicon with a bandgap of 1.1 eV is well suited for operation at wavelengths below 1.1 μm and generally offers the best solution for the 0.8–0.9 μm band.

The requirement for detection of light at 1.55 μm limits the choice of suitable materials to those of bandgap less than 0.8 eV. Materials with bandgaps much smaller than this will still respond to 1.55 μm radiation but will have the disadvantage of high levels of dark current and undesirable temperature sensitivity. A direct-gap semiconductor material is also an advantage as this results in more efficient light absorption. Germanium, with a bandgap of 0.7 eV and an indirect gap below 1.53 μm (0.8 eV), is an illustration of these points and although it can be used at 1.55 μm is far from ideal, particularly for high speed operation. Germanium has found better application at 1.3 μm, particularly when an APD is required.

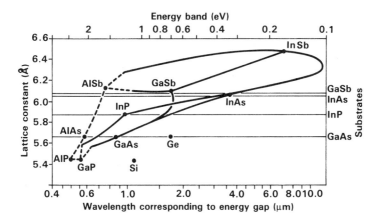

Fig. 4.5 Energy gaps for semiconductor materials.

Group III–V semiconductors also provide suitable detector materials for the range 1.3–1.55 µm. As can be seen from Fig. 4.5, none of the binary semiconductors, with the exception of GaSb, have bandgaps near 0.8 eV. It is possible, however, to form ternary and quaternary solid solutions, comprising three or four constituents from the group III and group V elements of the periodic table, and to tailor the bandgap to a desired value over a wide range. These solid solutions are usually prepared by epitaxial growth from either the vapor phase (vapor phase epitaxy) or the liquid phase (liquid phase epitaxy) onto a binary substrate. The preferred material system for 1.3–1.55 µm devices, based on proven performance, is the quaternary GaInAsP range of alloys which can be grown epitaxially lattice matched to InP with bandgaps between those of the binary InP (1.3 eV or 0.95 µm) and the ternary GaInAs (0.75 eV or 1.6 µm). The system AlInAs provides materials of larger bandgap and can also be grown lattice matched to InP, allowing a further degree of freedom in the design of more sophisticated detector structures.

A recent development in semiconductors is the concept of bandgap engineering achieved through the growth of superlattice structures (Capasso, 1983). These consist of a large number of very narrow layers of alternating semiconductor materials of different intrinsic bandgap. The superlattice or multi-quantum-well structures provide the capability of modifying the effective bandgap by varying the thickness of the semiconductor layers. This contrasts with the option of changing the composition of bulk ternary or quaternary materials.

4.4 Detector types

In this section we will describe the most common forms of semiconductor detector devices, i.e. the unity gain PIN diode, the APD and the photoconductor. The principles of operation of these detectors will be described in turn, together with a discussion of device design considerations and the important issues of bandwidth, gain (where appropriate) and noise performance.

4.4.1 Detectors without internal gain: the p–n and PIN junction diodes

The mode of operation of p–n and PIN devices has already been briefly described in Section 4.2. Whether the device structure is of the p–n or PIN type makes little difference to the basic principles. The choice of structure depends largely on the width of depletion region required, and this will be discussed shortly. However, first we consider some basic parameters which are necessary to characterize the device for use in an optical receiver.

4.4.1.1 Device capacitance
The small-signal equivalent circuit for the junction photodiode is shown

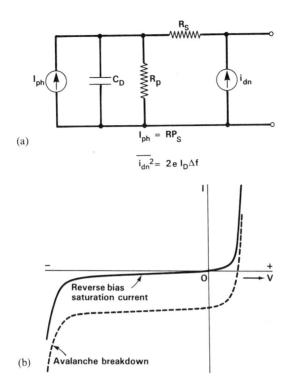

$$I_{ph} = RP_S$$

$$\overline{i_{dn}^2} = 2e\,I_D\Delta f$$

Fig. 4.6 (a) Equivalent circuit model for a reverse-biased photodiode; (b) current–voltage characteristic for a PIN photodiode in the dark (full curve) and when irradiated (broken curve).

in Fig. 4.6. This depicts the junction represented in terms of a capacitance C_D, a shunt resistance R_p and a series resistance R_S arising from the bulk resistance of the p and n regions plus the contact resistance. The photocurrent is represented by a current generator shunting the junction model for the diode. This model can be used as the basis for analyzing the detector performance when coupled to a following amplifier. As will be shown later, the detector capacitance is an important parameter in determining both the electrical and the noise characteristics of the optical receiver. For a PIN diode in which the i region is lightly doped the electric field is approximately uniform and the junction capacitance is easily shown to be that of a parallel-plane capacitor. The detector junction capacitance C_D is therefore given by

$$C_D = \frac{\varepsilon\varepsilon_0 A}{W} \tag{4.10}$$

where W is the depletion width. This also applies to the abrupt p–n junction case with W suitably interpreted.

4.4.1.2 Bandwidth

The frequency response, or impulse response, is ultimately limited by the transit time for carriers to drift across the depletion region. If we define τ_{av} as the mean of the transit times for electrons and holes then the detector 3 dB bandwidth is given by (Sze, 1981, p. 758)

$$f_{3\,dB} = \frac{0.44}{\tau_{av}} \qquad (4.11)$$

The bandwidth is here defined as the frequency at which the current falls by a factor of $\sqrt{2}$ for a sinusoidal modulation at frequency $f_{3\,dB}$.

4.4.1.3 Noise

In the dark the diode current–voltage characteristics can be represented by (Sze, 1981, p. 84)

$$I = I_0 \exp\left(\frac{eV}{nkT}\right) - I_D \qquad (4.12)$$

The two terms are respectively the forward and reverse current components for the junction. Under reverse bias the leakage current I_D flows through the device. This leakage current can arise from a variety of mechanisms: minority carrier injection, generation–recombination within the depletion region or band-to-band tunneling. The mechanism which occurs depends on the semiconductor material and the field conditions. When the diode is biased with a voltage V a net current I, which comprises the forward and reverse components described in eqn (4.12), flows through the junction. Current fluctuations appear at the device terminals owing to the random nature of the process by which the carriers traverse the depletion region. The process gives rise to what is known as shot noise, in which the mean square current fluctuations are proportional to the average detector current. The forward and reverse current components of eqn (4.12) are independent and each exhibits full shot noise. Therefore, for the dark current processes, the single-sided (positive frequencies only) noise spectral density function is given by (Van Der Ziel, 1970)

$$S_I = 2e(I + 2I_D) \qquad (4.13)$$

so that in a bandwidth Δf the total mean square fluctuations are

$$\overline{I_{dn}{}^2} = 2e(I + 2I_D)\,\Delta f \qquad (4.14)$$

Note that under zero bias conditions, although the net junction current I is zero, the mean square noise current is not zero but $4eI_0\Delta f$, representing the shot noise contributions from the independent forward and reverse current components I_0.

In the presence of light a photocurrent I_{ph} is generated which flows in the opposite sense to the forward current of the diode. The diode characteristic can therefore be represented by

$$I = I_0 \exp\left(\frac{eV}{nkT}\right) - I_D - I_{ph} \qquad (4.15)$$

The photocurrent I_{ph} also exhibits shot noise which results from the randomness in the rate of arrival of photons at the detector, and so

$$S_I^{PIN} = 2e(I + 2I_D + I_{ph}) \qquad (4.16)$$

4.4.1.4 Design considerations

One of the main design considerations is to ensure that most of the incident radiation is absorbed within the depletion region. For silicon operating at about 0.85 µm a depleted zone of typically 30 µm is required. In the case where wide depletion zones are necessary the PIN structure is preferred, since the lightly doped i material can be depleted at relatively low voltages. The reach-through structure of Fig. 4.7, so called because the depletion zone "reaches through" depleting the i region and stopping at the

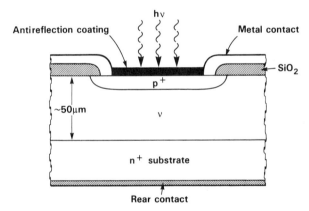

Fig. 4.7 Structure of a silicon PIN photodiode. The device is of the reach-through type in which the low-doped ν layer depletes through to the n^+ substrate at low voltages.

heavily doped substrate, is therefore adopted for silicon devices. When only a micron or so of material needs to be depleted, for example when using GaInAs for long wavelength detection (Fig. 4.8(a)), a p–n junction diode often suffices.

Another design point is the avoidance of absorption outside the depleted zone in order to reduce absorption loss and speed limitations. This can be achieved by making the heavily doped surface region very thin. The problem is particularly important when direct-gap semiconductors are used because substantial absorption can occur in the surface and within thin layers. This is avoided in the device shown in Fig. 4.8(b) by using a substrate entry structure

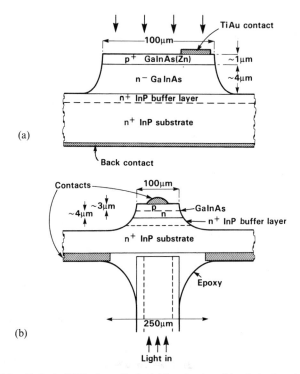

Fig. 4.8   GaInAs PIN photodiode: (a) front entry; (b) substrate entry.

in which the large bandgap of InP makes it transparent to the radiation. Absorption takes place within the n-GaInAs layer, which would be fully depleted so as to avoid a diffusion contribution to the photocurrent.

Alternative solutions to the avoidance of surface absorption are the use of heterojunction or Schottky barrier structures.

4.4.2   The avalanche photodiode

The APD is in essence a p–n junction diode reverse biased close to the point where the junction begins to break down. Under very high electric fields electrons and holes can impact ionize and give rise to carrier multiplication; for example, a highly energetic electron can collide with a valence band electron and transfer sufficient energy to it to cause excitation into the conduction band. In this way one electron gives rise to two free electrons in the conduction band and a free hole in the valence band. The basic processes are illustrated in Fig. 4.4. When the electrons initiating the ionization are photogenerated electrons the multiplication process gives rise to photocurrent gain at the device terminals. Gains of the order of 100 have been obtained in well-designed silicon devices.

Important material parameters determining the behavior of a device are the electron and hole ionization coefficients α and β. These quantities define the probability that an ionizing event takes place per unit distance traveled. They are strongly field dependent and are also temperature dependent. If, for example, $\alpha \gg \beta$ this would indicate that the impact ionization is predominantly due to electrons so that the current gain is associated with the primary electron photocurrent. Some typical ionization coefficient data are given in Fig. 4.9.

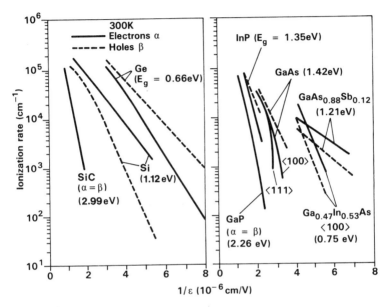

Fig. 4.9 Ionization rates at 300 K versus the reciprocal electric field for germanium, silicon, GaAs and some IV–IV and III–V compound semiconductors.

APDs have the advantage of providing current gain which can substantially improve the performance of an optical receiver. However, they do have the drawbacks that they require very high voltages to establish the device fields necessary and that the gain is very sensitively dependent on bias voltage and temperature so that the operating conditions need to be very stable. A typical gain–voltage characteristic for a silicon device is shown in Fig. 4.10(b).

4.4.2.1 Device capacitance
The capacitance behaves in the same way as for p–n junction diodes. The important parameters are device area and depletion width.

4.4.2.2 Bandwidth
We consider here the optimum situation where all carriers are generated

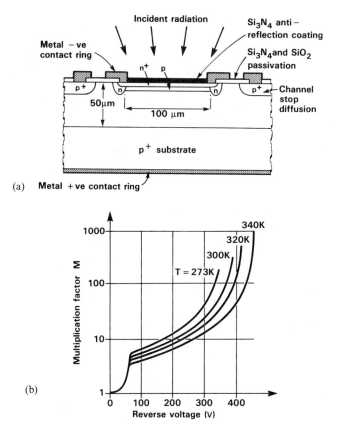

Fig. 4.10 A planar epitaxial silicon reach-through APD: (a) schematic cross-section; (b) variation in the avalanche multiplication factor M with applied voltage and temperature. (From Melchior et al., 1978.)

within the depletion region. The analysis of the bandwidth of an APD is a complex problem because the presence of the gain process results in a gain–bandwidth relationship. This has been analyzed by Emmons (1967) for a PIN diode structure in which the whole of the depletion region contributes to the multiplication process. In this case the transit time which enters the calculations is that of the depleted layer, which also defines the avalanche zone. If the width of the avalanche region is L_a and v is an effective drift velocity for the carriers, the transit time τ_a is given by L_a/v. It is found that, for a particular value of the multiplication factor M, the bandwidth is given by

$$f_{3\,dB} = \frac{\chi_a(M, \alpha/\beta)}{2\pi\tau_a} \tag{4.17}$$

where χ_a is a factor which depends on the gain M and the α/β ratio for the device, and can be extracted from Fig. 4.11. An effective transit time, or what is

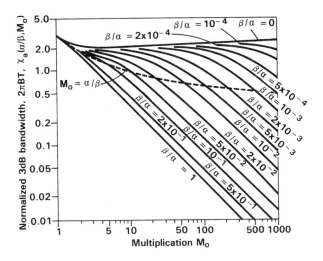

Fig. 4.11 Bandwidth as a function of multiplication and β/α for a PIN photodiode.

sometimes referred to as the avalanche build-up time, can be defined as follows:

$$\tau_a{}^{\text{eff}} = \frac{2.8\tau_a}{\chi_a(M, \alpha/\beta)} \qquad (4.18)$$

The factor of 2.8 enters as the limit of χ_a when the gain is unity so that this has the correct limiting form for a nonavalanching diode.

It can be seen from Fig. 4.11 that for $M < \alpha/\beta$ the bandwidth is approximately independent of the gain, whereas for $M > \alpha/\beta$ there is a constant gain–bandwidth product.

4.4.2.3 Noise

When the APD is operating at an average gain M not all photogenerated carriers are multiplied by exactly M. There is a distribution of gains which is produced by the statistical nature of the avalanche process and this introduces noise into the multiplication process. The problem has been analyzed by McIntyre (1966) who has shown that if a primary current I_0 is injected into the avalanche region the spectral density of the shot noise in the multiplied current is given by

$$S_I{}^{\text{APD}} = 2eI_0 M^2 F(M) \qquad (4.19)$$

where $F(M)$ is the excess noise factor and is the measure of how much the noise exceeds that of an ideal current multiplier. $F(M)$ depends on the material and junction characteristics through the ionization coefficient data, as well as on the nature of the primary excitation, i.e. electron injection, hole injection or both. If an effective ionization coefficient ratio $K_{\text{eff}} = (\beta/\alpha)_{\text{eff}}$ is defined for the avalanche zone and the avalanche is initiated by electrons (α), then

$$F(M) = M\left\{1 - (1 - K_{eff})\left(\frac{M-1}{M}\right)^2\right\} \qquad (4.20)$$

In the limit where the electron ionization coefficient is very much larger than that for holes ($K_{eff} \ll 1$), $F(M) \to 2$, independent of the gain, and this is essentially the result for a photomultiplier, which is the best which can be achieved. If $K_{eff} = 1$, then $F(M) = M$, yielding the strongest dependence of the excess noise factor on the gain, and reflecting the maximum feedback between the electrons and holes in the multiplication process and hence the greatest noise. However, if the ionization is initiated by electrons but the holes possess the largest ionization coefficient ($K_{eff} > 1$), then in the limit of large gain $F(M) \to M K_{eff}$. This emphasizes the importance of ensuring that the carrier with the largest ionization coefficient initiates the avalanche.

In the APD not only the photocurrent undergoes multiplication but any component of the device leakage current which flows through the junctions is also multiplied and contributes to the noise. Therefore the full noise spectral density can be repesented as

$$S_I^{APD} = 2e\{I_D^{(1)} + (I_D^{(2)} + I_{ph})M^2 F(M)\} \qquad (4.21)$$

4.4.2.4   Design considerations

The comments made in Section 4.4.1 concerning the requirements for achieving high quantum efficiency and bandwidth in the case of unity gain junction photodiodes apply equally well to the APD.

Material quality is very important. Defects and dislocations within the material can cause local enhancement of the electric field and thus cause premature avalanching in their vicinity, referred to as microplasmas. This can give rise to nonuniform carrier multiplication across the illuminated surface area of the device.

In structures requiring large optical absorption depths, such as those based on silicon, the simple PIN structure is unsatisfactory. Instead a similar reach-through structure is adopted but in this case the lightly doped region occurs after the n^+–p junction as depicted in Fig. 4.10(a). This has the effect of providing an appropriate thickness of depleted material for absorption, but the high field avalanching region is confined to the more heavily doped, but thin, n^+–p junction. This provides a much more stable device than would be the case if the whole of the lightly doped region sustained a breakdown field.

The device shown in Fig. 4.10(a) also indicates the use of a guard-ring structure. The ring of comparatively low n-type diffusion creates a p–n junction which consists of a wider depletion region and hence a lower field compared with the n^+–p junctions. This has the effect of confining the avalanche within the ring to inhibit premature breakdown near the surface at the n^+–p junction.

A choice of materials with high α/β ratios is clearly preferred, but it must also be ensured that the carrier with the largest ionization coefficient initiates the multiplication. These conditions influence the bandwidth of the device and its noise performance, and also ensure a more stable and uniform gain.

Work in developing APDs for long wavelength operation based on III–V materials has presented a new range of design problems. Because of the narrow bandgap associated with long wavelength detecting materials there is a tendency for band-to-band tunneling to take place before sufficiently high

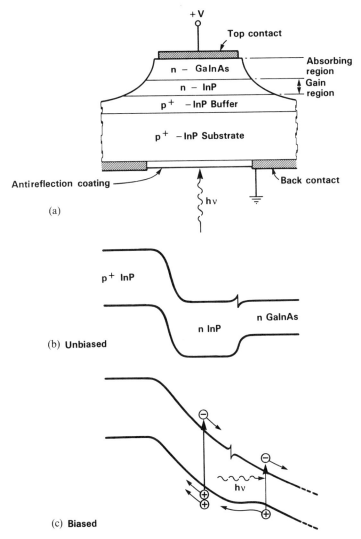

Fig. 4.12 The structure and band diagram of a GaInAs–InP SAM APD.

fields are reached to achieve carrier multiplication. The large tunneling currents which occur and their associated shot noise rule out the homojunction structures formed in, for example, GaInAs. To overcome this problem the structure depicted in Fig. 4.12 has been devised. This is referred to as a SAM APD (separate absorption and multiplication APD) (Kim *et al.*, 1981). Carriers are photogenerated in the narrow-gap material (GaInAs) where the field is high enough to cause depletion, but not tunneling or multiplication, and drift into the wide-gap more highly doped InP junction where the field is high enough to cause avalanching. The constraints imposed by the field requirements and depletion requirements for this structure make it a difficult device to fabricate.

The APD can also be used as a photon counter (Haecker *et al.*, 1971). This is essentially a digital counting technique and to be operated in this mode the APD is generally biased slightly above the breakdown voltage. The microplasma pulse switched on by the absorbed photon is a sensitive measure of the photon intensity. For this application the device must normally be cooled to low temperatures in order to reduce the noise due to dark current pulse generation.

4.4.3 The photoconductor

The photoconductor is conceptually perhaps the simplest form of photodetector and can operate from a bias of only a few volts. It consists of a slab of semiconductor material with ohmic contacts fixed at opposite ends. When light is absorbed by the material, carriers are generated which increase the carrier density in the material and hence its conductivity. This is the phenomenon of photoconductivity. Under an applied field the photogenerated carriers traverse the device and flow out of the contacts into the external circuit. Unlike a photodiode, where a photogenerated carrier traverses the junction depletion region and then recombines rapidly in the heavily doped n and p regions in a photoconductor, a photogenerated carrier can make many passes through the device before recombining. This produces an effective increase in the quantum efficiency of the device which can now be greater than unity owing to the fact that in the steady state one photon can give rise to more than one electron in the external circuit. The photocurrent produced by the device can be expressed by

$$I_{ph} = e \frac{\eta P_r}{h\nu} G \qquad (4.22)$$

G represents the photoconductive gain which can be shown to be given by (Sze, 1985)

$$G = \frac{t_r}{t_T} \qquad (4.23)$$

where t_r is the carrier recombination time and t_T is the device transit time.

Photoconductors can be either of the intrinsic type, where carriers are generated by band-to-band transitions, or the extrinsic type, where the generation process is via energy levels in the energy gap.

4.4.3.1 Bandwidth

The current response of the photoconductor to an optical impulse exhibits an exponential decay with a time constant equal to the carrier recombination time. In the frequency domain this yields a 3 dB bandwidth given by

$$f_{3\,dB} = \frac{1}{2\pi t_r} \qquad (4.24)$$

The photoconductor is therefore intrinsically slower than a PIN diode because not only do the physical dimensions tend to be rather larger but the time constant determining the device bandwidth is the recombination time which is much larger than the carrier transit time. Indeed, the photoconductor is a gain–bandwidth-product-limited device so that gain G is only available at the expense of speed. This is readily seen by using eqn (4.23) to re-express eqn (4.24) in the form

$$f_{3\,dB} = \frac{1}{2\pi G t_T} \qquad (4.25)$$

4.4.3.2 Noise

At frequencies above a few kilohertz the noise in a photoconductor arises principally from two sources: Johnson noise (Kittel, 1958) associated with the thermal noise from the bulk resistance of the photoconductor slab, and generation–recombination noise (Burgess, 1956) arising from fluctuations in the generation and recombination rates of photogenerated electron–hole pairs. The noise current spectral density for the Johnson noise contribution is given by

$$S_I = \frac{4kT}{R} \qquad (4.26)$$

where R represents the photoconductive resistance of the device. The generation–recombination noise has a noise current spectral density which can be expressed as

$$S = \frac{4eI_{ph}G}{1 + 4\pi^2 f^2 t_r^2} \qquad (4.27)$$

This noise source is fundamental to the photoconductive process and is unavoidable. A well-designed photoconductor would be arranged so that this source of noise dominates over the Johnson noise contribution at all but the highest frequencies.

At very low frequencies the noise spectrum of photoconductors increases with an approximately $1/f$ frequency dependence. $1/f$ or flicker noise is the form of low frequency noise which is characteristic of nearly all semiconductor devices and indeed a broad range of nonsemiconductor phenomena (Bell, 1980). The origin of $1/f$ noise is poorly understood and has been the subject of theoretical and experimental investigations since the early 1950s. Because $1/f$ noise appears in such a broad range of phenomena there have been attempts (Hooge, 1976) to construct universal theories to describe the behavior of all systems exhibiting this characteristic form of noise. However, such attempts have met with limited success. It is clearly particularly important to be aware of sources of $1/f$ noise in the design of low frequency sensor systems. Empirical formulae have been established to describe the behavior of many semiconductor devices, but in general it is necessary to characterize the devices in question in order to select a design for a particular application.

4.4.3.3 Design considerations

Present-day photoconductor developments employ either planar or vertical geometry. In the planar configuration the area between the contact bars is illuminated and the active device volume is formed by epitaxy on a semi-insulating substrate (Gammel et al., 1981a). In the vertical configuration the device is formed by epitaxy on a conducting substrate which forms one of the electrodes (Gammel et al., 1981b). The other electrode is formed on the top surface which is illuminated. In the design of a photoconductor the device geometry must be optimized to achieve high quantum efficiency and high resistance, to maximize the signal and to minimize Johnson noise. For the planar configuration the active layer thickness should be sufficient to ensure efficient optical absorption, but an increase in this dimension decreases the device resistance. The interelectrode spacing is determined from the illumination spot size, but as this dimension is increased the speed of the device decreases and the resistance increases, so that there may be a design trade-off between noise, quantum efficiency and speed depending on the application.

It is important to maximize the device resistance and hence minimize the Johnson noise by optimizing the device dimensions and fabricating the device from high resistivity material. This means the use of near-intrinsic material of low impurity concentration to ensure high resistivity without the concomitant trap-related generation–recombination noise associated with highly compensated material.

4.5 Detector technology: present and future

Silicon detectors at present offer the best solution for $0.85–1.0\,\mu m$ wavelength operation. The technology is well developed and excellent performance can be obtained from both PIN diodes and APDs. Commercially available silicon PIN diodes can typically achieve quantum efficiencies of about 75% and subnanoampere leakage currents at 25 °C. When operating at 10 V reverse bias, a bandwidth of typically 500 MHz is achievable. The silicon APD is an excellent device because the ionization coefficient for electrons is much greater than that for holes ($\alpha \gg \beta$). Devices exhibit values of K_{eff} in the range 0.1–0.01, with 0.03 being typical. Coupled with subnanoampere leakage currents, this results in a very low noise APD which permits the device to be operated at multiplication factors of around 100. Bias voltages of 200–300 V are required to achieve such a gain, although it can be obtained simultaneously with a frequency response of up to about 500 MHz. The APD can offer very significant receiver sensitivity improvements over the PIN diode as illustrated in Fig. 4.13 for digital (10^{-9} bit error rate) detection.

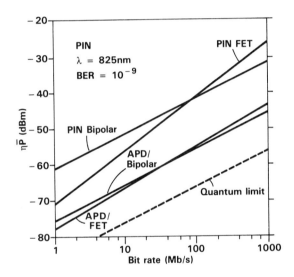

Fig. 4.13 Calculated receiver sensitivity of silicon PIN diodes and APDs ($K = 0.03$).

Germanium detectors, although capable of operation out to 1.55 μm, have predominantly been used at a wavelength of 1.3 μm. The germanium APD has found the greatest application because, until recently, it has been the only commercially available APD at this wavelength. The device which is easiest to fabricate, and hence the commonest, uses the n^{+}–p configuration produced by diffusing n-type donors into a p-type substrate. This structure sustains the avalanching field near the n^{+} layer and hence electrons predominantly initiate the ionization. Unfortunately, in germanium the ionization coefficient for electrons is less than for holes ($\alpha < \beta$), although only slightly, with the result that the excess noise factor $F(M) \approx M$ gives rise to a noisy device. Leakage currents in germanium devices tend to be rather high, being typically 0.1 μA unmultiplied at room temperature. This limits the useful gain in a receiver to around 10, beyond which the receiver noise increases more rapidly than the signal and hence the SNR degrades. Operating voltages for germanium APDs are lower than for silicon devices, being typically 30–40 V, and bandwidths of up to about 1 GHz are available from commercial devices.

Operation can be extended out to 1.55 μm, but large depletion depths of about 10 μm are required. A $p^{+}-n-n^{-}$ structure of the reach-through type has been developed for this wavelength and has the added advantage that the ionization is initiated by holes (Niwa et al., 1984). The result is that a K_{eff} of less than unity has been achieved, with the corresponding $F(M) < M$ so that avalanche noise is reduced. Leakage currents have been reduced somewhat by using diodes of smaller area (30 μm in diameter as opposed to the more conventional 100 μm). Operation at 1.55 μm tends to be a feature of the move to ever higher data rates and it is in this respect that the germanium APD has limited application. The best reported results indicate a bandwidth of 700 MHz at a gain of 10 (Niwa et al., 1984).

At long wavelengths (1.3–1.55 μm) the GaInAs PIN diode is the detector best established for high data rate operation. For the lowest receiver noise this is usually coupled to a GaAs field effect transistor (FET) preamplifier. The GaInAs PIN–GaAs FET front-end is the basis of commercially available receivers for data rates of up to 565 Mbit s^{-1}. Although the bandgap and wavelength of peak response of a III–V detector could be optimized by appropriate choice of the GaInAsP alloy compositions, most long wavelength detectors in this system have in fact been developed using $Ga_{0.53}In_{0.47}As$ which is lattice matched to InP and responds to wavelengths out to 1.7 μm. This results in a broadband detector with a response from 0.8 to 1.7 μm, although the quantum efficiency is usually optimum near 1.3 μm and 1.55 μm, being typically 75% and 90%. Interestingly, the device has a useful response at 0.85 μm ($\eta \approx 40\%$). Both the top entry and substrate entry devices of Fig. 4.8 have been successfully developed. In both cases a depleted GaInAs layer of about 3 μm is used which provides high quantum efficiency and bandwidth. Low doping permits full depletion of the GaInAs at low reverse bias. Because of the narrow depletion layers and the associated short transit times the device is intrinsically very fast with a theoretical bandwidth of approximately 15 GHz. However, the bandwidth of commercially available packaged detectors is usually limited to 1–2 GHz owing to the properties of the package. The devices operate under a reverse bias of approximately 5 V and exhibit low leakage currents of typically 10 nA or less. Low capacitance is a very important feature of the PIN diode detector and a device capacitance of less than 0.5 pF is normal. With one particular design of substrate entry device in which the detector is a flip-chip bonded GaAs FET integrated circuit (IC) preamplifier, a detector capacitance of about 0.05 pF has been achieved (Sussmann et al., 1985).

In recent years considerable research and development effort worldwide has been aimed at producing a III–V APD for long wavelength operation which will surpass the performance offered by germanium. The SAM APD structure illustrated in Fig. 4.12 has been the subject of most investigation. Promising device and system results have been reported in the literature, and the first commercially produced devices have recently become available. Typical performance specifications are as follows: external quantum efficiency better than 80%, leakage current (unmultiplied) of 10 nA or less, capacitance of less than 0.5 pF and an operating voltage of about 100 V. The effective α/β ratio for the InP junction used in the device is approximately 0.5 which, coupled with the lower leakage current, suggests a lower noise performance compared with germanium APDs. As indicated in Section 4.4 the gain–bandwidth relationship for an APD is complex. However, although representing incomplete information, it is useful to note that at a gain of 10 a bandwidth of about 2 GHz is achievable with this device.

Telecommunications is the main driving force behind present-day detector research and development, and hence the emphasis is on higher data rates (over 1 Gbit s^{-1}), higher receiver sensitivity and probably 1.55 μm wavelength operation. Detector developments are continuing with the aim of achieving wider bandwidths, lower noise and lower internal gain and will clearly have a spin-off for sensor applications. We have already mentioned in Section 4.1 systems based on the principle of coherent detection. In a coherent receiver the LO power provides the gain mechanism and, if adequate LO power to achieve shot-noise-limited operation is assumed, the ideal detector is a low noise unity gain PIN diode. The motivation for future detector development is therefore to enhance the performance of direct detection systems, and a common theme which features in these developments is to seek structures with internal gain.

In the last few years new concepts have been emerging for APDs with the aim of achieving higher effective α/β ratios and hence lower noise. Two such ideas have arisen from work on semiconductor superlattices. The first is depicted in Fig. 4.14 and represents a structure comprising alternate layers of wide- and narrow-bandgap materials (Chin et al., 1980). By choosing materials such that the conduction and valence band discontinuities are significantly different it is possible to achieve an effective α/β ratio for the structure which is very different from unity, even though the ratio may be close to unity for the constituent bulk semiconductors. The concept has been realized in the GaAs–GaAlAs system but not yet in materials suitable for long wavelength operation. A second multilayer concept is shown in Fig. 4.15. This is referred to as the staircase APD (Capasso et al., 1983). Device operation is based on the idea that if the conduction band discontinuity is sufficiently large the electrons drifting across it will find themselves with sufficient energy to impact ionize immediately in the narrow-gap region. This device could operate on a very low bias voltage, and in the limit of no hole impact ionization it becomes a solid state photomultiplier with an excess noise factor of unity! The present

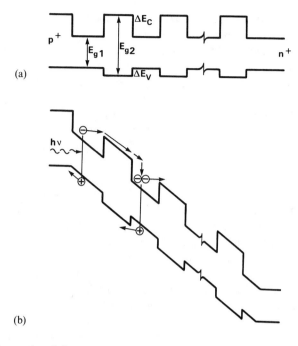

Fig. 4.14 Energy band diagram of the superlattice APD: (a) unbiased; (b) biased. The structure would comprise about 100 layers of alternate wide- and narrow-gap semiconductors.

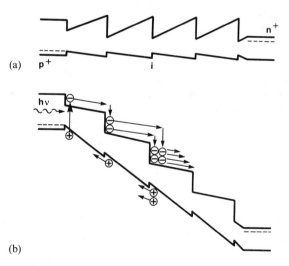

Fig. 4.15 The staircase APD shown in the photomultiplier mode with an electron multiplication of two at each stage and no hole ionization: (a) the situation for the unbiased device; (b) the device biased for normal operation.

challenge is to find suitable materials with which to realize the structure. The band structure requires the ability to grade continuously in alloy composition. The only suitable candidate material system to date is GaAlAsSb.

A third idea for improving the ionization coefficient ratio arises from the observation that in certain material systems the hole ionization coefficient exhibits a resonant characteristic as a function of the alloy composition (Hildebrand et al., 1981). The phenomenon is a band structure effect and occurs when the bandgap energy becomes equal to the spin–orbit splitting energy. The two material systems which have been found to exhibit this behavior and which are suitable for long wavelength operation are $Ga_{1-x}Al_xSb$ and $Hg_{1-x}Cd_xTe$. At resonance an enhancement in the α/β ratio by a factor of up to about 20 has been observed. However, considerable improvement in the quality of these materials is necessary before high performance devices will be forthcoming.

The phototransistor and photoconductor are also included in our category of future developments. These are not so new in concept but are included here because at present no suitable devices are commercially available for long wavelength operation. The heterojunction phototransistor (HPT) has been investigated for a number of years as an alternative to the APD (Campbell, 1985). The HPT combines the detection process at the base–collector junctions and current gain, but is more analogous in operation and performance to an integrated PIN diode and bipolar transistor than an APD. The InGaAs–InP HPT has been the subject of most development work but results to date suggest that it will not be a serious contender for receivers with a high data rate and high sensitivity.

4.6 Direct detection receivers

In this section we deal with the design and performance of direct detection optical receivers. The receiver comprises the photodetector, a bias circuit, a preamplifier and filtering. This is depicted in the equivalent circuit representation of Fig. 4.16. With suitable interpretation of the detector equivalent circuit elements and equivalent noise generators this representation holds for PIN diode, APD and photoconductor-based receivers.

The design of the optical receiver front-end is of critical importance since, as in all communication systems, it is at this point that the received signal is weakest and must be amplified with the introduction of minimum noise. It is here that the system SNR is determined which in a digital system will determine the minimum received signal power to achieve a given bit error rate (BER).

The detector noise sources were discussed in the previous section and can be represented by the shunt noise current generator and the series noise voltage generator as shown in Fig. 4.16. To summarize, a description of these noise generators for each device type is given in Table 4.1.

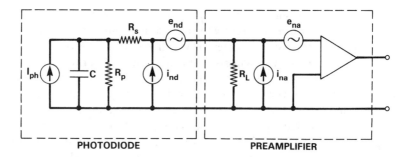

Fig. 4.16 Equivalent circuit representation of an optical receiver front-end. The circuit also depicts the equivalent noise current generators i_{nd} and i_{na} for the detector and preamplifier respectively, and the equivalent noise voltage generators e_{nd} and e_{na}.

The preamplifier noise depends on the circuit design and the transistor type. At present the choice of transistor tends to be between the silicon junction FET (JFET), the silicon bipolar transistor and the GaAs FET. Which is the most appropriate depends on the noise and frequency performance required. Table 4.2 contains a summary of the relevant attributes of these devices and gives a guide to their regimes of application. More exotic forms of device such as the GaAs heterojunction bipolar transistor (HJBT) and the GaAs high electron mobility transistor (HEMT) are now becoming available with attractive attributes, particularly for high speed ultralow noise receivers.

Table 4.1   Equivalent noise current and voltage generators for photodetectors

Detector type	Noise spectral density	
	$\overline{i_{nd}^2}/\Delta f$	$\overline{e_{nd}^2}/\Delta f$
PIN	$2e(I + 2I_D + I_{ph})$	$4kTR_S$
APD	$2e(I + 2I_D + I_{ph})M^2 F(M)$	$4kTR_S$
Photoconductor	$\dfrac{4kT}{R_p} + \dfrac{4eI_{ph}G}{1 + 4\pi^2 f^2 \tau_C^2}$	

Table 4.2   Attributes of transistor types for use in optical receiver front-ends

	Input voltage noise	Input current noise	1/f noise	C_{in}	Frequency response
Si JFET	High	Very low	Low	Fair	Fair
Si bipolar	Low	High	Low	Fair	Can be very high
GaAs FET	Fair	Very low	High	Very low	Very high

An important aspect of the receiver design concerns the form of input termination employed, which determines the receiver bandwidth and also influences its noise performance. The most straightforward method of designing the front-end is to terminate the input to the preamplifier with a load resistor R_L such that in conjunction with the input capacitance C_T the bandwidth B of the input admittance is equal to or greater than that required to pass the signal undistorted. This requires

$$R_L \lesssim \frac{1}{2\pi B C_T} \qquad (4.28)$$

For this design approach only a final filter is subsequently required to perform noise filtering and pulse shaping (in digital systems). The suitability of this approach depends on the application and whether the magnitude of the load resistance for the bandwidth required is not so small that its noise contribution dominates the system performance. Where this is the case two alternative design approaches are commonly used: the high impedance (or integrating) front-end design and the transimpedance feedback amplifier design.

The high impedance front-end design starts with the objective of minimizing all noise sources within the receiver, which fixes the magnitude of the bias resistance R_L. The resistance R_L is generally too large to satisfy condition (4.28) and so results in a front-end frequency response which falls as

$$\frac{1}{2\pi f R_L C_T} \qquad (4.29)$$

reflecting the RC effect of the input capacitance and load resistance. This design approach produces the lowest receiver noise, but an equalization circuit is subsequently needed to produce a flat frequency response over the bandwidth required and hence to restore the signal shape.

The transimpedance feedback amplifier design is perhaps the most commonly employed approach in optical fiber applications. The basic electrical circuit is shown in Fig. 4.17. Its attraction lies in the feature that a wideband receiver can be achieved, avoiding the need for equalization, whilst the noise performance is in practice not much poorer than in the high impedance approach. With an amplifier gain A the receiver bandwidth is given by

$$B = \frac{A}{2\pi C_T R_F} \qquad (4.30)$$

which is increased through the use of the transresistance R_F. In the case where R_F is equal in magnitude to R_L the noise performance would be the same as that of a high impedance design. In practice this is rarely possible because the use of large feedback around a high gain, high input impedance amplifier makes the circuit prone to instability.

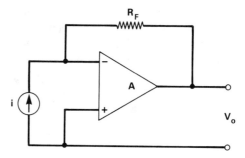

Fig. 4.17 Circuit representation of a transimpedance amplifier. R_F denotes the feedback resistance.

The SNR of a digital receiver described by the equivalent circuit of Fig. 4.16 can be expressed in the form (Smith and Personick, 1980; Haykin, 1983)

$$\text{SNR} = \frac{M^2 R^2 P_r^2}{(S_1 + 4kT/R_L)I_2 B + \overline{I_C^2}} \tag{4.31}$$

In this expression S_1 refers to the noise current spectral density for the detector, the second term describes the thermal noise associated with the bias resistor R_L and $\overline{I_C^2}$ represents the noise contribution from the preamplifier circuit, which can be related to the noise current and voltage generators i_{na} and e_{na}. These equivalent noise generators located at the input port of the amplifier are defined and constructed such that the effect of the following amplifier and circuit is to produce the correct noise magnitude at the output of the receiver. The quantity I_2 is a dimensionless parameter and denotes a noise integral defined in such a way that, at a data rate B, $I_2 B$ represents the effective receiver noise bandwidth.

For a receiver based on a silicon JFET or a GaAs FET the noise generators i_{na} and e_{na} are descriptions of the gate leakage noise and the FET channel thermal noise respectively. The noise spectral densities of these generators are given by

$$\frac{\overline{i_{na}^2}}{\Delta f} = 2e I_G \tag{4.32}$$

and

$$\frac{\overline{e_{na}^2}}{\Delta f} = \frac{4kT\Gamma}{g_m}\left(1 + \frac{f_k}{f}\right) \tag{4.33}$$

The FET gate leakage noise is described as shot noise attributable to the leakage current I_G. The channel thermal noise is empirically described by the form above where g_m is the FET transconductance and Γ is an empirical factor which is close to unity for both the silicon JFET and the GaAs metal–semiconductor FET (MESFET) (Baechtold, 1972). This expression also takes into account $1/f$ noise from the FET channel which is characterized by a corner or knee frequency f_k in the spectrum. The calculation of $I_C{}^2$ is described in many texts (Muoi, 1984) and will not be repeated here; instead we will give only its form containing the dominant noise terms, which is

$$\overline{I_C{}^2} = 2eI_G I_2 B + 4\pi^2 C_T{}^2 \frac{4kT\Gamma}{g_m}(I_3 B^3 + I_3' B^2 f_k) \tag{4.34}$$

The parameters I_3 and I_3' are also noise integrals. The mathematical expressions for I_2 and I_3, which depend on the input and output pulse shapes for the receiver, are described and evaluated by Smith and Personick (1980). The parameter I_3' is not normally found in the literature and so we give it here using the notation of Smith and Personick:

$$I_3' = \int_0^\infty \left| \frac{H_{out}'(y)}{H_p'(y)} \right|^2 y \, dy \tag{4.35}$$

For the case of rectangular nonreturn-to-zero (NRZ) optical pulses and a full raised cosine output from the receiver the noise integrals I_2, I_3 and I_3' take the values 0.5639, 0.0868 and 0.1838 respectively.

Equations (4.31) and (4.34) can also be used in the analysis of analog systems. In this case eqn (4.31) must be modified by including the multiplying factor $m^2/2$ where m is the modulation index, assuming baseband amplitude modulation. The parameter B should be interpreted as the receiver bandwidth, and the factors I_2, I_3 and I_3' then take the values 1, $\frac{1}{3}$ and $\frac{1}{2}$ respectively.

From consideration of these equations it can be seen that if a PIN diode detector is used with an FET preamplifier the thermal noise from the load resistance and the shot noise attributable to detector and FET gate leakage currents dominate at low data rates. In this regime the sensitivity of a digital receiver, defined as the minimum received optical power to achieve a specified BER, is proportional to $B^{1/2}$. This can be seen from studying eqns (4.31) and (4.34). The receiver sensitivity is proportional to the square root of the denominator of eqn (4.31), which yields the $B^{1/2}$ dependence. As the data rate increases, noise from the FET becomes more important and eventually dominates, yielding a $B^{3/2}$ dependence for the receiver sensitivity. Therefore at low data rates low leakage current for the PIN diode is important to reduce the detector contribution to the receiver shot noise, whereas at high data rates the emphasis is on reducing the detector capacitance in order to minimize the effect of the FET channel noise.

Depending on the magnitude of I_G, the parameter $C_T{}^2/g_m$ and the $1/f$ knee frequency f_k, an intermediate regime may exist where the $1/f$ noise from the FET channel dominates, yielding a receiver sensitivity proportional to B. At data rates above the frequency f_k, $1/f$ noise is not significant. The magnitude of the knee frequency can depend on device design, material quality and device processing. Silicon JFETs exhibit very low $1/f$ knee frequencies, but GaAs

MESFETs currently being produced exhibit f_k typically in the range 1–100 MHz.

For an APD the SNR is a function of the multiplication factor M, through both the signal and the noise. Examination of the expression for the SNR indicates that it can be improved initially by increasing the gain M until the point is reached when the APD noise dominates the receiver noise. Any further increase in gain degrades the SNR. Hence there exists an optimum value for the APD gain which maximizes the SNR for the receiver. The value of the optimum gain, and hence the SNR, depends on the excess noise factor, the magnitude of the unmultiplied leakage current and the noise from the following amplifier. At low data rates, where the preamplifier noise contribution is small, the value of the optimum gain is also relatively low. At higher data rates, where the preamplifier noise is dominant, the optimum gain can be large, emphasizing the need to achieve high gain from the APD.

For the case of a preamplifier using bipolar transistors, $\overline{I_C^2}$ is given by (Muoi, 1984)

$$\overline{I_C^2} = 2eI_bI_2B + 2e\frac{I_C}{g_m^2}(2\pi C_T)^2 B^3 I_3 \tag{4.36}$$

where I_b and I_c refer to the base and collector current. Although the absolute magnitude of the transistor noise is different for bipolars and FETs, the comments on detector requirements apply equally well in both cases. The detector parameter requirements for the PIN diode and the APD are summarized in Table 4.3.

The SNR, or receiver sensitivity in a digital system, depends on a number of critical parameters for any given design. For very low bandwidths or data rates the dominant noise sources tend to be shot noise from the leakage current of PIN diodes or APDs, gate leakage from FETs and shot noise from the base

Table 4.3 Assessment of the relative importance of detector characteristics to the optical receiver performance

Detector attribute	PIN diode		APD	
	Low data rate	High data rate	Low data rate	High data rate
Low leakage current	3	1–2	4	2–3
Low capacitance	1–2	3	1	2
High quantum efficiency	4	4	4	4
High bandwidth	1	4	1	4
High gain	1	1	2	3
Large ratio of ionization coefficients	1	1	3	3

1, Not significant/not applicable; 2, significant; 3, important; 4, highest importance.

current of bipolar transistors. The importance of minimizing these device parameters is obvious. Much work has been carried out on the design and characterization of PIN–FET receivers for telecommunications. For this component, the principal noise sources above about 50 Mbit s^{-1} are the thermal noise from the bias resistor (high impedance) R_L or the feedback resistor (transimpedance) R_F and the channel noise from the FET. Under these conditions the sensitivity is strongly dependent on the parameter $C_T/g_m^{1/2}$, which is regarded as a figure of merit. Below about 50 Mbit s^{-1} noise associated with the detector and FET gate leakage currents tends to be important. For the PIN–bipolar receiver the dominant sources of noise are the shot noise associated with the base and collector currents and the thermal noise of the base resistance. If biased for minimum noise the receiver sensitivity is proportional to the factor $C_T^{1/2}/\beta_0^{1/4}$ (Muoi, 1984), where β_0 is the small-signal gain of the transistor. For nonoptimum bias of the bipolar transistor the parameter dependence of the receiver sensitivity is more complex, but again it indicates the desirability of minimizing the total input capacitance and maximizing β_0.

The difference between the high impedance and the transimpedance receivers using FETs and bipolar transistors can be usefully illustrated by an analysis of the performance of designs for operation at 200 Mbit s^{-1} (Plessey in-house design information). Results for the receiver sensitivities and dynamic range are shown in Table 4.4. A PIN diode of diameter 100 μm and a bias resistor of 1 MΩ in the case of the high impedance design and a feedback resistance of 15 kΩ for the transimpedance case are assumed in the calculations. The greater dynamic range achievable with the transimpedance receiver is clearly evident. The difference in performance between high impedance and transimpedance designs is more marked for the case of the PIN–FET receiver because for this case the feedback resistor is found to contribute a significantly larger proportion of the total noise in the FET design than for the bipolar case.

A large number of sensor applications involve the detection of modu-

Table 4.4   Receiver sensitivity and dynamic range predictions for receiver designs for 200 Mbit s^{-1} operation

Preamplifier type	High impedance receiver		Transimpedance receiver	
	Receiver sensitivity (dBm)	Dynamic range (dB)	Receiver sensitivity (dBm)	Dynamic range (dB)
GaAs FET	−42.6	23	−39.3	36
Bipolar	−37.0	17	−36.5	33

Data from Plessey.
Receiver sensitivities are calculated for a BER of 10^{-9} and a temperature of 25 °C.

lation signals of 1 kHz or less and the detection of continuous wave (CW) signals; a d.c. receiver response is also a common requirement. Although this removes the need for the high bandwidth detector and circuit techniques associated with, for example, receivers for OTDR systems, d.c. detection can present its own problems, and care must be taken when it is desired to optimize the performance for low level detection.

The first change, which arises at low frequencies, is advantageous. Below 100 kHz the impedance of the diode and the amplifier capacitance are very high and the terms in the earlier noise equations which involve the capacitances now become negligible. This results in a noise model in which the only significant contributions are the amplifier noise current (the amplifier noise voltage is only significant when the shunt diode impedance is low, i.e. at high frequency when the capacitive reactance is low), the Johnson noise from the various resistors, the photon noise contribution from both the signal and dark currents and finally the $1/f$ noise contribution from the amplifier. The amplifier noise current can be kept very low using an FET amplifier, and in order to take full advantage of this low noise it is necessary to use very high values of the feedback resistor R_f, which is the other main contributor to the noise.

Values of R_f as high as 1 GΩ are common in low level d.c. detection circuits and care must be taken to avoid electrical surface leakage currents in both R_f and the printed circuit board. In addition, the d.c. offsets of the amplifier become much more critical. Figure 4.18 shows a d.c. equivalent model for a detector–amplifier combination. It can be shown, using straight-forward circuit analysis techniques, that the d.c. output voltage V_o when the

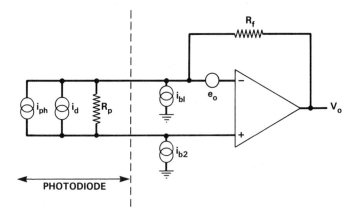

Fig. 4.18 D.c. equivalent circuit model for photodiode–operational amplifier trans-impedance receiver: i_{ph}, detector signal current; i_d, detector dark current; R_p, detector parallel resistance; e_o, amplifier offset voltage; i_{b1}, i_{b2}, amplifier input bias currents.

noninverting input is grounded is given by the approximate expression

$$V_o \approx e_o + e_o \frac{R_f}{R_p} + i_b R_f + (i_{ph} + i_d)R_f \qquad (4.37)$$

(it is assumed that the gain of the amplifier is high). The first three terms are undesirable d.c. offsets arising from the amplifier d.c. offsets and the fourth term contains both a signal term $i_{ph}R_f$ and a d.c. offset $i_d R_f$ due to the leakage current. At low frequencies this final component $i_d R_f$ can be removed, without significant penalty, by simply not biasing the diode. The third term in eqn (4.37) can be reduced by taking advantage of the balanced nature of operational amplifiers, or more specifically the fact that

$$i_o = \overline{i_{b1} - i_{b2}} \ll \overline{i_{b1}} \approx \overline{i_{b2}} \qquad (4.38)$$

where i_o is the input offset current, which is generally significantly less than the bias current for a well-designed operational amplifier.

The circuit shown in Fig. 4.19 is a simple circuit, optimized for d.c. and low frequency operation, where the contributions to the bias current have been balanced (as well as can be arranged without prior knowledge of the value of each) by the inclusion of an input resistor R, of similar value to R_f, in the noninverting input circuit. The capacitor C is included to decouple R and remove its Johnson noise contribution.

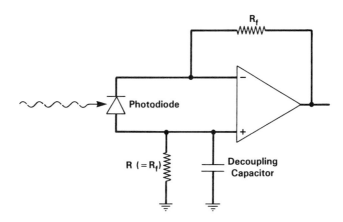

Fig. 4.19   Potential circuit for a low frequency receiver with a d.c. response.

The reduced d.c. output voltage V_o for the revised circuit of Fig. 4.19 is now given by

$$V_o = e_o + e_o \frac{R_f}{R_p} + i_o R_f + i_{ph}R_f \qquad (4.39)$$

For silicon detectors at room temperature the second term is normally not a significant factor, as R is then usually very high. The final term is, of course, the desired signal term.

Although the parasitic capacitances of the diode and amplifier have no significant effect on the noise model at low frequencies (i.e. usually below $100\,\mathrm{kHz}$), they may still, as a result of the ultrahigh feedback resistor values used, play a role in reducing the bandwidth of the receiver. We will therefore calculate the bandwidth of the receiver shown in Fig. 4.19.

The effective input impedance R_{in} at the amplifier input as a result of the effects of the feedback circuit is given simply by

$$R_{in} = \frac{R_f}{A(f) + 1} \approx \frac{R_f}{A(f)} \qquad \text{if } A(f) \text{ is high} \qquad (4.40)$$

where $A(f)$ is the frequency-dependent gain of the amplifier. As this input impedance is effectively in parallel with the capacitance C_T, which represents the sum of the amplifier and photodiode capacitances, the $3\,\mathrm{dB}$ breakpoint $f_{3\,dB}$ in the frequency response is given by

$$f_{3\,dB} = \frac{1}{2\pi R_{in} C_T}$$

$$= \frac{A(f)}{2\pi R_f C_T} \qquad (4.41)$$

If $A(f)$ is described in terms of a gain–bandwidth product GB such that GB $= fA(f)$, then

$$f_{3\,dB} = \frac{GB/f_{3\,dB}}{2\pi R_f C_T}$$

Therefore

$$f_{3\,dB} = \left(\frac{GB}{2\pi R_f C_T} \right)^{1/2} \qquad (4.42)$$

Thus the substitution allows the $3\,\mathrm{dB}$ frequency response to be determined in terms of the gain–bandwidth product of the amplifier, which is a commonly quoted parameter on data sheets.

As final notes, it should be added firstly that the use of an APD detector at low frequency will in general confer no significant advantage, except at ultralow levels when its use in the photon-counting mode could perhaps find an application in more sophisticated systems. Secondly, in such low frequency circuits it is much more common for the performance to reach the photon-noise limit in view of the much smaller amplifier and thermal noise contributions relative to the high signal voltages developed in the high resistance loads.

A major thrust in receiver development, particularly for high data rates, has arisen from the requirements for telecommunications. Although the bandwidths are much greater than needed for many sensor applications the design and constructional techniques are relevant, in particular to sensor systems such as OTDR that require high bandwidths.

GaInAs PIN–GaAs FET receiver design and development has produced components which are now available for data rates up to 565 Mbit s^{-1}, with 2.4 Gbit s^{-1} becoming available. In the main, construction is based upon hybrid technology using discrete chip components glass- or solder-bonded onto a ceramic substrate. Designs tend to be predominantly of the high impedance type in order to achieve maximum sensitivity. Representative sensitivity figures for commercial devices are shown in Table 4.5. A photograph of a typical module is shown in Fig. 4.20.

Table 4.5 Representative PIN–FET sensitivities

Data rate (Mbit s^{-1})	Minimum sensitivity ($-$dBm) (line coded, NRZ)		Temperature derating at $+55\,°C$ (dB)
	Standard	High	
8	50	53	-2.5
34	47	50	-2.0
140	40	43	-1.5
565	34	36	-0.7
1200	31 typical (prototypes)		
2400	28 typical (prototypes)		

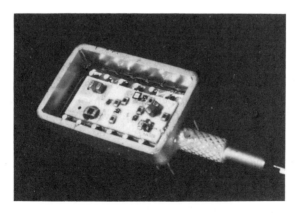

Fig. 4.20 Photograph of a GaInAs PIN–GaAs FET optical receiver based on hybrid technology. This component is designed to operate at a digital rate of 565 Mbit s^{-1}.

The use of GaAs IC technology is increasing rapidly. A "semi-integrated" version of a 565 Mbit s^{-1} PIN–FET receiver has been reported (Moseley et al., 1985). This component is based on a GaAs IC version of the FET preamplifier and a discrete GaInAs PIN diode flip-chip bonded onto the GaAs substrate. The PIN diode, which is a substrate entry device, is designed to achieve ultralow capacitance, measuring approximately 0.05 pF after bonding and under normal operating conditions. The preamplifier design is based on FETs with a gate length of 0.6 μm. This component has demonstrated a best receiver sensitivity of −37.5 dBm at 680 Mbit s^{-1}. A similar approach is being used at present to design GaAs IC preamplifiers for operation at 1.2 and 2.4 Gbit s^{-1}.

Data links for local area networks have also been the subject of considerable research and development. Receiver sensitivity is not the most significant parameter for these applications. Cost is of critical importance and so commercial receiver components feature silicon IC technology. Silicon bipolar ICs have been developed for receivers based on transimpedance designs operating at up to 200 Mbit s^{-1}.

Future developments in optical receivers will continue to move away from hybrid construction and concentrate more on IC technology. For certain applications an evolution of receivers based on silicon bipolar technology is anticipated as devices with smaller feature size and higher f_T become available. This will enable lower noise, wider bandwidth receivers to be developed. A 1 μm bipolar process will be available shortly with devices achieving f_T values in excess of 10 GHz. There is at present a major research activity in the GaAs heterojunction bipolar transistor and this device has considerable potential for use in optical receiver ICs based on GaAs technology. Another future prospect is a fully integrated receiver in which both the detector and the preamplifier, and possibly other functions, are integrated on a single substrate. This may involve either GaAs- or InP-based IC technology.

4.7 Coherent detection

Coherent detection has attracted increasing interest in recent years because of the prospects of achieving higher sensitivity than in direct detection systems. Research and development into sensors and communications applications has grown, spurred on by improved component technology, in particular with the semiconductor laser. The main applications being researched using this technique include sensors (see Chapter 10), fiber optic telecommunications (Kimura, 1987), free-space communications between ground-based stations (Giannaris and Mooradian, 1977) and between orbiting satellites (Furuhama et al., 1987), and the optical control of phased-array radar (Forrest et al., 1982).

The basic principle of coherent detection was described in Section 4.2. Figure 4.21 shows a functional diagram of a coherent optical transmission

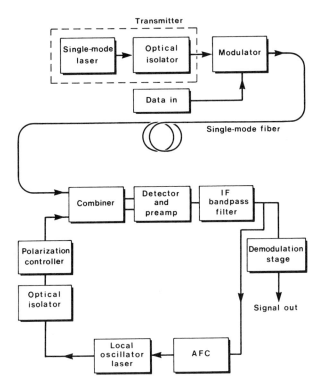

Fig. 4.21 An illustration of the functional requirements of a coherent optical transmission system using the heterodyning principle.

system based on the heterodyning principle. The transmitter consists of a laser source operating in a single transverse and longitudinal mode possibly coupled to an external modulator in order to impart the amplitude, phase or frequency modulation. At the receiver the weak signal field from the transmitter laser is combined with the field from the LO laser in such a way that the wavefronts of the two laser fields are matched for the most efficient detection. In a fiber-based system this is usually achieved using a taper-fused fiber coupler. The combined signal is fed to a square-law detector and preamplifier to provide the mixing, gain and low noise amplification. In a heterodyning system the signal modulation appears on an IF electrical carrier as indicated by eqn (4.9). This then goes through an IF filter which is sufficiently wide to pass the modulated carrier prior to recovery of the modulation.

Figure 4.21 indicates the provision of an automatic frequency control (AFC) loop in order to maintain a stable IF. The IF is equal in magnitude to the difference between the frequencies of the transmitter and LO lasers so that fluctuations in the frequency of either laser will cause fluctuations in the IF.

The demodulation stage will require a certain level of IF stability in order to recover the signal and so the IF must be actively controlled. This is achieved by providing temperature and drive current stabilization of the lasers to establish a sufficient level of absolute laser frequency stability so that the signal can be located within the IF filter and thus permit additional electronic means to lock the IF to its prescribed value. Thermal fluctuations are the main cause of IF drift with semiconductor lasers, and temperature stabilization of the order of millidegrees is required in order to achieve intrinsic IF stability of the order of tens of megahertz. At the output of the IF filter the carrier frequency is sampled electronically in order to sense deviations from its prescribed value. A control signal is then fed to the drive current of the LO laser in order to modify its output frequency and thus bring about a return of the IF to the correct value.

The receiver can be configured in such a way that the IF is zero; this is referred to as homodyning. In this case it can be seen from eqn (4.9) that the modulation at the output of the preamplifier appears at baseband and no further demodulation is necessary. The system is completed by suitable low pass filtering. This receiver architecture is particularly efficient in the use of receiver electrical bandwidth, but demands that not only the frequency between the transmitter and the LO laser but also the phase is controlled. The design and implementation of the optical phase-lock loop is particularly demanding and to date has resulted in only limited investigations of homodyne detection systems.

In many sensor applications the self- or pseudo-heterodyning or homo-dyning configuration is adopted where the signal and LO sources are derived from the same laser. This arrangement avoids the need for the stringent laser stability and frequency tracking required in communications systems employing independent transmitter and LO lasers.

In order to maximize the magnitude of the received signal a coherent system requires that the polarization states of the signal field and LO field at the detector are identical. In a fiber-based system this could be achieved through the use of polarization-maintaining fiber. In systems employing standard single-mode fiber the polarization state of the signal field at the detector can be arbitrary and change with time owing to the birefringence of the fiber. The receiver therefore requires that some means be introduced to control the polarization of the LO laser actively in order to match that of the signal field, or alternatively to adopt a receiver configuration which can operate passively and is insensitive to the states of polarization of the lasers. The latter is referred to as polarization diversity and various schemes have been proposed for achieving it (Kuwahara *et al.*, 1986). Active polarization control is potentially more efficient but requires electromechanical or electro-optic polarization transformers (Noe, 1986) and the associated control electronics.

The exact form of the demodulation circuit depends on the modulation format employed. As already indicated, amplitude, phase and frequency modulation are possible, which in the case of digital modulation are referred to as amplitude shift keying (ASK), phase shift keying (PSK) and frequency shift keying (FSK). The first two formats are best implemented using external modulators whereas FSK is normally achieved through d.c. modulation of the laser. The different modulation formats achieve varying levels of performance in terms of receiver sensitivity. PSK systems offer the greatest sensitivity and ASK the least. (Homodyning provides 3 dB better sensitivity than heterodyning for the same modulation format.) The SNR at the output of a coherent digital receiver can in general be expressed in the form

$$\xi = \frac{\alpha R^{2} M^{2} P_{L} P_{S}}{eRP_{L} M^{2} F(M) I_{2} B^{+} \overline{I_{C}^{2}}} \tag{4.43}$$

In this expression P_S refers to the average received power per bit time and $\overline{I_C^2}$ represents the mean square noise current arising from the preamplifier circuit. The probability of a bit error rate corresponding to the SNR ξ is given by

$$\text{BER} = \frac{1}{2} \text{erfc}\left(\frac{\xi^{1/2}}{\beta}\right) \tag{4.44}$$

In eqns (4.43) and (4.44) α and β represent numerical parameters whose values are shown in Table 4.6 for the modulation formats indicated. The first term in the denominator of eqn (4.43) is described explicitly because in the limit of large LO power P_L this noise contribution dominates. It represents the shot noise in the detector current associated with the detected LO laser power. As the LO power increases the SNR approaches a limiting value and is referred to as the LO shot noise limit. Because the LO laser essentially provides signal gain it can be seen from eqn (4.43) that in the limit of large LO power the unity gain PIN diode is the optimum form of detector. There is little to be achieved from the use of APDs with their additional gain and associated noise, except perhaps in the case where the LO power is sufficiently weak that the SNR is considerably degraded relative to the LO shot noise limit.

Table 4.7 illustrates the theoretical performance which can be attained in the LO shot noise limit. The table gives the receiver sensitivity for digital

Table 4.6 Numerical values of parameters α and β (eqns (4.43) and (4.44)) which characterize the signal-to-noise ratio and probability of error for digital coherent receivers

Format	α	β
PSK homodyne	4	$\sqrt{2}$
PSK heterodyne	1	1
FSK heterodyne/synchronous	1	$\sqrt{2}$
ASK homodyne	8	$2\sqrt{2}$
ASK heterodyne	2	2

Table 4.7 The theoretical limits for receiver sensitivity of coherent detection systems

Modulation format	Receiver type/demodulation technique[a]		
ASK	Heterodyne/envelope 87	Heterodyne/synchronous 81	Homodyne 41
FSK	Heterodyne/envelope Single filter 87 Dual filter 45	Heterodyne/synchronous 41	
PSK	Heterodyne/differential (DPSK) 22	Heterodyne/synchronous 20	Homodyne 10

[a] The numbers indicate the number of photons which must be detected for a transmitted mark in order to achieve a BER of 10^{-9}.

systems in terms of the minimum number of received photons per transmitted mark required to achieve a BER of 10^{-9}. This is a useful way of presenting the sensitivity, because for coherent receivers this quantity is independent of data rate. For comparison, present-day direct detection telecommunication systems require around 1000 photons per mark over the data rate range 34–565 Mbit s^{-1}. Thus it can be seen that there is the potential for an improvement of between 10 and 20 dB in receiver sensitivity compared with direct detection.

4.8 Conclusions

In this chapter we have presented a broad introduction to the field of detectors and detection circuits for sensors. The bandwidth range for sensor receivers extends from low frequency or d.c. for low cost discrete configurations through radiofrequency for heterodyne (or frequency-modulated carrier wave) systems (100 kHz to 40 MHz) to very high frequencies (40 MHz to several gigahertz) for OTDR and distributed sensors. We have presented the basic detection principles (Section 4.2) and detector types (Section 4.4) suitable for such systems, together with future trends in detector developments (Section 4.5). Ultrawide bandwidth (1–20 GHz) direct and coherent detection techniques are currently attracting considerable research and development effort as a result of telecommunications applications; the reader should consult recent specialist conference proceedings and journals as the state of the art progresses, for example the Proceedings of the European Conference on Optical Communications, the Optical Fiber Communications Conference and the Integrated Optics and Optical Communications Conference.

We have also presented an analysis of direct detection and coherent receiver circuits detailing the major noise sources; the reader will be able to use the analysis to calculate the bandwidth, noise and dynamic range of practical receiver circuits for a particular application.

Acknowledgments

We would like to thank Dr J. P. Dakin for his useful comments on the manuscript and his contribution to the discussion of low frequency and d.c. sensor circuits in Section 4.6.

References

Baechtold, W. (1972). Noise behavior of GaAs field-effect transistors with short gate lengths, *IEEE Trans. Electron. Dev.*, **19** (5), 674–680.
Bell, D. A. (1980). A survey of 1/*f* noise in electrical conductors, *J. Phys. C*, **13**, 4425–4437.

Burgess, R. E. (1956). The statistics of charge carrier fluctuations in semiconductors, *Proc. Phys. Soc. B*, **69**, 1020–1027.

Campbell, J. C. (1985). Lightwave communications technology. In *Semiconductors and Semimetals*, Vol. 22, Part D, *Photodetectors*, Chapter 5, Academic Press, New York.

Capasso, F. (1983). Band-gap engineering via graded gap, superlattice, and periodic doping structures: applications to novel photodetectors and other devices, *J. Vac. Sci. Technol. B*, **1** (2), 457–461.

Capasso, F., Tsang, W. T. and Williams, G. F. (1983). Staircase solid state photomultipliers and avalanche photodiodes with enhanced ionisation rates ratio, *IEEE Trans. Electron. Dev.*, **30** (4), 381–389.

Chin, R., Holonyak, N., Stillman, G. E., Tang, J. Y. and Hess, K. (1980). Impact ionisation in multi-layer heterojunction structures, *Electron. Lett.*, **16** (12), 467–468.

Emmons, R. B. (1967). Avalanche photodiode frequency response, *J. Appl. Phys.*, **38** (9), 3705.

Forrest, J. R., Richards, F. P., De Salles, A. A. and Varnish, P. (1982). Optical fibre networks for signal distribution and control in phased array radars, *Proc. Radar 1982*, Institution of Electrical Engineers, Stevenage.

Fukuhama, Y., Yasukawa, K., Kashiki, K. and Hirata, Y. (1987). Present status of optical ISL studies in Japan. In *Optical Systems for Space Applications*, Vol. 810, pp. 141–149, SPIE.

Gammel, J. C., Ohno, H. and Ballantyne, J. M. (1981a). High speed photoconductive detectors using GaInAs, *IEEE J. Quantum Electron.*, **17** (2), 269–272.

Gammel, J. C., Ohno, H. and Ballantyne, J. M. (1981b). A photoconductive detector for high speed fiber communication, *IEEE Trans. Electron. Dev.*, **28** (7), 841–849.

Giannaris, R. J. and Mooradian, G. C. (1977). Shipboard electro-optic system integration. In *Systems Integration and Optical Design II*, Vol. 103, pp. 120–125, SPIE.

Haecker, W., Groezinger, O. and Pilkuhn, M. H. (1971). Infra-red photon counting by Ge avalanche diodes, *Appl. Phys. Lett.*, **19** (4), 113–115.

Haykin, S. (1983). *Communication Systems* (2nd edn), Chapter 9, Wiley, New York.

Hildebrand, O., Kuebart, W., Benz, K. W. and Pilkuhn, M. H. (1981). GaAlSb avalanche photodiodes: resonant impact ionisation with very high ratio of ionisation coefficients, *IEEE J. Quantum Electron.*, **17** (2), 284–288.

Hooge, F. N. (1976). $1/f$ noise, *Physica B*, **83**, 14–23.

Kim, O. K., Forrest, S. R., Bonner, W. A. and Smith, R. G. (1981). A high gain InGaAs/InP avalanche photodiode with no tunneling leakage current, *Appl. Phys. Lett.*, **39** (5), 402–404.

Kimura, T. (1987). Coherent optical fiber transmission, *J. Lightwave Technol.*, **5** (4), 414–428.

Kittel, C. (1958). *Elementary Statistical Physics*, p. 141, Wiley, New York.

Kuwahara, H., Chikama, T., Ohsawa, C. and Kiyonaga, T. (1986). New receiver design for practical light-wave transmission system, *Proc. 12th European Conf. on Optical Communications, Barcelona*, Vol. 1, pp. 407–410.

McIntyre, R. J. (1966). Multiplication noise in uniform avalanche diodes, *IEEE Trans. Electron. Dev.*, **13** (1), 164–168.

Melchior, H., Hartman, A. R., Schinke, D. P. and Seidel, T. E. (1978). Planar epitaxial silicon avalanche photodiodes, *Bell Syst. Tech. J.*, **57**, 1791–1797.

Moseley, A. J., Hankey, J., Debney, B. T., Monham, K. I., Stone, L. G. and Cooper, P. D. (1985). GaInAs PIN–GaAs IC preamplifier receiver for high data rate long wavelength optical fiber systems. In Pearsall, T. and Noblanc, J. P. (eds), *Proc. 2nd Int. Tech. Symp. on Optical and Electro-Optic Applied Science and Engineering, Cannes, 1985*, Vol. 587, pp. 195–200, SPIE, Washington, DC.

Muoi, T. V. (1984). Receiver design for high speed optical fiber systems, *J. Lightwave Technol.*, **2** (3), 243–267.

Niwa, N., Tashiro, Y., Minemura, K., Iwasaki, H., Sussman, R. S., Ash, R. M., Moseley, A. J. and Goodfellow, R. C. (1984). High sensitivity Hi–Lo germanium avalanche photodiode for 1.5 μm wavelength optical communication, *Electron. Lett.*, **20** (13), 552–553.

Noe, R. (1986). Endless polarisation control experiment with three elements of limited birefringence range, *Electron. Lett.*, **22** (25), 1341–1343.

Smith, R. G. and Personick, S. D. (1980). Receiver design for optical fiber communication systems, *Semiconductor Devices for Optical Communication*, Chapter 4, Springer, New York.

Sussman, R. S. *et al.* (1985). Ultra-low capacitance flip chip bonded GaInAs PIN photodetector for long wavelength high data rate fibre optic systems, *Electron. Lett.*, **21** (14), 593–595.

Sze, S. M. (1981). *Physics of Semiconductor Devices* (2nd edn), p. 758, Wiley, New York.

Sze, S. M. (1985). *Semiconductor Devices: Physics and Technology*, p. 281, Wiley, New York.

Van Der Ziel, A. (1970). Noise in solid-state devices and lasers, *Proc. IEEE*, **58** (8), 1178–1204.

Chapter 5

Optical Sources

A. M. YUREK AND A. DANDRIDGE

5.1 Introduction

5.1.1 Source requirements

Fiber optic sensors exploit a very wide range of operating principles. Consequently the range of optical sources for such sensors is also very diverse, ranging from hot filament lamps to semiconductor lasers. The purpose of this chapter is to provide some background to the operating principles and optical properties of typical sources. Prior to embarking on a detailed discourse, it may be useful to review briefly some types of sources and their potential roles in sensors.

The light-emitting diode (LED) is normally the preferred choice for simple incoherent sensors using multimode fiber, except where the higher power capability of lasers is required. For interferometric sensors, the use of lasers is essential when there is a significant length difference between the interfering optical paths. However, for certain interferometric sensors using well-balanced optical paths, high radiance broadband sources such as superluminescent diodes (SLDs) or very multimoded lasers or even in some cases normal high radiance LEDs may be advantageous, as then any undesirable reflection will not generally cause problems in the interferometer. As the sources and the sensing systems have yet to be described in detail, we will now concentrate on the principles of operation of the devices themselves and then describe their properties in more detail.

5.1.2 The emission process

The concepts of spontaneous and stimulated emission were discussed in Chapter 3, but we shall now recapitulate and expand on the treatment. In a semiconductor the choice of a direct-bandgap material is necessary for efficient emission as a result of the need to conserve momentum during the

151

electron–hole recombination which gives rise to the emission of a photon. All semiconductor emitting diodes are forward-biased junction diode devices where carriers are injected as a result of the current flow. The energy available from each recombination process is approximately equal to the bandgap energy E_g, and hence the photon emission frequency v is given by

$$v = \frac{E_g}{h}$$

where h is Planck's constant, because the photon energy hv must be equal to the energy lost during recombination.

Not all recombinations, however, result in photon emission as there are competing nonradiative processes which result in energy loss to heat. The efficiency of the photon-generation process is defined by two quantum efficiencies: the internal quantum efficiency which, as the name implies, is the ratio of the number of photons generated to the number of electron–hole pairs which recombine, and the external quantum efficiency which is the ratio of the number of photons emitted from the device package to the number of pairs which recombine. The latter thus takes into account the losses occurring after the generation process.

It is relatively easy to produce a population inversion in semiconductor devices where there are more excited states than ground states in the emitting region. Under these conditions the stimulated emission rate exceeds the self-absorption rate and a very high gain per unit length can be achieved compared with most other forms of lasing medium. Thus in high radiance LEDs, which have high injection current densities, it is quite likely that significant single-pass gain will occur as the light travels from the emitting region to the surface of the device. This gain may give rise to so-called superluminescent behavior if it occurs in the direction of primary emission. The process can result in a much increased output from the device and also in a significant linewidth reduction as a result of greater gain at the center of the gain curve. (A normal LED has a typical natural linewidth in the range 30–100 nm depending on the materials used, whereas superluminescent devices may show a linewidth which may be narrowed by a progressively increasing amount until the onset of lasing action.)

The construction of a laser requires some form of resonant feedback system in order to produce a self-maintaining oscillation during repeated light reflections between the reflective mirrors through the amplifying medium. As already stated, in semiconductor devices the gain per pass is extremely high and a simple cleaved facet at each end of the device, with a Fresnel reflection of only 30%, will usually provide sufficient feedback to cause lasing action.

The individual devices and their forms of construction will now be described. The main descriptions in the earlier sections will deal with the more straightforward aspects, leaving more complex aspects relevant to interferometric sensors to the later sections.

5.1.3 Electrical properties and drive circuitry

The equivalent electrical circuit of a semiconductor diode device is shown in Fig. 5.1(a). This circuit applies to all the semiconductor light emitters discussed in the following sections. The basic elements include a series resistor

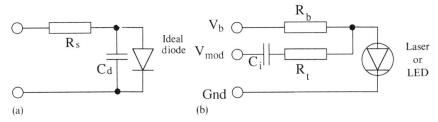

(a)   (b)

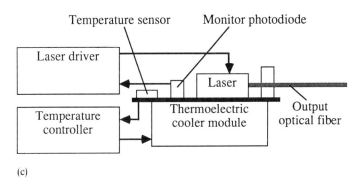

(c)

Fig. 5.1 Electrical drive considerations of semiconductor light-emitting devices: (a) equivalent circuit of an LED or laser; (b) drive circuit for high frequency modulation; (c) temperature and power output control circuit for a laser diode module.

R_s, a junction capacitance C_d and a diode with the traditional diode voltage–current relationship

$$I_f \approx I_0 \exp\left(\frac{qV}{kT}\right)$$

where I_f is the forward diode current, V is the forward voltage, q is the electronic charge, k is Boltzmann's constant and T is the absolute temperature. We will now calculate the limitations that the electrical parasitics impose on the modulation behavior of the diode, before going on to the more fundamental physics limitation internal to the device which will be considered later. Differentiating the above equation yields

$$dI_f \approx \frac{I_0 q}{kT} dV \exp\left(\frac{qV}{kT}\right)$$

and the dynamic resistance $R_d = dV/dI_f$ has a value given by

$$R_d = \frac{dV}{dI_f} = \frac{kT}{qI_f}$$

kT/q has a value of 25 mV at room temperature and hence, at typical forward bias currents of 50 mA, a dynamic resistance of $0.5\,\Omega$ is obtained.

Thus although the parasitic capacitance C_d may have a value of several hundred picofarads under forward bias conditions, it is not normally a severe constraint on the frequency response. If we neglect the series resistor R_s in Fig. 5.1(a) in view of the very low values of this component in practical devices, the 3 dB frequency $f_{3\,dB}$ is given by

$$f_{3\,dB} = \frac{1}{2\pi R_d C_d}$$

under current drive conditions, and hence $f_{3\,dB} = 320$ MHz even when a value of C_d as high as 1000 pF is chosen.

The circuit of Fig. 5.1(b) shows a suitable circuit for biasing a laser or LED diode from a constant voltage source V_b and giving provision for an amplitude modulation either directly from a radiofrequency voltage source or indirectly via a transmission line. In the case of the latter, the resistance R_T should be chosen to match the line impedance. The decoupling capacitor C must have a negligibly low impedance at all the drive frequencies of interest.

The final circuit in Fig. 5.1(c) shows a typical functional block diagram of a control system for stabilizing both the temperature and the optical output of a laser. Similar circuits can be used for an LED, except that for surface-emitting and forward-emitting extended LEDs (ELEDs) the monitor photodiode will generally need to receive a proportion of the light from the front of the device. The temperature control is achieved using a temperature monitor and a Peltier temperature controller. Many commercial laser modules now contain such temperature-control and light-output-monitoring devices within the laser package.

5.1.4 Modulation behavior of semiconductor diode light sources

The electrical drive limitations of devices were described in the previous section. However, once the electrical circuit has been arranged for the desired internal injection-current modulation, the physical light emission processes will determine the effects of this bias current on the output beam.

The most fundamental aspect affecting the speed of response of the light emission process is the lifetime of the injected carriers. In simple surface-emitting LEDs, this is determined primarily by carrier recombination time. The recombination time τ describing the exponential decay of injected carriers is given by the well-known empirical relationship

$$\tau = \frac{1}{bn}$$

where n is the impurity doping level and b is a constant depending on the material. The value of b is remarkably similar for commonly used materials, having a value of 1.1×10^{-10} for GaAs and $(1.2–1.3) \times 10^{-10}$ for GaInAs. The value of τ determines the "fall-time" when an LED is excited by a square-wave signal and hence determines the maximum modulation frequency. Typical GaAlAs LEDs can be modulated up to a (-3 dB) frequency of 100 MHz.

In a device where stimulated emission processes may occur, the stimulation processes can lead to a greatly increased recombination rate for the injected carriers. Thus, as the degree of stimulated emission increases, the effective recombination rate and hence the speed of the devices increases. Lasers operated above threshold have very fast modulation capability, usually extending into the 1–10 GHz region, and in some cases as high as 30–50 GHz. The main problems that can occur in some devices are usually due to relaxation oscillation or "ringing" resulting from heavy depletion of carriers in response to a current increase followed by heavy repopulation when the light has decayed.

The other aspect relevant to laser modulation is the frequency modulation (sometimes termed "chirping") which occurs when the bias current is changed. This is a cause of great concern in direct detection communication systems as it can lead to a great bandwidth penalty when transmitting through fibers with significant modal or material dispersion. For sensors it can be a convenient means of frequency sweeping the source either to resolve fringe ambiguity problems or to create so-called "pseudo-heterodyne" signals, when light from a frequency-swept source is guided to a detector via an unbalanced interferometer path.

The frequency fluctuation of the laser has two components: the first is very fast and is due to refractive index changes which occur as a direct consequence of the bias current (e.g. changes in the complex refractive index due to the gain, which will be discussed further in Section 5.3.1), and the second is due to thermal changes which also result in refractive index changes. The thermal time constants are, in fact, remarkably rapid, considering their nature, because of the small dimensions of the active region and the good thermal conductivity of the materials. The thermal effects can therefore still be effective at rates of a few megahertz. As most sensor applications use slow "sawtooth" modulation of laser diodes, the thermal effects usually predominate. A typical laser will show a frequency shift in its output of 2 GHz mA^{-1} in response to changes in its bias current, a very fast slew rate in electronic terms, which is extremely useful for generating pseudo-heterodyne signals using frequency-modulated carrier wave (FMCW) techniques (see Chapter 14). However, it represents only a small change in optical terms and hence is not relevant to LEDs, with their much broader linewidth.

5.2 Light-emitting diodes

LEDs are spontaneous emission light sources. They usually emit light into a wide approximately Lambertian spatial cone (with an approximately $\cos \theta$ variation in the polar diagram for the simplest form of surface emission). They typically have an emitting diameter in excess of 50 μm and therefore only couple efficiently into multimode fibers. LEDs have both very short coherence lengths (typically less than 30 μm) and poor spatial coherence and are therefore incompatible with most forms of interferometric sensors. The only exceptions to this are the so-called super-radiant diodes in which the spatial coherence is substantially improved so that they may be compatible with zero-order (or almost zero-order) fringe interferometric sensing with closely balanced path lengths.

LEDs are invariably used as an optical source for incoherent sensors. As these sensors generally use multimode fiber, the problems of light launching are far less than with single-mode fiber. LEDs are generally less expensive than lasers or SLDs and are therefore excellent optical sources for low cost systems.

5.2.1 Device construction

Two basic LED structures have been developed, initially for telecommunications applications where high radiance and ease of coupling into optical fibers are important considerations. These are the surface-emitting and edge-emitting types.

A schematic diagram of a high radiance surface-emitting LED is shown in Fig. 5.2 (Burrus and Dawson, 1970). It consists of a number of n-doped and p-doped layers with one p–n junction. To provide close access to the emitting region and a convenient location for an optical fiber a well is etched into the substrate side. This well also reduces the self-absorption in the material between the emitting region and the output fiber, a problem that can be further alleviated by the use of layers of different composition (higher bandgap) in this intervening region. This means that the well need not be so deep, hence keeping surface defects further from the active region (Personick, 1985). The well also allows the junction region to be placed much closer to the heat sink than would otherwise be the case. The current contact is situated under the well to create strong current confinement in the desired emitting region.

A number of variants on this system are possible in which microlenses are formed in the material. The use of lenses would not normally improve the launching efficiency from a large area radiance-limited emitting device into a fiber. It does mean, however, that an emitting area much smaller than the fiber can be used and matched, using the lens to couple more efficiently into the fiber. This now gives rise to the possibility of increasing the radiance of the device by closer current confinement into the smaller active area with better heat transfer away into the surrounding material. It is therefore an indirect

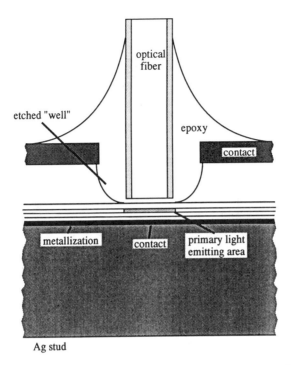

Fig. 5.2 Schematic diagram of a surface-emitting LED showing one technique used to couple to an optical fiber.

effect of the lens that allows a higher radiance device to be constructed and matched to a fiber of larger diameter.

The second commonly used LED structure is the edge-emitting hetero-junction type. This structure is similar to a laser diode except that the length of the emitting region is usually shorter, typically around 100 μm, and reflective feedback from at least one of the mirrors is generally suppressed to prevent lasing action (Kressel and Ettenberg, 1975). Schematic diagrams of LEDs incorporating a restricted edge-emitting diode (REED) structure are shown in Fig. 5.3. In Fig. 5.3(a) the active area is defined by the location of the contact on the junction side of the diode. In Fig. 5.3(b) a groove has been cut or etched behind the active area to increase the optical power output. This increase is due both to the increased confinement of the active area and to the (approximately 30%) reflection at the uncoated rear surface. A further increase in optical power output can be obtained by metallizing the grooved portion and applying an antireflection coating to the output face of the LED (Wittke *et al.*, 1976). The width of the junction region in these REEDs is generally chosen to be 50–70 μm for optimum coupling to multimode optical fibers (Kressel and Ettenberg, 1975; Wittke *et al.*, 1976). Edge-emitting LEDs can be mounted

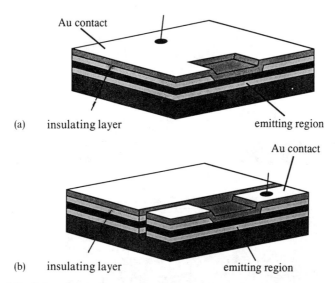

(a)   insulating layer   emitting region

(b)   insulating layer   emitting region

Fig. 5.3 Edge-emitting structures: (a) the whole surface of the diode is metallized for ease of contact; (b) a groove is added at the back of the square contact area to provide a partially reflecting surface.

junction side down (in order to provide improved heat transfer from the active region) on copper heat sinks.

SLDs are edge-emitting LEDs driven with a sufficiently high current density to produce a strong population inversion and provide a significant single-pass gain by stimulated emission amplification. A laser-like guiding structure can be used to enhance the gain. SLDs were originally developed for telecommunications in order to boost the launch power and reduce the linewidth compared with a normal LED. The REED ELED structure is capable of superluminescent behavior but is less effective if no light-guiding stripe is used to confine the light in a high current density region.

Three methods can be employed to prevent lasing action in SLDs: (a) the cleaved end-facets of the cavity can be antireflection coated; (b) an unpumped (and hence absorbing) region can be included at one end of the device to act as an energy sink; (c) the light-guiding stripe of a conventional semiconductor laser can be produced with an angular offset such that the end-facets are no longer normal to the axis of the stripe, thereby preventing efficient reflection back into a guided mode (Fig. 5.4). SLDs can be fabricated to produce single-spatial-mode radiation which can be coupled into single-mode fiber. This is particularly useful in fiber gyroscopes (see Chapter 11).

Both the angular emission pattern and the spectral linewidth of ELEDs are narrowed compared with conventional LEDs as a result of the gain process. The linewidth narrowing of the ELED as a result of the higher gain at the center of the gain curve has already been mentioned. The narrowing of the angular emission pattern is shown in Fig. 5.5.

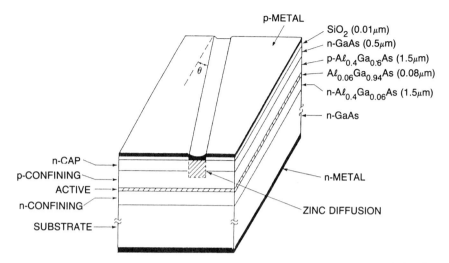

Fig. 5.4 Layer structure and composition of an inclined-stripe SLD (device by courtesy of David Sarnoff Research Laboratory).

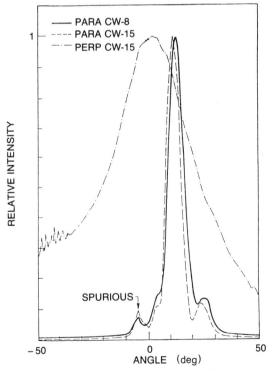

Fig. 5.5 Far-field output intensity versus output angle for a typical inclined-stripe SLD: para, plane parallel to the layers; perp, plane perpendicular to the layers; cw-x indicates the output power with x in milliwatts.

5.2.2 Optical properties

5.2.2.1 Wavelength and linewidth

The center emission wavelength λ of an LED depends on the bandgap energy E_g of the semiconductor material:

$$\lambda = \frac{hc}{E_g} \approx \frac{1.24}{E_g} \, \mu m$$

where h is Planck's constant and c is the velocity of light. The linewidth of the radiation from an LED is typically of the order of 5% of the central emission wavelength except in super-radiant diodes where the selectivity of the gain across the linewidth may produce narrowing.

Four materials are commonly used to produce LEDs (emission wavelengths given in parentheses):

GaP (700 nm)   red
GaAlAs (650–850 nm)   red to near-infrared
GaAs (900 nm)   near-infrared
InGaAs (1200–1700 nm)   near-infrared

The bandgaps of the ternary and quaternary mixtures can be varied by changing the mixture of these compounds. In addition to the above, there have been significant developments of longer wavelength devices such as HgCdTe structures for mid-infrared operation, and these may have significant interest for gas-sensing applications.

5.2.2.2 Output power and coupling into optical fibers

The output power of 850 nm LEDs is frequently in the region 1–10 mW. The power available decreases dramatically for devices below 850 nm as the efficient GaAlAs system can no longer be used. At longer wavelengths (except for the GaAs system, which can result in high output devices in the wavelength region 900–940 nm) the power output of available LEDs also tends to be somewhat less, although in this region it may be partly due to lack of developmental attention compared with that for the mass-market areas below 900 nm.

The optical power launched into optical fibers from LEDs is generally far lower than their total output capability, as the launch efficiency of such wide-emission-angle devices into fibers with their relatively low acceptance angles is inevitably rather poor (Wittke *et al.*, 1976; Kressel and Butler, 1977; Personick, 1985). For butt mounting of an LED of radiance R to a step-index fiber of core radius r and numerical aperture NA, the launch power P_{IN} is given by

$$P_{IN} \approx \pi^2 r^2 (NA)^2 R$$

The radiance in watts per steradian per square centimeter represents the brightness of the LED, i.e. the power radiated per unit area per unit solid angle. For a graded-index fiber with half the mode volume of a step-index type, the corresponding relationship is

$$(P_{IN})_{GRIN} \approx 0.5\pi^2 r^2 (NA)^2 R$$

In both cases the assumption is made that NA is small (less than 0.3 gives a negligible error) and that only truly guided modes are launched (i.e. "leaky" modes with an angle to the axis of the fiber which is beyond the guidance limit for rays launched onto the center of the core are ignored).

The ray model used to derive the above relationship no longer applies for monomode fibers, although the formula still provides an order-of-magnitude estimate of launched power. For accurate results a more exact model taking into account spatial mode matching must be used.

A typical launch figure for a graded-index fiber with a core of radius 50 μm and an NA of 0.2 from an 815 nm high radiance LED is 50 μW (-13 dBm). Launch powers of up to 1 mW can be achieved for fibers with larger diameters and high NA. The figures for visible LEDs are generally at least a factor of 10 lower than for near-infrared devices. However, such powers are more than adequate for most low speed sensing applications (e.g. 0–5 kHz) where received powers of only 10^{-10}–10^{-12} W may be all that is necessary to achieve the necessary signal-to-noise ratio. The use of lens-focusing arrangements cannot increase the above figures (and will in fact introduce additional reflection losses) unless the fiber core area is greater than the LED emitting area. As already discussed, however, the incorporation of a lens allows an LED with a much more confined active area to be used and higher current densities can be applied to increase the radiance without the attendant thermal problems that would otherwise occur with larger areas. Thus the use of a lens, particularly a microsphere lens, attached on or close to the LED surface is an attractive option for LED packaging. Figure 5.6 shows a lens-assisted coupling arrangement using a sphere lens between the LED and the fiber tail. Such an arrangement can be used for surface-emitting LEDs, ELEDs and SLDs, although there is generally more to be gained from the surface-emitting type with their wider output angle (Botez and Ettenberg, 1979).

5.2.2.3 Noise

In most optical fiber sensor systems incorporating simple surface-emitting LEDs as the optical source, the system noise limitation is primarily that due to the detection system as the spontaneous emission process is relatively low noise, except for the fundamental discrete photon nature of the light. Thus, as was discussed in more detail in Chapter 4, the receiver thermal noise will predominate at low light levels unless avalanche photodiodes (APDs) are used. At higher received levels the photon noise will be the dominant factor (and of course the use of APDs would no longer be necessary).

5.2.2.4 Operating lifetime

After the simple PIN detector, the simple LED is one of the most reliable

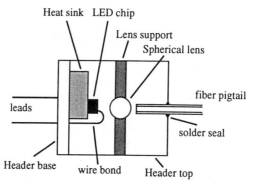

Fig. 5.6   Schematic diagram showing lens-assisted coupling from an LED to an optical fiber.

of optoelectronic components. The primary cause of LED degradation, and eventual failure, is the growth of crystal defects (the so-called "dark-hole" defects) in the junction region. These defects tend to increase the level of nonradiative processes, and their growth is a function of both temperature and drive current.

In order to reduce problems with dark defects, the starting material must be carefully manufactured or selected. It is common practice in high reliability LED manufacture to "burn in" devices at high temperature and select out devices which exhibit a noticeable degradation in external quantum efficiency as a function of time. Devices with small active areas tend to have better yields as the likelihood of including a dark defect is reduced.

The mean time before failure (MTBF) is defined as the average time taken for a test batch to have their outputs reduced to 50% of the original value. Twu and Kung (1982) concluded that the MTBF can be expressed as

$$\text{MTBF} = k'J^n \exp\left(\frac{E_a}{kT}\right)$$

where k' is a constant, J is the current density, E_a is the activation energy, k is Boltzmann's constant and T is the absolute temperature of the substrate. A typical value for E_a is 0.46 eV, and n has a value of 2 for a surface-emitting LED and 2.3 for a planar LED.

Figure 5.7 shows a family of MTBF characteristics in which two types of surface-emitting LEDs, one with an etched well and one without, are compared for a particular set of conditions. The packaging of LEDs may either improve or degrade the MTBF depending on whether the additional mechanical stress degrades it or the improved thermal heat sinking improves it. Modern high quality LEDs generally achieve an MTBF of 10^6–10^7 h at room temperature, and problems are only likely if they are run continuously at very high temperatures or if they are accidentally overstressed mechanically or electrically.

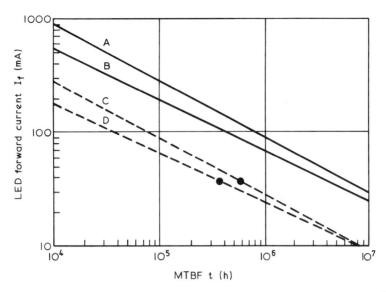

Fig. 5.7 MTBF versus current at two temperatures (at 40 mA, $J = 1200 \, \text{A cm}^{-2}$ for both devices): line A, etched well, 25 °C; line B, planar, 25 °C; line C, etched well, 70 °C; line D, planar, 70 °C.

5.2.3 Operation of light-emitting diodes and superluminescent diodes in sensors

In this section we shall attempt to summarize the typical applications of LEDs in sensors. However, at this point in the text the description must necessarily be brief as many of the types of optical sensors have yet to be described.

The main source likely to be used in sensors of the cheaper incoherent type will be the surface-emitting LED, as it is more generally available at low cost. This simple compact device is a near-ideal source for many such applications. Three main types are worthy of consideration: the fiber-tailed type and the packaged LED microlens type (each of these two usually emits at 820–850 nm and is generally based on GaAlAs technology), and the larger area 940 nm GaAs type which is frequently used in punched-card readers, infrared proximity detectors and remote control devices. The GaAlAs types are capable of high speed modulation if desired (typically about 80 MHz), whereas the 940 nm GaAs types are only capable of about 500 kHz modulation.

All LEDs change their output power and output wavelength with temperature. At 850 nm the typical temperature coefficients of output power and wavelength are 0.5% °C^{-1} and 0.3 nm °C^{-1} respectively. Consequently simple analog intensity sensors and even some forms of dual-wavelength-referenced sensors will produce output signals which are dependent on the LED temperature. Thermal stabilization is thus very important in many such sensors.

The use of LEDs in wavelength-filtering systems is somewhat hampered by their relatively narrow linewidth compared with that obtainable using a tungsten filament lamp. Although this problem can be solved by combining many LEDs of different wavelengths, production of a flat spectral characteristic is not easy. The alternative of operating over a narrower spectral band is less attractive, as channel separation is less easy and temperature variation of the spectrum may be troublesome.

The range of mid-infrared LEDs for gas sensing and other spectrophotometric measurements is expanding, as is the availability of compatible infrared fiber. The lead salt LEDs are the most promising in this area.

Finally, we make a brief comment on LEDs in interferometers. The short coherence length of about 20 nm means that the fringe contrast is extremely low unless very accurate path-length balancing is carried out (Dandridge, 1983). However, for intrinsically well-balanced interferometers such as the bidirectional Sagnac loop interferometer, where the light travels along the same path in opposite directions, the short coherence length can be used to advantage as the desired interference still has a high fringe contrast whereas virtually all the undesirable additional paths arising as a result of reflection and scattering mechanisms have much longer path differences and hence poor fringe visibility. In this case, however, it is necessary to use the extra radiance that SLDs can provide in order to launch sufficient energy into the monomode fiber.

5.3 Semiconductor diode lasers

Semiconductor lasers (also called injection lasers or diode lasers) differ from LEDs as a result of the optical feedback from some form of resonant cavity. This results in multiple passes through the gain region which, if it has a sufficiently high population inversion, will overcome the losses at each reflection from the external mirror (or an equivalent reflecting arrangement such as a grating). Even with the relatively low Q cavity typical of such lasers, each mode in the spectrum generally has a much reduced linewidth compared with an LED from the same material.

5.3.1 Laser structures and types

The simplest form of laser is the Fabry–Pérot cavity type, which has mirrors placed at each end of the lasing cavity. These mirrors are generally produced simply by cleaving the crystal along a crystalline plane, although more recently surface passivation coatings are often applied in order to increase the threshold at which optically induced mirror damage may occur.

The concept of the Fabry–Pérot resonator was introduced in Chapter 3. As the Fresnel reflections at each surface have a magnitude of only 30% or so, a net gain of at least a factor of 3 is required on each pass through the amplifying medium. The output of the laser corresponds to all the cavity resonant lines at which there is sufficient gain to maintain oscillation, and the typical spectrum of a multimode type is as shown in Fig. 5.8. It is beyond a general text of this type to describe all the forms of Fabry–Pérot laser that have been devised. The most common feature is that the devices almost invariably consist of a series of stratified layers called heterostructures which confine the light within a planar waveguiding structure. The simplest forms of such lasers emit over very broad stripes (typically 20–200 μm wide, but only a few microns thick). These broad-stripe lasers, which were one of the first structures to be produced, require very high operating currents to reach lasing thresholds as a result of the wide stripe (which gives a larger product of current density and area) and the poor optical confinement. Therefore they will only operate in pulsed mode at room temperatures. If operated continuously, they would rapidly overheat and be destroyed. In addition, they are highly multimoded, being able to support a large number of transverse and longitudinal modes. Such lasers find their main applications, such as range-finding systems, in optical lidar and have analogous applications in time-division multiplexing of sensors where a pulsed source is desired. However, they can only be launched efficiently into large core multimode fiber.

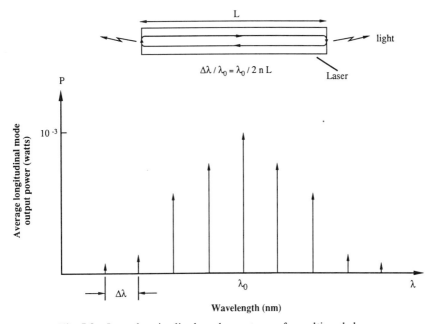

Fig. 5.8   Laser longitudinal mode spectrum of a multimode laser.

In order to produce continuous-wave (CW) operation at room temperature, it is necessary to confine the optical beam and the injection current to a long thin stripe such that the local heating can be readily conducted away and the light is carefully guided between the mirrors with low optical losses. The narrow stripe also ensures that the emitting region is more compatible with the dimensions of optical fibers and can produce a single-transverse-mode structure, but usually there is some degree of astigmatism in the mode pattern owing to the rectangular cross-sectional stripe in the laser. These narrow-stripe laser structures can be categorized according to whether they have gain-guided or index-guided structures (Fig. 5.9). Both structures confine the optical beam in the vertical direction by virtue of the refractive indices of the stratified layers, in a similar way to that in planar waveguides. The two structures differ, however, in their method of optical confinement in the horizontal direction. In the gain-guided structure horizontal confinement is achieved by the localization of population inversion to the area under the electrode. This produces a refractive index gradient in the active layer. The gradient here is largely in the imaginary term of the index (i.e. because of the local gain), in contrast with index guiding which is enhanced by confinement due to a gradient in the real part of the refractive index. Clearly all lasers will have some contribution from gain guiding. In the index-guided laser structure, a refractive index profile is designed into the device in the horizontal direction in order to confine the propagating light in the direction parallel to the junction. In the latter case, guidance occurs even in the absence of injected carriers. A representative example is shown in Fig. 5.9(b) where the *effective* refractive index of the lower cladding layer is modified by a change in its thickness.

5.3.2 Single-mode operation

Most early lasers would support oscillation in a number of transverse and longitudinal modes. The narrow-stripe lasers discussed earlier solve the multiple-transverse-mode problem. This removes the difficulty of efficient coupling to monomode systems, particularly if the astigmatism is corrected by suitable lenses. However, the problem of multilongitudinal mode operation remains. This can give rise to a form of intensity noise called mode partition noise. The division of optical power between the various longitudinal modes radiated by the laser fluctuates erratically whilst the total output power from the laser may remain constant. Transients are observed during the fluctuation from one spectral distribution of output to another. These transients are observed as intensity noise on the optical signal. Additionally, many sensor systems are to some extent wavelength selective so that these mode partition fluctuations can be further exacerbated after transfer through the wavelength-selective characteristic of the sensor. Another aspect of this behavior is a tendency to produce a nonlinear output power versus current characteristic. As the distribution of power within the modes alters, new modes become

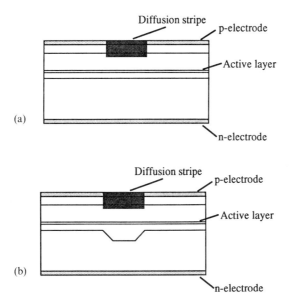

Fig. 5.9 (a) Typical gain-guided laser architecture; (b) index-guided structure. The diagrams show an end view.

supported or supportable at higher levels of gain. These give rise to "kinks" in the characteristic. It is particularly troublesome to have multimode operation in interferometric systems as each mode will result in a different fringe pattern response, and these may cancel or reinforce depending on the length imbalance.

In principle, the simplest way to achieve single-mode operation is to use a short lasing cavity. However, it is fundamental to the design of such a cavity that its lowest-order resonant frequency should exceed the gain linewidth of the lasing medium which, for a semiconductor source, is typically of the order of 2000 GHz. This requires that the cavity length is less than 75 μm in air or less than about 20 μm in the typical III–V semiconductors used for lasers. This, in turn, requires that the gain in the laser cavity should exceed $1500\,\mathrm{cm}^{-1}$, corresponding to excessively high drive currents. In practice, a somewhat longer cavity is more typical, giving rise to several resonances within the gain curve. However, mode selection effects can be exploited in order to give almost pure single-mode operation. The behavior of such devices is quite complex, however, and in particular they may be susceptible to mode jumping as the mode at which the gain selectivity peaks moves around with changes in operating current and/or temperature.

Other techniques can be used to enhance the gain selectivity by "tuning" the response of the cavity to enhance a particular resonance. The basic Fabry–Pérot cavity has a "comb" response in which each resonant peak is approximately equal in size. The basic philosophy of all the single-mode selection processes is to enhance one of these resonant peaks by using another external resonant structure.

One approach is to use a separate Fabry–Pérot cavity coupled to the first but with a different frequency spacing. The coupled cavities will produce a composite spectrum which will have a preferred mode. One version of this is the so-called C^3 laser in which a long laser cavity is literally cut into sections of different lengths. Similar effects can be obtained by using external mirrors mounted within or external to the laser package, although these produce a closely spaced "comb" response which requires very careful adjustment and matching to the laser cavity.

One of the most effective ways of ensuring stable single-mode operation in a monolithic structure is referred to as the distributed feedback laser. In essence this laser uses Bragg gratings formed on a surface close to the active region. These grating elements only become efficient distributed reflectors at the wavelength at which the reflection from each individual line perturbation of the grating reinforces that from each of the adjacent ones. The net result is a series of reflections which, even though each individual line reflection has a low value, coherently reinforce to produce the reflection coefficients of a few tens of a per cent required to allow lasing action. This lasing action must then be at a precisely defined wavelength, as determined by the grating spacing.

Interferometric sensors often require highly coherent sources particularly for those operating on nonzero path differences. For such sensors the frequency stability of the source is extremely important since instabilities, conveniently regarded as frequency modulation (FM) noise, may produce fluctuations in the output from the interferometer which cannot be removed using signal processing. This is considered in more detail later in this chapter.

A final comment regarding single-mode lasers is pertinent. Having produced the desired single-mode output, they are generally rather susceptible to external reflections which can effectively create a large number of new resonant oscillatory modes in the laser by formation of a new series of coupled cavity modes. Care must therefore be taken to prevent return reflection into the cavity. This will be dealt with in more detail later.

5.3.2.1 Phased-array lasers

Phased-array lasers are essentially a series of thin stripe lasers on a single chip. The stripes are arranged to be close and parallel to each of their neighboring stripes, so that a degree of coupling of energy occurs between them. It is this coupling which can lead to the phase-locking condition where all the stripes have a fixed relative optical phase. The output should in theory consist of two degenerate far-field emission lobes which are the far-field diffraction pattern from the phase-locked array. The reason for twin emission lobes, rather than a single central lobe, is that the phases of adjacent stripes do not match in the phase-locked condition but vary periodically (in principle between zero and 180°) along the structure as a result of the coupled-mode relationships.

In practice, however, not all commercial lasers of the so-called phased-array type exhibit the true phase-locked nature and the output mode pattern is often highly complex. Despite this, they have found extensive uses in view of their high CW power output (powers of several tens or even hundreds of watts have been reported) and devices are commercially available with CW powers of several watts. Devices pigtailed to multimode fibers are available with launched powers of up to 500 mW. Amplitude noise levels of typically 60 dB below the CW power level can be obtained with commercial devices.

5.3.3 Optical properties

5.3.3.1 Wavelength

The construction of semiconductor lasers is feasible, in principle at least, at all wavelengths where LEDs can be constructed, provided that the population inversion conditions necessary for gain can be achieved. However, the efficiency of the processes decreases in the visible region and it becomes extremely difficult to produce lasers at shorter wavelengths than the red region of the spectrum despite intense commercial interest for improved resolution in optical data storage and readout systems (e.g. laser printers, compact disk (CD) players etc). In the near-infrared region sources are available for CD players (700–850 nm, CW types), laser range finders (850 nm, pulsed sources) and telecommunications (850, 1300 and 1550 nm CW single-mode types).

The development of mid-infrared sources could have important prospects for chemical analysis by spectrophotometry, and may also be important for long distance telecommunications in mid-infrared fibers with their potentially much lower loss. Only a very limited number of research devices are available in this area at present. Thermal and current-induced variations in the length and refractive index of the cavity of a semiconductor laser produce very large changes in operating wavelengths. There are no convenient natural features such as the Lamb dip seen in gas lasers which can be exploited for wavelength stabilization.

5.3.3.2 Linewidth

The linewidth of semiconductor lasers varies over an enormous range from the 10–100 MHz typical of Fabry–Pérot and distributed feedback types to a few kilohertz or less for the lasers coupled to long external cavities.

5.3.3.3 Output power

The output power of lasers varies from the 1–10 mW typical of telecommunications monomode lasers to the kilowatt peak pulsed powers possible from arrays of broad-stripe single heterostructure lasers. In the last 2–3 years dramatic strides have been made in the powers available from commercial lasers, with single-mode lasers of up to 1 W CW power being reported and phased-array lasers of several watts becoming commonplace. The normal limitation on laser output power for narrow-stripe devices has been the optically induced facet damage at the active surface layer. However, surface passivation techniques appear to have improved dramatically in the last 2–3 years, giving rise to at least an order-of-magnitude power increase over this period.

The coupling efficiency of a monomode fiber can in theory approach 100% with an optimal lens system. In practice, however, a figure of 50% is a more realistic expectation for low cost micro-optical systems. Figures of less than this are achieved when it is necessary to include an optical isolator device.

The coupling of stripe lasers to multimode fiber can be maximized much more easily and figures of 80% for launching efficiency are readily obtained. The only difficulty with coupling semiconductor lasers into multimode fibers occurs when a light-emitting region which is wider than the fiber core diameter is used, leading to a loss which is not easily avoidable using lens systems because of the poorly defined mode pattern of this type of laser.

5.3.3.4 Operating lifetime

Laser diodes are generally reliable and long lived at room temperature if they are treated as recommended in their application notes. Extrapolated room temperature lifetimes of over 100 years have been reported from studies of accelerated high temperature tests. The lifetime of a semiconductor laser depends most strongly upon the operating temperature and drive current and can be rapidly terminated by even a transient overdrive current. The dependence of the laser lifetime on temperature is shown in Fig. 5.10. It can be seen that the lifetime decreases by an order of magnitude for a 40 °C rise in case temperature.

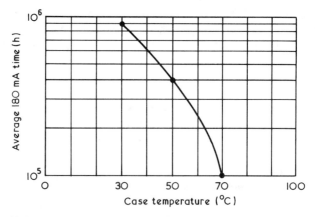

Fig. 5.10 Lifetime versus case temperature for a laser diode. The curve is for an NEC model NDL1308 laser diode, but the trend is similar for all laser diodes.

The other important requirement, to prevent the premature death of laser diodes, is the elimination of current transients and spikes. If their amplitude is large enough, transients of the order of a few nanoseconds in duration are enough to cause irreversible damage. The damage mechanism is usually the almost instantaneous overheating of the laser facet.

5.3.4 Noise and noise reduction

In the preceding sections we have discussed the optical properties of sources which determine the types of sensor in which they can be usefully employed. In this section, we will examine the noise properties of semiconductor diode lasers which will result in degradation of the sensor resolution performance. We will concentrate on the aspects relevant to interferometric sensors as they provide the most challenging requirements. In addition to their behavior under constant-current-drive conditions, both the amplitude and frequency of diode lasers vary with the drive current, with the amplitude being proportional to the current above threshold and the frequency varying (or "chirping") with a coefficient of typically $2\,\text{GHz}\,\text{mA}^{-1}$ in response to drive current changes. Consequently, well-smoothed power supplies or even batteries are often required. Single-mode diode lasers will be considered initially.

The development of semiconductor diode lasers was driven by the optical communications industry, where the high frequency noise properties of the laser are important. Although some fiber sensors operate in the hundreds of megahertz regime, many typically operate in the low frequency (d.c. to $50\,\text{kHz}$) region. Consequently, it was not until the early 1980s that the low frequency properties of these devices were examined in any detail. The earliest studies concentrated on the amplitude modulation (AM) noise properties (Dandridge et al., 1980), which were shown to exhibit an $f^{-0.5}$ frequency dependence on their output intensity (Fig. 5.11). Later studies deconvoluted the output into the two orthogonal polarizations emitted by the laser, i.e. the intensity $I_\parallel$ parallel to the junction and the intensity $I_\perp$ perpendicular to the junction (Dandridge et al., 1986). The variation in $I_\parallel$ and $I_\perp$ with drive current for a channel–substrate planar device is shown in Fig. 5.12. As expected, below threshold $I_\parallel$ and $I_\perp$ both represent predominantly spontaneous emission and above threshold (the threshold current is $28\,\text{mA}$ for this device) $I_\parallel$ increases rapidly, primarily because of the onset of stimulated emission. Thus, above threshold, the total intensity I_T is primarily governed by $I_\parallel$. The two noise terms $dI_\parallel$ and $dI_\perp$, as measured at $100\,\text{Hz}$ in a $1\,\text{Hz}$ bandwidth, are shown in Fig. 5.13. For a drive current varying between $10\,\text{mA}$ and threshold, $dI_\parallel$ increases by three orders of magnitude; however, above threshold $dI_\parallel$ is independent of current. Between $15\,\text{mA}$ and threshold, $dI_\perp$ increases less than an order of magnitude, but as the device starts to lase this quantity drops $5\,\text{dB}$ before becoming constant. This behavior can be understood by the following

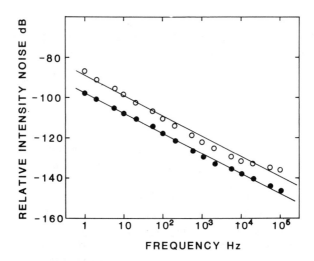

Fig. 5.11 Relative intensity noise dI/I as a function of frequency for an 830 nm GaAlAs laser diode (●) and a 1300 nm GaInAsP laser diode (○). (From Dandridge *et al.*, 1983.)

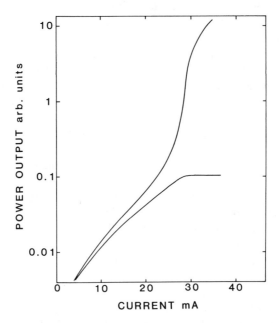

Fig. 5.12 Variation in laser orthogonal mode output intensity with forward drive current: upper curve, light polarized parallel to the junction ($I_{\parallel}$); lower curve, light polarized perpendicular to the junction ($I_{\perp}$). The threshold current is 28 mA.

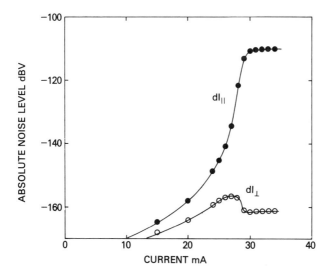

Fig. 5.13 Variation in $dI_\parallel$ (●) and $dI_\perp$ (○) with forward drive current. Measurements were made at 100 Hz with a 1 Hz bandwidth.

simple picture (this is discussed in greater depth by Dandridge *et al.* (1986)). Below threshold, the spontaneous emission noise fluctuations in the TE and TM modes are both driven by the current density n via the effective current density fluctuations ΔJ_e. Here, the effective current is defined as that component of the total current J which contributes to the carriers in the active region. Above threshold, the absolute value of $dI_\parallel$ becomes constant and is independent of the forward driving current. This has been explained by assuming that the amplitude of the effective fluctuations ΔJ_e, for a given frequency, is independent of the total injection current. The fluctuations ΔJ_e are probably related to the presence of carrier traps at or near the junction interfaces. The carrier density above threshold in the active region is almost constant and is very weakly affected by current fluctuations. The 5 dB drop in the noise of $dI_\perp$ at the lasing threshold indicates a reduction in the spontaneous emission noise above threshold drive as a result of carrier density clamping. Residual noise in the $I_\perp$ component above threshold is probably due to fluctuations in the current density outside the active region when the carrier density is not clamped to the value at the lasing threshold.

In most coherent fiber sensor systems, the signal is generally proportional to the total intensity I_T, or more precisely to the stimulated (coherent) portion of I_T (above threshold, $I_{STIM} \approx I_T \approx I_\parallel$). The optical spectral distribution of $I_\perp$ is very broad and contains many modes compared with the single $I_\parallel$ mode. Consequently, above threshold, the signal-to-noise ratio can be represented by $dI_\parallel/I_T$ and $dI_\perp/I_T$. Typical values are shown in Fig. 5.14. As expected, the signal-to-noise ratio is dominated by $dI_\parallel$ and $dI_\parallel/I_T$ is improved above

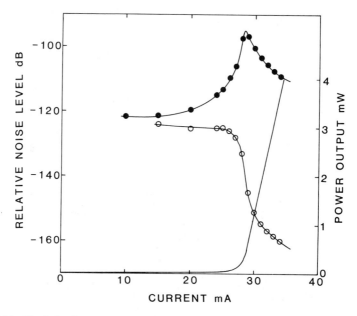

Fig. 5.14   Variation in the relative intensity noise of the orthogonally polarized output components $dI_{\parallel}/I_T$ (●) and $dI_{\perp}/I_T$ (○) as a function of the forward driving current. Measurements were made at 100 Hz with a 1 Hz bandwidth.

threshold by maximizing the laser drive current. Typically, the fringe visibility V of interferometric sensors is not unity. The AM limitation to phase detectability can be shown to be given by $(dI_{\parallel}/I_T)(1/V)$, which, in the best case for the conditions in Fig. 5.14 and with a fringe visibility of 50% ($V = 0.5$), corresponds to an amplitude-noise-limited phase resolution of only 10 μrad. The $dI_{\perp}/I_T$ value is two orders of magnitude below typical system requirements. Numerous successful approaches to overcoming laser AM noise have been demonstrated: (a) electronic feedback to the bias current from error signals derived from a separate monitor photodiode near a laser; (b) balanced homodyne optical receivers and heterodyne detection. The results of a simple optical subtraction technique, equivalent to a balanced receiver, are shown in Fig. 5.15. The development of sources for CD players has led to the development of substantially quieter diode laser sources (Dandridge *et al.*, 1982).

A rather more basic limitation of semiconductor diode lasers, where unbalanced interferometric sensors are concerned, is their FM noise component (Dandridge *et al.*, 1981). Although the AM noise of a diode laser is actually less than that for most stabilized gas lasers over a wide AM frequency band (Dandridge *et al.*, 1980), the low Q cavity and wide gain curve of the diode laser result in a poor frequency stability or high FM noise. The frequency instability is most conveniently measured using an unbalanced interferometer.

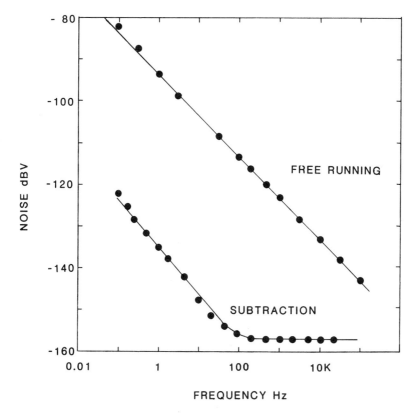

Fig. 5.15 Variation in the relative intensity noise of a buried heterostructure 830 nm laser diode with frequency: upper curve, free-running laser noise; lower curve, simple electronic subtraction technique. (From Dandridge, 1980.)

As most fiber interferometers are generally some form of two-beam instrument (e.g. Michelson, Mach–Zehnder, low reflectance Fabry–Pérot or Fizeau) we will use this as an example. The optical phase shift $\Delta\varphi$ in an interferometer with two optical paths l_1 and l_2 arising from a source frequency instability dv is given by

$$\Delta\varphi = \frac{2\pi dl_{12} dv}{c}$$

where dl_{12} is the optical path difference $l_1 - l_2$ and c is the velocity of light in free space. The variation in $\Delta\varphi$ as a function of the optical path difference at 2 kHz is shown for a number of lasers in Fig. 5.16. Although the level for each device is shifted because of the different values of dv, the dependence on path-length difference is confirmed. Thus, at 2 kHz, the r.m.s. frequency instability of the laser output is between 9 and 20 kHz as measured in a 1 Hz detection bandwidth. The frequency noise of the laser is equivalent to a phase noise error

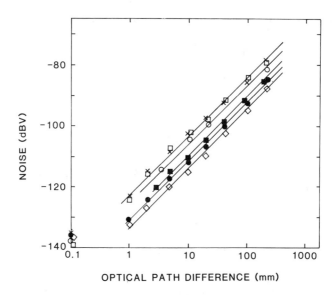

Fig. 5.16 Variation in the noise output of an interferometer as a function of the optical path difference for six different types of 830 nm laser diode. Note that the noise levels in dBV also correspond to dB with reference to a phase shift of 1 rad. Measurements were made at 2 kHz with a 1 Hz bandwidth.

at the sensor output and consequently neither the balanced optical receiver approach nor heterodyne detection will reduce this noise term. As can be seen, the noise is quite severe; for example, a Hitachi HLP 1400 laser was found to exhibit a noise-limited phase detection capability of about $100\,\mu$rad with a 20 cm path difference (Dandridge and Tveten, 1981b). Although the fringe visibility at a path difference of 20 cm would be close to unity, the signal-to-noise performance of the sensor would be rather poor. The suitability of sources for high sensitivity unbalanced interferometric sensors cannot therefore simply be assumed from a knowledge that the coherence length of the source is greater than the imbalance. The latter condition merely ensures that good fringe visibility is achieved. Above threshold, this frequency noise term is almost independent of current drive level (Fig. 5.17) (Dandridge and Taylor, 1982).

The FM noise has similar characteristics to the AM noise and, as shown in Fig. 5.18, exhibits an $f^{-0.5}$ frequency dependence. This similarity of behavior suggests that the AM and FM noise might be driven by the same mechanism. However, measurements of the correlation of these noise terms yielded significant values ($\gamma^2 \approx 0.5$) well above threshold, which slowly increased as threshold was approached. This study also led to the surprising observation that even the AM noise emitted from one facet of the laser was not well correlated with that from the other, as shown in Fig. 5.19(a) (Dandridge and Taylor, 1982). The AM noise term is well correlated at threshold, but γ^2

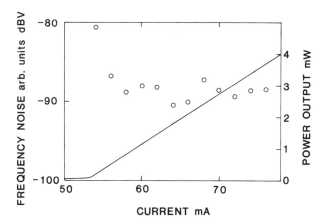

Fig. 5.17 Variation in the FM noise for an 830 nm laser with laser drive current (○). The power output is also shown (right-hand axis). The device threshold is 53 mA.

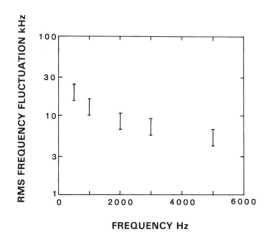

Fig. 5.18 Variation in the r.m.s. frequency fluctuation (FM noise) with the frequency of a 1300 nm laser diode.

decreases to about 0.7 well above threshold although the value of the modulation depth dI/I is the same for each facet, as shown in Fig. 5.19(b). Even more extreme behavior is noted when the laser mode hops, where the correlation may drop to zero (Dandridge, 1982). Dandridge and Taylor (1982) have developed a model that qualitatively predicts the behavior described above. The effects are explained in terms of fluctuations in ΔJ_e and the backscattering within the laser cavity. The backscattering of the guided light is assumed to result from irregularities at the hetero-epitaxial layers bounding the active region. The large refractive index discontinuity (about 0.2) at these

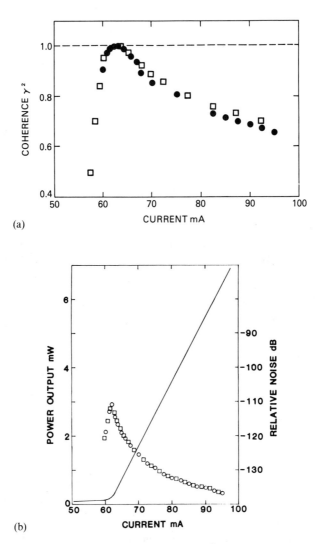

Fig. 5.19 (a) Variation in the coherence function γ^2 with the drive current for light emitted from the front and back laser facets. The device was an 830 nm laser diode with a threshold of 61 mA, and measurements were made at 100 Hz. Results from two devices are shown. (b) Variation in the relative intensity noise from the front (◯) and rear (☐) facets of an 830 nm laser with drive current. The laser output characteristic from the front facet is also shown.

interfaces means that a small displacement of the boundary can cause a significant amount of backscattering. The analysis is simplified by assuming in the model that a single reflector can replace the presumed numerous discontinuities. The backscatter terms act as intracavity mirrors and correspondingly allow the behavior described above.

The FM noise of diode lasers and the complexity of arrangements to reduce it have meant that great care must normally be taken in path balancing the arms of interferometers (Dandridge, 1983). Sensing approaches which introduce large path imbalances will lead to large values of phase noise as observed in coherence-multiplexed systems (Brooks et al., 1985). In the coherence-multiplexed sensor approach the effect of the laser frequency noise can be reduced by high frequency modulation of the emission frequency of the laser. The laser frequency modulation has little or no effect on the nominally path-balanced interferometers, but the "noisy" unbalanced interferometers now have a high modulation index β such that the noise is disposed to harmonics of the modulation frequency and the amplitude of the baseband noise is reduced by a factor $J_0(\beta_1)$ where J_0 is the zeroth-order Bessel function (Kersey and Dandridge, 1986).

Although the AM and FM noise characteristics of diode lasers deviate from those of the "ideal" quantum-limited source, they have the advantage that it is possible to modulate both their amplitude and their emission frequency (see above). In general, diode lasers exhibit both effects under current modulation; there are different device structures, however, which reduce the unwanted term. Even though fiber sensors do not generally require high speed source modulation, it should be noted that the intrinsic modulation limits are associated with the recombination lifetime of an electron–hole pair in the junction. Circuit limitations, including device capacitance, also limit the maximum modulation frequency. Owing to their light output characteristics, lasers may have a greater modulation index than LEDs for a given current modulation. Because the laser modal output deteriorates under on–off modulation, running the laser CW and using an external modulator (either acousto-optic or integrated optic) is preferred for applications that require a pulsed output from the source.

Current modulation of the laser also produces a change in the emission frequency; typical low frequency (d.c. to 100 kHz) values are 3 GHz mA^{-1} for lasers operating at 830 nm. At low frequencies the effect is dominated by the thermally induced changes in the refractive index and the length of the laser Fabry–Pérot cavity; the exact frequency dependence of this contribution is governed by the device structure and heat sinking. Modulation frequencies above 1 MHz are dominated by the charge-carrier-density-induced index change in the laser active region; this contribution is relatively constant below 1 GHz and has typical values of a few tenths of a gigahertz per milliampere. The ability to frequency modulate the optical source is often employed in demodulation schemes for interferometric sensors.

SLDs also exhibit a small degree of AM and FM noise; however, as the interferometric fiber gyroscope is essentially path balanced, the FM noise term is not of great importance and the AM noise can be reduced by power monitoring and division. It should be noted, however, that long-term drifts in the mean output wavelength may result in significant scale factor errors in the

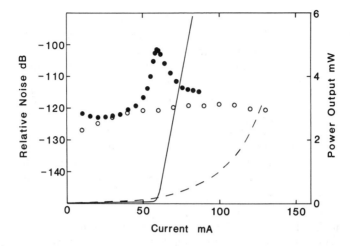

Fig. 5.20　Relative output noise of an SLD (○) and of a laser from the same wafer (●) as a function of current ($f = 1\,\text{kHz}$; $\Delta f = 1\,\text{Hz}$). Also shown is the power output characteristic of the laser (——) and the SLD (– – –). (From Dandridge and Taylor, 1987.)

gyroscope output. The AM noise terms of SLDs originate not only from the $f^{-0.5}$ noise (Dandridge and Taylor, 1987) but also from quantum-fluctuation noise effects (Yurek *et al.*, 1986) which give a flat frequency spectrum and are seen above 100 kHz. Typical low frequency noise behavior of an SLD is shown in Fig. 5.20. The behavior of the laser diode before SLD processing is also shown.

　　　Although most of the examples cited in Section 5.3.4 refer to sources operating at 830 nm, similar laser noise behavior has been noted for longer-wavelength semiconductor sources.

5.3.4.1　Optical feedback

　　　For laser diodes, the use of optical feedback into the lasing cavity may be either advantageous or highly disadvantageous depending on the type of feedback and its intensity. Initial measurements showed how uncontrolled optical feedback could induce laser mode hopping (Miles *et al.*, 1981); thus feedback increased both AM and FM noise. Optical feedback was also shown to produce satellite mode generation (i.e. sidelobes), multimode operation and apparent line broadening (Miles *et al.*, 1980). An example of the optical spectrum of a deteriorating modal output is shown in Fig. 5.21. This was found to have a strong effect on the fringe visibility of an interferometer (Fig. 5.22). Moreover, some of these effects can be induced with levels of feedback as low as 0.001%, i.e. a level which requires great practical care to avoid unintentional feedback effects. In this regime, where small amounts of optical feedback are applied, the optical phase of the feedback into the laser cavity is extremely important as changes in this phase can trigger mode instabilities. If the optical

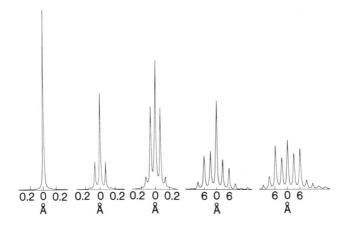

Fig. 5.21 Variation in the modal output of an 830 nm laser diode with varying optical feedback: (a) no feedback; (b) 0.041% feedback; (c) 0.06% feedback; (d) 0.3% feedback; (e) 1.5% feedback.

phase can be carefully controlled, line narrowing can actually occur and the characteristics of the laser can be greatly improved. By increasing the amount of phase-controlled feedback, the laser line can be narrowed by many orders of magnitude (Saito and Yammamoto, 1981). Although this narrowing does not affect the AM noise, the FM noise is reduced by the square root of the ratio of the free-running linewidth to the feedback-improved linewidth (Goldberg *et al.*, 1982). This technique has been investigated as a method of source linewidth control for sensors and for coherent communications.

In many optical systems it is possible to use polarizers and phase plates to reduce the extent of specularly reflected feedback into the laser from lenses etc. However, it has been shown that, for a laser coupled to more than a few tens of meters of optical fiber, Rayleigh backscattered light, the phase and polarization properties of which are quasi-random, can induce unstable operation (Dandridge and Miles, 1981). Such systems employ bulk optic isolators to achieve state-of-the-art performance, although pigtailed lasers with in-line isolators within the laser module package are commercially available at longer wavelengths. However, typical isolators achieve only − 30 dB isolation, and so care is still required to ensure that no residual deleterious effects due to reflections from fiber ends and so forth will occur.

5.3.4.2 Electronic feedback

It is relatively easy to reduce the AM noise of a laser diode using negative electronic feedback, and in fact this is now a standard feature in many laser modules to stabilize their output. A small proportion of the emitted light is detected using the monitor diode, amplified and then fed back to the laser current supply to form a negative feedback control loop. Depending on the

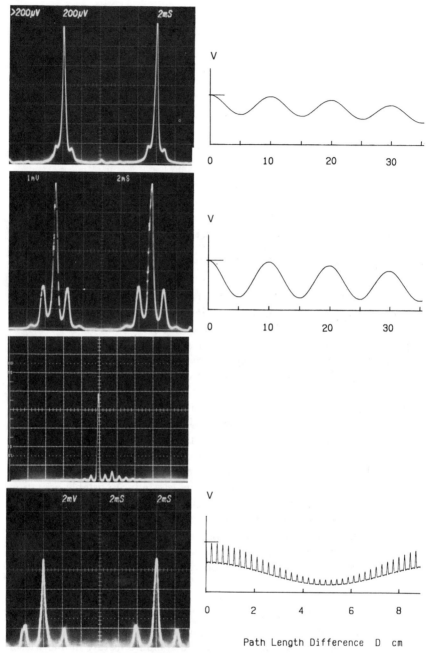

Fig. 5.22 Variation in the interferometer fringe visibility V as a function of the optical path difference D for the three optical spectra shown on the left. Note that, for the third case, the upper photograph shows the multimode operation while the lower photograph shows the satellite mode generation. (From Dandridge and Tveten, 1981a.)

frequency regime, a reduction of one or two orders of magnitude in AM noise can typically be achieved. It should again be noted that the correlation effect of light emitted from the front and back facets of the laser may play an important role. Many pigtailed lasers have a built-in detector to measure light level and noise from the rear facet; this often limits AM noise reduction to less than 10 dB owing to the poor correlation γ^2 of only 0.8 between the emissions from the front and rear facets. However, light from the front facet can be extracted using couplers or beam splitters. Typically, electronically reducing the level of the AM noise has a minimal effect on the FM noise (Dandridge and Tveten, 1983). However, Dakin and Withers (1986) have found high levels of FM noise reduction (about 29 dB) with some lasers using only AM feedback.

A stable frequency discriminator or filter is required to reduce the FM noise of the laser. A portion of the emitted light can be monitored using a Fabry–Pérot or unbalanced Mach–Zehnder interferometer. Such an optical frequency discriminator transforms the frequency fluctuations to corresponding intensity fluctuations which are detected, amplified and fed back as a control signal to the bias supply of the laser (Dandridge and Tveten, 1981c). An improvement of two to three orders in stability can be achieved using this approach. This allows high performance signal-to-noise ratios to be obtained without resorting to very short optical path differences (i.e. less than 1 mm).

The approach indicated above works well for reducing the alternating FM noise (1 Hz or above), but thermal drifts in the compensating interferometer, particularly if a fiber interferometer is used, render this a poor method for stabilization and care must still be taken to prevent reflection back into the controlled laser. Low frequency (quasi-d.c.) stabilization can be achieved by using a more stable form of optical frequency detector. Typical approaches use a monochromator, diffraction grating or interference filter to provide a simple frequency-dependent output (Webb et al., 1988). Care must be taken to ensure that errors due to intensity fluctuations are corrected. Temperature control of the device is also necessary to ensure that the correcting variations in the device drive current do not deviate too far from the optimum operating point.

5.3.5 Operation in sensors

It is clear that laser diodes offer numerous advantages over conventional lasers, particularly for fiber interferometric sensors. Advantages range from size and ruggedness to the ability to amplitude or frequency modulate their output easily by merely changing their bias current. Other advantages include relatively good AM stability, a long lifetime and relatively high efficiency.

Although few commercial interferometric sensors using diode lasers are currently available, a number of important field demonstrations have been made which would have been impossible without the use of diode laser sources. Although most prototype systems using diode lasers have been constructed using 830 nm devices, there is a clear trend towards the use of longer wavelengths. This will be particularly important for relatively large multiplexed systems which need to be operated over long lengths of fiber. The transition to long wavelengths should beneficially affect the ultimate cost of these sensors, allowing for low cost connectors and minimizing the pigtail stability problems which occur at 830 nm.

SLDs are at present strong candidates for the fiber gyroscope source—the competition is the fiber laser (see Section 5.4.2 and Chapter 8). High power SLD devices, which allow 5 mW to be launched into a single-mode fiber, are available at 830 nm. Present 1300 nm devices are an order of magnitude below this. Of major concern in this application are the wavelength stability and aging effects of these sources as these can affect the scale factor and hence the accuracy.

The use of lasers in noninterferometric sensors is limited to two basic types. The first is the use of high power pulsed lasers (almost invariably in the 820–900 nm wavelength region) in optical radar or lidar systems (such as optical time domain reflectometers and other time-distributed or time-division-multiplexed systems—see Chapters 14 and 15). The second is the use of phased-array lasers to provide high CW power for multiplexed sensors and for the photovoltaic powering of hybrid sensors (i.e. sensors based on traditional electrical concepts but powered and interrogated via optical links—see Chapter 12). In addition these lasers are often used to pump NdYAG and similar crystal host lasers to provide high power collimator sources.

Apart from these applications, the use of lasers with multimode fiber has generally been unnecessary in view of the higher coupled efficiency of LEDs into these fibers compared with that into monomode fibers. There is a possibility that high CW power transmitted along optical fibers may represent a safety hazard in flammable atmospheres, although recent studies have indicated that the practical hazard is likely to be small owing to the reduced spatial coherence obtained from multimode fibers.

5.4 Other optical sources

Although the majority of fiber optic sensors use LEDs or semiconductor diode lasers, there has been, and is likely to continue to be, interest in the use of alternative sources. Some sensors require narrow linewidths; as yet these are not commonly available from diode laser sources. Other sensors may require white light sources. These alternatives and others are discussed below.

5.4.1 Gas lasers

Much of the early interferometric sensor work was carried out using 630 nm He–Ne lasers, and this continues today for many laboratory prototypes. The frequency stability of the He–Ne laser allows many meters of optical path imbalance between the interferometer arms and therefore path balancing is not required. A compact stabilized 1 mW He–Ne laser has a well-defined Gaussian beam of circular cross section which allows more than 50% of the light to be coupled easily into a single-mode fiber (over 95% is theoretically possible). Where a longer wavelength is required He–Ne lasers operating at 1150 nm have allowed outputs of 8 mW to be obtained. Ar$^+$ lasers can be employed for specialized high power applications.

5.4.2 Fiber lasers

A number of rare-earth-doped single-mode optical fibers have recently been found to exhibit tunable laser action when externally pumped. These will be discussed in more detail in Chapter 8 on special fibers.

5.4.3 Glass and crystal host lasers

There has recently been a great deal of interest in compact crystal lasers which have semiconductor diode laser pumps. These sources have longer coherence lengths than diode lasers and their output beams are less astigmatic, allowing for more efficient coupling into optical fibers. Most of these solid state lasers use Nd:YAG or Nd:YLF as their active material, and so the output wavelengths are 1060 nm or 1319 nm. The output power currently available is of the order of tens of milliwatts.

5.4.4 White light sources

Sensors utilizing some form of spectral filtering of a broadband source can make use of incandescent sources with blackbody radiation characteristics. Small lensed tungsten filament lamps with an output overlapping the spectral range of main interest (400–1000 nm) and a total drive power requirement of only 100 mW are available. Lifetimes of commercially available sources are in the range 100–100000 h, but these can generally be extended by running at reduced power. These lamps can be used for simple intensity modulated sensors as well as for the excitation of phosphors and photoluminescent materials.

References

Botez, D. and Ettenberg, M. (1979). Comparison of surface- and edge-emitting LED's for use in fiber-optical communications, *IEEE J. Electron. Dev.*, **26**, 1230–1238.

Brooks, J. L., Wentworth, R. H., Youngquist, R. C., Tur, M., Kim, B. Y. and Shaw, H. J. (1985). Coherence multiplexing of fiber optic interferometric sensors, *IEEE J. Lightwave Technol.*, **3**, 1062.

Burrus, C. A. and Dawson, R. W. (1970). Small-area high-current-density GaAs electroluminescent diodes and a method of operation for improved degradation characteristics, *Appl. Phys. Lett.*, **17**, 97–99.

Dakin, J. P. and Withers, P. B. (1986). The reduction of semiconductor laser phase noise for sensor applications, *Opt. Acta*, **33**, 489.

Dandridge, A. (1980). *Naval Research Laboratory Internal Memo.*

Dandridge, A. (1982). Correlation effects in 0.83 μm GaAlAs lasers, *Int. Conf. on Lasers, New Orleans, LA, December 1982.*

Dandridge, A. (1983). Zero path length difference in fiber optic interferometers, *IEEE J. Lightwave Technol.*, **1**, 514.

Dandridge, A. and Miles, R. O. (1981). Spectral characteristics of semiconductor laser diodes coupled to optical fibers, *Electron. Lett.*, **17**, 273.

Dandridge, A. and Taylor, H. F. (1982). Correlation of low-frequency fluctuations in GaAlAs lasers, *IEEE J. Quantum Electron.*, **18**, 1738.

Dandridge, A. and Taylor, H. F. (1987). Noise and correlation effects in GaAlAs broadband sources, *J. Lightwave Technol.*, **5**, 689.

Dandridge, A. and Tveten, A. B. (1981a). *Naval Research Laboratory Internal Memo.*

Dandridge, A. and Tveten, A. B. (1981b). Phase noise of single mode diode lasers in interferometric systems, *Appl. Phys. Lett.*, **38**, 530.

Dandridge, A. and Tveten, A. B. (1981c). Phase noise suppression in diode lasers, *Electron. Lett.*, **17**, 937.

Dandridge, A. and Tveten, A. B. (1983). Properties of diode lasers with intensity noise control, *Appl. Opt.*, **22**, 310.

Dandridge, A., Tveten, A. B., Miles, R. O. and Giallorenzi, T. G. (1980). Laser noise in fiber-optic interferometer systems, *Appl. Phys. Lett.*, **37**, 526.

Dandridge, A., Tveten, A. B., Miles, R. O., Jackson, D. A. and Giallorenzi, T. G. (1981). Single mode diode laser phase noise, *Appl. Phys. Lett.*, **38**, 77.

Dandridge, A., Goldberg, L. and Miles, R. O. (1982). Intensity noise and spectral properties of low noise GaAlAs lasers, *Naval Research Laboratory Memo Report 4908*, September.

Dandridge, A., Goldberg, L. and Miles, R. O. (1983). Noise and spectral properties of semiconductor lasers operating at 1.3 μm, *OFC '83, New Orleans, LA.*

Dandridge, A., Miles, R. O. and Taylor, H. F. (1986). Polarization resolved low frequency noise in GaAlAs lasers, *IEEE J. Lightwave Technol.*, **4**, 1311.

Goldberg, L., Taylor, H. F., Dandridge, A., Weller, J. F. and Miles, R. O. (1982). Spectral characteristics of semiconductor lasers with optical feedback, *IEEE J. Quantum Electron.*, **18**, 555.

Kersey, A. D. and Dandridge, A. (1986). Phase-noise reduction in coherence-multiplexed interferometric fibre sensors, *Electron. Lett.*, **22**, 616.

Kressel, H. and Butler, J. K. (1977). *Semiconductor Lasers and Heterojunction LEDs*, pp. 485–500, Academic Press, New York.

Kressel, H. and Ettenberg, M. (1975). A new edge-emitting (AlGa)As heterojunction LED for fiber-optic communications, *Proc. IEEE*, **63**, 1360–1361.

Miles, R. O., Dandridge, A., Tveten, A. B., Taylor, H. F. and Giallorenzi, T. G. (1980). Feedback induced line broadening in CW channel substrate planar laser diodes, *Appl. Phys. Lett.*, **37**, 990.

Miles, R. O., Dandridge, A., Tveten, A. B., Giallorenzi, T. G. and Taylor, H. F. (1981). Low frequency noise characteristics of channel substrate planar laser diodes, *Appl. Phys. Lett.*, **38**, 848.

Personick, S. D. (1985). *Fiber Optics Technology and Applications*, pp. 46–65, Plenum, New York.

Saito, S. and Yammamoto, Y. (1981). Direct observation of Lorentzian lineshape of semiconductor laser and linewidth reduction with external grating feedback, *Electron. Lett.*, **17**, 325.

Twu, B. and Kung, H. (1982). Reliability of fiber optic emitters, *Proc. SPIE, Integrated Optics II*, **321**, 86.

Webb, D. J., Jones, J. D. C. and Jackson, D. A. (1988). Laser diode frequency stabilization technique for interferometric sensors, *Fiber Optics '88, London, April 1988*.

Wittke, J. P., Ettenberg, M. and Kressel, H. (1976). High radiance LED for single-fiber optical links, *RCA Rev.*, **37**, 159–183.

Yurek, A. M., Taylor, H. F., Goldberg, L., Weller, J. F. and Dandridge, A. (1986). Quantum noise in superluminescent diodes, *IEEE J. Quantum Electron.*, **22**, 522.

Chapter 6

Materials Interactions in Optical Fiber Sensors

A. M. SMITH

6.1 Introduction

The materials used to construct any optical fiber sensor system bear a central role in determining the ultimate performance in terms of sensitivity, selectivity, cost benefit and suitability for use in the operating environment. In this chapter the basic materials interactions used in optical fiber sensors will be discussed and a foundation laid for the later chapters describing applications, in particular the growing area of chemical and biomedical sensors (Chapter 16).

The choice of optical fiber used, the nature of any specialized sensing or transducing layer and the overall sensor construction components need to be governed by materials considerations. In addition, the matching of the properties of the individual components both within the sensor and to the operating environment is necessary. Each of these areas will be considered, but the emphasis will be on the nature of the phenomena being used for sensing.

6.2 Extrinsic, intrinsic and evanescent sensors

The relative importance of materials factors depends strongly on the configuration of the optical fiber sensor system. For example, the constraints on materials for an *in vivo* pH measurement system are naturally very different from those associated with an undersea hydrophone. Within the sensing transducer itself, there are a variety of optical effects which can be utilized and their relative applicability will depend on the sensor design.

The concept of "extrinsic" and "intrinsic" sensors was introduced in Chapter 2, and the nature of the field distribution propagating within an optical fiber was discussed in Chapter 3. In this chapter these areas will be further developed with particular reference to chemical sensing. It is appropriate to consider three basic sensor configurations: extrinsic, intrinsic and evanescent. All these are being investigated actively for chemical sensing.

Many optical fiber sensors consist of an optical fiber transmission path used to interrogate a remote transducer. In these "extrinsic" sensors the performance of the device should be independent of the fiber and depend only on the nature of the sensing element. For a chemical or biomedical sensor the transducer at the remote end of the fiber will consist of a "reagent phase" which has direct access to and interacts with the local environment of the sensor. Various optical effects can be utilized in order to sense a change in the environment, and these are detailed in subsequent sections.

In "intrinsic" sensors the fiber construction materials are deliberately chosen in order to give sensitivity to one or more parameters. Often it is not cost effective to make highly specialized fibers for sensing applications; therefore intrinsic sensors may utilize readily available fiber in specialized configurations and in conjunction with sophisticated instrumentation. Thus the optical fiber Sagnac interferometer (see Chapter 11), often called the "fiber gyroscope", which senses rotation may use "off-the-shelf" single-mode fiber in conjunction with carefully designed ancillary optics and signal processing. Work on specialized fibers for sensing applications is detailed in Chapter 8. Intrinsic sensing is not normally used for chemical species and will not be considered further in this chapter. Examples of intrinsic sensors for physical parameters are given in Chapters 10 and 11.

A third class of sensor occupies the middle ground between extrinsic and intrinsic devices. In "evanescent" sensors a length of the fiber is stripped of its lower refractive index cladding, thus allowing access to the propagating electromagnetic wave within the guide, as described in Chapter 2. The sensing transducer is then composed of the naked fiber core and whatever sensing layer (reagent phase) is positioned on, or close to, the surface of the fiber. The major area where evanescent sensors have been investigated is in the monitoring of antibody–ligand reactions (Place *et al.*, 1985). The nature of the evanescent field was introduced briefly in Chapter 3, and its use for monitoring both absorbing and fluorescent species will be covered in Section 6.7. The application of evanescent field sensing in the planar integrated optics geometry is covered in Chapter 9.

6.3 Absorption

As has already been outlined in Chapter 3, a range of optical phenomena can be used within practical optical fiber sensor systems for chemical species, and also some physical parameters. The simplest of these is the absorption of radiation at a specific wavelength. Absorption is used primarily with extrinsic sensors, where a single fiber or fiber bundle brings light to the measurement cell and the transmitted light is returned to a remote measurement instrument via a further fiber or fibers. The extent of the absorption depends on the absorption cross-section of the transducing molecule, the optical path length and the illumination wavelength. For a collimated beam of light the intensity of light measured at a distance z into an absorbing medium is given by

$$I(z) = I(0)\exp(-\alpha z)$$

The absorption coefficient α is related to the absorption cross-section c_s of the absorbing molecule (expressed in square meters) and the concentration c_m of the molecule (expressed in moles per cubic meter) by

$$\alpha = \frac{c_s c_m}{N}$$

N is Avogadro's number and is numerically equal to $6.022 \times 10^{23}\,\text{mol}^{-1}$.

In most systems relevant to optical fiber sensing there is some divergence of the light beam, and the optical detector is unable to collect all the transmitted light. These effects make the dependence of the transmitted intensity on distance rather more complicated. For example, in a system consisting of an illumination fiber with radius r_1 and a collecting fiber of radius $r_2 (r_2 < r_1)$ a distance z away in an absorbing medium, to first order the collected light intensity will be given by

$$I(z) = I(0)\left(\frac{r_2}{r_1 + z\tan\varphi}\right)^2 \exp(-\alpha z)$$

where φ is the divergence angle of the light emerging from the end of the input fiber. In this expression it is assumed that the illumination of the expanding disk of light remains uniform and that the divergence angle is small. More explicit formulae need to be derived to model real systems where the expanding light cone is unevenly illuminated.

Changes in chemical environment can modify the absorption of carefully chosen reagent chemicals, and this modification is monitored as a change in transmitted intensity within the sensor. The aim in designing a sensor system is to ensure that the reagent chemical species and concentration are chosen in order to satisfy two important criteria.

(1) The difference in transmitted light intensity corresponding to the possible dynamic range of the parameter of interest (e.g. the minimum and maximum concentrations of a particular chemical that is to be measured) must be sufficiently great to give adequate sensitivity. In general terms a change of one to two orders of magnitude in signal intensity over the range of interest is appropriate. However, this is only a guide because for many measurands there is a requirement to have different levels of precision within the overall dynamic range. In this case a nonlinear intensity function is needed, with a maximum change in signal occurring in the measurand range where maximum precision is required.

(2) The optical transmission of the reagent chemical in the maximum absorption condition must be sufficiently high for there to be an adequate

signal relative to the noise sources present. In practical terms, this means that the "insertion loss" of the sensing element (determined partly by the sensor reagent and partly by the sensor geometry) must not be so high that the transmitted signal becomes difficult to separate from effects such as ambient light leakage. This requirement does not necessarily mean that the transmitted signal has to be larger than the ambient light signal. If light-source modulation methods and narrowband detection methods are used, for example, a much smaller signal can be tolerated provided that care is taken that the total light levels do not saturate the photodetector or processing electronics.

To take a practical example, work has been carried out using the indicator dye phenol red (molecular weight, $354 \, \text{g mol}^{-1}$) for measuring changes in pH close to neutral pH 7.0. The absorption spectra of the dye at pH 6.40 and pH 8.05 are shown in Fig. 6.1. It can be seen that at a wavelength of 560 nm the absorption varies by over an order of magnitude for the pH range of interest. The data were obtained in a cuvette of 10 mm path length for a 10 ppm (28 μM) concentration of the dye. At 560 nm the absorption is 1.07 for pH 8.05, giving a molar absorbance of $3\,790\,000 \, \text{m}^{-1} \, \text{mol}^{-1} \, \text{L}$. Hence if the path length of an optical fiber sensor is 5 mm and the minimum acceptable transmission of the cell (at maximum absorption pH 8.05) is, say, 2% (equivalent to an absorbance of 1.70), the required concentration of dye within the measurement cell can be calculated from the expression

$$\text{concentration} = \frac{\text{required absorbance}}{(\text{path length}) \, (\text{molar absorbance})}$$

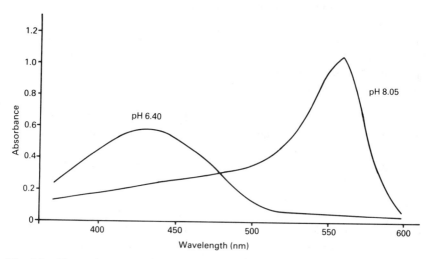

Fig. 6.1 Absorption spectra for aqueous phenol red dye at pH 6.40 and pH 8.05. The measurements were taken for 10 ppm concentrations in a buffer with a 10 mm path length.

In the numerical example, the required concentration will be 89 µM.

In general, for precise absorption measurements, at least two wavelengths of light are monitored simultaneously. These wavelengths are chosen such that the absorption in one case is sensitive to the local environment whilst the absorption at the other wavelength is insensitive to these changes. A two-channel system of this type allows compensation for common-mode effects, such as changes in the efficiency with which light is launched into the fiber, changes in the light source intensity, or aging of the fiber, the photodetector or any other optical components. It can be seen from Fig. 6.1 that wavelengths near 600 nm are suitable for referencing in this case. A general introduction to the need for referencing methods is given in Chapter 2, and more specific applications of these techniques in intensity-modulation-based sensors are given in Chapter 12.

6.4 The use of scattering in absorption measurements

The fundamental problem with the use of a simple absorption phenom-enon is the need to monitor in transmission, since in general it is highly advantageous to have a "single-ended" optical fiber system. This problem can be resolved by the use of a mirror (or other reflective element) or, more usually, by utilizing the light-scattering properties of an ancillary material in order to backscatter the partially absorbed light into the collecting fiber.

6.4.1 Membrane sensors

In the simplest arrangement, which is shown schematically in Fig. 6.2, the reagent is bound to the surface of a colorless membrane material and this is abutted to the end of the fiber (Kirkbright et al., 1984). The diffuse reflectivity of the membrane is chosen to be quite high and results from light scattered not only from the surface but also from within the membrane. Incorporation of the absorbing reagent will therefore modify the intensity of the backscattered light, and this can be monitored in the preferred single-ended manner by placing a receiving fiber alongside the illumination fiber. In practical

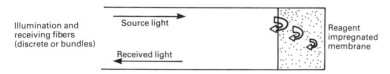

Fig. 6.2 Schematic diagram of a membrane absorption–scattering sensor. The source light is scattered by the membrane and the amount of backscattered light received is modified by changes in the optical absorption of the reagent impregnating the membrane.

arrangements a bifurcated fiber bundle may be used to provide multiple illumination and receiving fibers. In general, it is impractical to approach the design of this type of sensing element from a purely analytical base. It is important, however, to choose a reagent support material which has the following characteristics.

(1) The membrane should allow chemical coupling or entrapment of the reagent without impeding the chemical sensing capacity of the reagent. In general, reagents coupled to surfaces do not react in an identical manner to the free solution forms; however, any changes that occur should be small. It is worth noting that in some cases coupling can lead to increased reagent stability.

(2) The pore structure of the membrane needs to be sufficiently permeable to allow adequate diffusion of the chemical species to be measured within the time response period appropriate to the application. Thus a membrane of very low porosity that only allowed the internal solution to come into equilibrium with the external measurement environment after 30 min would not be appropriate for an application where information on the measurand was required on a minute-by-minute basis.

(3) The wetting properties of the membrane need to be compatible with the environment to be measured. A hydrophobic membrane will not be appropriate for use when measuring materials which are soluble in water. Similarly a lipophilic (i.e. oil-wettable) membrane will be needed when the measurements are performed in oils or fats.

(4) The diffuse "reflected" light from the membrane alone should, if possible, be unchanged in spectral composition. This requirement means that the membrane should preferably not contain absorbing species. Even a perfect scattering material will tend to have some wavelength variability, but this is usually not serious. In practice most common membrane materials (e.g. cellulose acetate and polytetrafluoroethylene) meet this constraint.

(5) The "reflected" light should result from scattering at depths of about 0.01–0.5 mm from the membrane surface. This range of values results from two competing constraints. If the light scattered from the surface of the membrane is too high, a large amount of the light detected by the receiving fiber will not be affected by the changes in the measurand. This will limit the dynamic range of the sensor, cause saturation problems in the instrumentation and reduce the measurement sensitivity. If, however, the received light results from scattering from a substantial depth of material, the scattering is too weak. If a membrane of this type is filled with a light-absorbing material only light scattered back from the first 0.5 mm or so will make a contribution; thereafter the light will become too heavily attenuated. In the ideal membrane case the scattered light from the side of the membrane furthest from the fibers should make a very small contribution (i.e. less than about 1%) to the received signal. The

concentration of the reagent used within the membrane can then be chosen to optimize the sensitivity.

One disadvantage of the general approach of using a membrane material is that typically a relatively small proportion of the modified incident light is subsequently collected by the fiber. In general, the light will be scattered fairly isotropically (i.e. into 4π sr), whereas the numerical aperture of the receiving fiber will be perhaps 0.2 (equivalent to $0.01 \times 4\pi$ sr); thus 1% at most of the light is received. However, in practice systems are rarely performance limited by lack of light intensity.

6.4.2 Scattering cell sensors

A more significant problem is that it is not always possible or advantageous to use a membrane material. It may be that the preferred reagent cannot be attached to a suitable membrane and retained in an active form, or that the geometry of the membrane sensor (which has an inherently small area of sensor interacting with the measurement environment) is unsuitable for the particular application. A more elongated sensor configuration, shown schematically in Fig. 6.3, has been adopted by some workers as an alternative approach for using absorption in a single-ended geometry. This type of device utilizes small spectrally inert scattering particles within a chemical cell arrangement at the end of a pair of fibers (Peterson and Vurek, 1984). The chemical reagent is present within the cell either in solution or bound to the surface of a suitable support. The wall of the cell is composed of a selectively permeable membrane which allows the measurand to percolate into and out of the measurement area but does not allow the reagent material

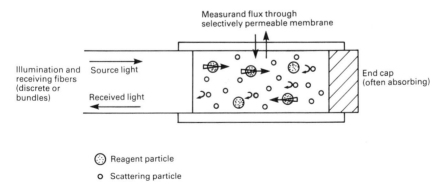

Reagent particle

Scattering particle

Fig. 6.3 Schematic diagram of a scattering cell absorption sensor. The source light is attenuated by the reagent which is often bound to solid particles. Scattering is enhanced by micron dimension particles within the cell. The selectively permeable membrane allows relatively free movement of the measurand but stops out-diffusion of the reagent.

to pass. Cellulosic dialysis tubing is often used for aqueous measurements (Peterson *et al.*, 1980), whereas a hydrophobic membrane of silicone rubber is more appropriate for gas analysis (Peterson *et al.*, 1984).

When the cell is illuminated there is absorption of light and this is monitored by collecting the scattered radiation from the particles. The particle sizes chosen are typically of micron dimensions for visible wavelength spectroscopy. Particles of this size are Mie scatterers (Van de Hulst, 1957) and give substantial backscattered intensities. Polyacrylamide gels and polystyrene "latex" dispersions are good sources of scattering particles.

6.5 Fluorescence

The phenomenon of fluorescence is directly related to absorption since it requires the absorption of light energy prior to the re-emission of radiation at a longer wavelength. The subject is well covered by numerous texts (e.g. Guilbault, 1973), and only the aspects of the phenomenon relevant to optical fiber sensing of chemicals will be mentioned here. The efficiency of fluorescence generation is dependent on the concentration, absorption cross-section and quantum efficiency of the fluorophore (the probability that an excited molecule will decay by emitting a photon rather than by losing its energy nonradiatively) and on the optical path length. In practice, quantum efficiencies in aqueous solutions vary from values close to 1.0 (e.g. fluorescein (Weber and Teale, 1957)) down to still useful values of around 0.05. The other parameters can be adjusted in an experimental system to ensure that maximum use is made of the excitation (pump) radiation.

A fluorescent molecule has a distinct range of wavelengths (excitation spectrum) over which the molecule can be excited. Once excited the molecule decays after a short time period (typically about 1 ns for simple organic molecules), and again the spectrum of the emission is well defined. The excitation and emission spectra of a simple fluorescent molecule (rhodamine B) are shown in Fig. 6.4. It can be seen that the emission occurs at a longer wavelength and that the peak wavelengths for excitation (564 nm) and emission (583 nm) are distinct. The difference in peak wavelength is known as the Stokes shift and has a value of around 10–20 nm (300–600 wavenumbers) for molecules such as fluorescein or rhodamine. Larger values are possible using more complicated molecules such as the phycobiliproteins (Glazer and Stryer, 1984).

In order to use fluorescence in an optical fiber sensor, it is important that the spectral characteristics of the light source, dye and detector system are carefully matched. The light source and detector will typically be broadband devices which have been restricted to operate over a more narrow wavelength range by the addition of filters. It is possible to construct a number of spectral

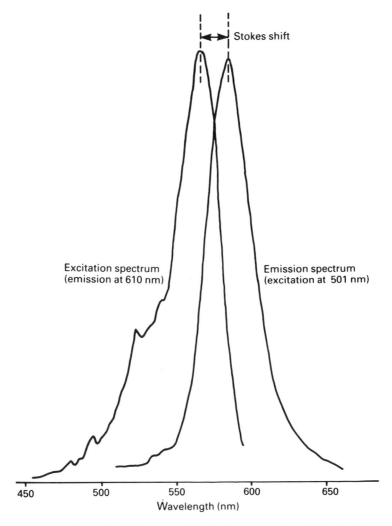

Fig. 6.4 Excitation and emission spectra for the fluorescent dye rhodamine B in water. The data were obtained using a Perkin–Elmer LS5 scanning spectrofluorimeter.

overlap integrals which aid in optimizing system design. There are four relevant spectral responses which need to be related:

$S(\lambda)$, the light output from the filtered source;
$Ex(\lambda)$, the excitation (absorption) spectrum of the dye;
$Em(\lambda)$, the emission spectrum of the dye;
$F(\lambda)$, the spectral sensitivity of the filtered detection system.

The overlap integrals are as follows.

The source overlap integral (SOI) gives a measure of the efficiency with which the dye is being pumped:

$$SOI = \int S(\lambda) \, Ex(\lambda) \, d\lambda$$

The detector overlap integral (DOI) gives a measure of how well the detection system monitors the fluorescent radiation:

$$DOI = \int F(\lambda) \, Em(\lambda) \, d\lambda$$

The pump rejection integral (PRI) indicates how well the filtering of the source and detector have been designed in order to reject scattered pump light:

$$PRI = \int S(\lambda) \, F(\lambda) \, d\lambda$$

In order to optimize the performance of a fluorescence system the aim is to design $S(\lambda)$ and $F(\lambda)$ so that SOI and DOI are as large as possible, while PRI remains as small as possible. In most optical fiber sensors there are many parts of the system which can scatter the pump light. These include the fiber itself, the end of the fiber abutting the sensor element and the various components of the sensor. As a result of this it is usually more important for PRI to be minimized than for the other two integrals to have their absolute maximum value. A useful general dimensionless "figure of merit" for comparing alternative systems is given by

$$\text{figure of merit} = \frac{SOI \times DOI}{PRI^2}$$

When a fluorescent molecule interacts with light of the correct wavelength, an electric dipole is created within the molecule and its initial orientation will be parallel to the incident electric field. If the molecule moves thermally (Brownian motion), the orientation of the dipole when a photon is emitted may be different. In general the emitted light will be depolarized to some extent, and in all cases there will be no "memory" of the direction from which the molecule was excited. A direct consequence of this is that the emission of fluorescence is equal in both the forward-scattering and backscattering directions. Thus for optical fiber sensing, fluorescence lends itself to a single-ended configuration without the requirement for additional scattering particles. In practice the polarization of the pump radiation will always be essentially random when using multimode fibers for transmission, and therefore the fluorescent radiation will also be randomly polarized.

However, it is worth noting that for low molecular weight fluorophores bound to surfaces there can be substantial retention of polarization states from the pump to the emission radiation. The reason for this retention is that the fluorescent molecule is sufficiently constrained to avoid a change in its orientation between the excitation and emission events. Monitoring of the polarization of fluorescence emission can be used to detect whether a fluorophore is attached to a surface (polarization retention) or is free in solution (the polarization is not retained because the molecule is rapidly moving and therefore will have changed orientation before it emits). This method could be used within a fiber sensor system as long as a polarization filter was incorporated at the sensor head.

The primary advantage of fluorescence is that it allows discrimination between the substance of interest (labeled with a fluorophore) and other species present within the region of measurement. In addition, the deleterious effects of light scattering and surface roughness are minimized by the wavelength shift. In practical optical fiber sensor arrangements, fluorescence has been used in two basic ways.

(1) As a labeling method: the fluorescent material moves into or out of the pump illumination in response to external parameters such as a chemical in the measurement environment, and this leads to a change in the detected emission. An optical fiber glucose sensor has been realized using this effect (Schultz *et al.*, 1982).

(2) As a chemical detector: fluorescence can be quenched by any process that can de-excite the molecule faster than the normal fluorescence emission; the most common quenching comes from low molecular weight molecules (e.g. oxygen) which are highly mobile and can move very close to the fluorophore to de-excite it. This phenomenon has been used to advantage in optical fiber gas sensing (Wolfbeis, 1985).

6.6 Phosphorescence

Organic chemicals exhibiting fluorescence usually have short lifetimes since the molecule only remains in its excited state for a period of a few nanoseconds. In addition, molecules which do have excited states with longer lifetimes are usually quenched rapidly by other species within their immediate environment. In the solid state much longer lifetimes are possible and in particular the phenomenon of phosphorescence can be used. The excited state of a phosphorescent molecule is not linked to the ground state by a quantum mechanically "allowed" transition, and therefore it may have a lifetime ranging from microseconds to hours. These "phosphorescent" molecules can be excited with a short burst of light and then the emission can be detected during a subsequent time period. As with fluorescence there are two basic modes of utilization of these molecules.

(1) As a label: here the advantage over fluorescence is that, since the

emission can be monitored after the pump radiation has been removed, it is possible to remove all the effects of pump light scattering which often limit the performance of a fluorescence system.

(2) As a detector: phosphorescence can be quenched, and this phenomenon can be used for sensing. A good example is the quenching of rare earth phosphors at elevated temperatures which is used in a commercial optical fiber temperature measurement system (Wickersheim and Alves, 1979).

The principal disadvantage of phosphorescence is that the instantaneous light output is low. Integration of the output signal is normally carried out to minimize this problem.

6.7 The evanescent field

The use of the evanescent field surrounding the naked core of an optical fiber requires some discussion. The principle underlying the evanescent field involves a more precise electromagnetic wave treatment of the well-known phenomenon of total internal reflection. When light is incident at the interface between two optically transparent regions of high (n_1) and low (n_2) refractive index, as shown in Fig. 6.5, for angles of incidence greater than the critical

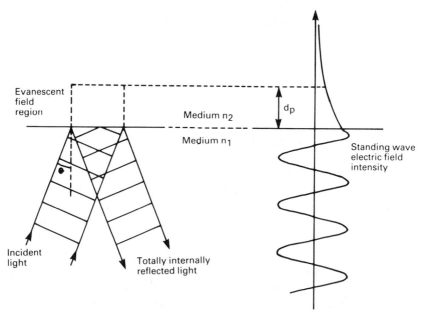

Fig. 6.5 An evanescent field is generated in conditions of total internal reflection. An oscillatory standing wave is set up in the medium with higher refractive index n_1 and this decays exponentially in the medium with lower refractive index n_2.

angle θ_c (where $\sin \theta_c = n_2/n_1$) all light is reflected. The incident light and the reflected light interact and the result is a standing wave disturbance close to the interface. In general, the phase of the light will change on reflection, and as a consequence the standing wave amplitude at the interface will be finite. Detailed solution of Maxwell's equations shows that this standing wave decays exponentially away from the interface into the low refractive index material. The detailed explanation of this phenomenon is given in many texts (e.g. Harrick, 1967). For the purposes of sensing, a key parameter is the depth of penetration of the exponentially decaying evanescent field, which is given by

$$d_p = \frac{\lambda}{2\pi(n_1{}^2 \sin^2 \theta - n_2{}^2)^{1/2}}$$

or

$$d_p = \frac{\lambda}{2\pi n_1(\sin^2 \theta - \sin^2 \theta_c)^{1/2}}$$

This is the distance from the surface over which the electric field of the standing wave disturbance decays to $1/e$ of its value at the interface. θ is the angle of incidence at the interface ($\theta > \theta_c$) and λ is the free-space wavelength of the light. For a typical optical fiber sensor arrangement n_1 has a value of around 1.5 and, if the medium of investigation is aqueous, n_2 is 1.33. In this case the depth of penetration has a minimum value of around $\lambda/5$ at grazing incidence ($\theta = 90°$) and increases to about one wavelength for angles about $1°$ greater than the critical angle. As can be seen from the above formula the depth of penetration goes to infinity at the critical angle, but in practical systems there is always light leakage and scattering at near-critical angles as a result of surface roughness. From this discussion it can be seen that in approximate terms only material located within about one wavelength of an interface between two transparent materials can interact with the evanescent field to any extent. More substantial penetration will not occur unless highly collimated beams incident at angles very close to the critical angle are used.

In an optical fiber the evanescent field around the naked fiber core is a superposition of the field distributions of all the modes propagating within the fiber. Nonetheless, the depth of penetration is still given, to first order, by the same expression.

The simplest form of interaction with the evanescent field is absorption. If a light-absorbing material is brought within the field region there is attenuation of the reflected energy. This phenomenon has been used widely in commercially available internal reflection spectrometers for some years, particularly at wavelengths in the near-infrared. The instruments typically use a slab waveguide of macroscopic dimensions and, by taking measurements of the attenuation of the reflected light as a function of wavelength for a fixed angle of incidence, it is possible to identify the composition of thin layers of material close to the surface of the waveguide. Exactly the same process can be repeated using a fiber-based system; however, it is usually more practical to excite all the modes in the fiber and therefore measure the spectrum of interaction for a range of angles of incidence. This approach has a lower sensitivity than the single-angle approach since many of the modes within the fiber are paraxial and thus have relatively small penetration depths (θ close to 90°). In principle a narrow range of angles (modes) could be excited within the fiber by applying spatial filtering to the launched radiation. In practice, however, this would yield a system that was very sensitive to external perturbations, since any mechanical stresses or variations in the fiber geometry would lead inevitably to excitation of other modes and hence a change in the range of angles being excited. The use of absorption of the evanescent field for sensing methane gas has been demonstrated in a recent study (Tai et al., 1987).

An important extension of the use of the evanescent field is the excitation of fluorescence. If a fluorescent molecule comes within the evanescent field region, then as long as the wavelength of the radiation is matched to the absorption spectrum of the fluorophore the molecule will be elevated to an excited state. After a short period of time the molecule will emit a longer-wavelength photon. This emission may appear as a ray of light propagating away from the interface in the medium with the lower refractive index; however, it is also possible for the emission to "tunnel" into the waveguide and thereafter be guided. The phenomenon of fluorescence coupling has been investigated experimentally (Lee et al., 1979) and theoretically (Carniglia et al., 1972) and forms the basis of a number of sensor configurations.

The evanescent field sensor configuration is particularly advantageous for monitoring the binding of ligands to layers of antibody material immobilized onto the surface of the waveguide. An antibody is a molecule of large molecular weight ($150\,000\,\mathrm{g\,mol^{-1}}$) which undergoes a highly selective affinity binding reaction with another molecule (ligand). This molecule may be another protein (an antigen, i.e. a material which will stimulate the production of antibodies in a mammal) or a material with a relatively low molecular weight (a hapten, i.e. a material which is not antigenic in its own right but for which antibodies can be produced by binding it to a material with a higher molecular weight). Antibodies have dimensions of around 10 nm and they can be bound to the surface of the waveguide using a variety of chemical procedures. This means that the molecular interaction between the antibody and its partner is well within the evanescent field penetration depth. Molecular detection sensitivities of around 1 nM have been demonstrated using fluor-escently labeled molecules (Sutherland et al., 1984).

The practical difficulty with the use of evanescent field sensors is that they can be highly sensitive to unwanted effects. Any material adsorbed by or bound to the surface of the guide may give rise to absorption, scattering or fluorescence signals which can be erroneously interpreted as indicating the presence of the measurand. Similarly, long-term out-diffusion of sodium ions from soda glass waveguides can lead to surface refractive index changes, which in turn change the device sensitivity. Despite these difficulties, devices have been shown to work in "dirty" environments such as biological samples as long as appropriate measures are taken (e.g. the use of surfactants to reduce nonspecific binding of protein).

6.8 Surface plasmon resonance

The evanescent electric field intensity at the interface between two transparent materials is relatively weak, since the energy stored in the standing wave disturbance is only of similar magnitude to the instantaneous maximum value of the energy flux of the electric field of the incident light exciting the disturbance. It is therefore very valuable to modify the interface in order to enhance the field intensity and thereby generate a more sensitive device. The phenomenon of surface plasmon resonance has been investigated in order to enhance the field intensity (Agranovich and Mills (1982) give a comprehensive treatment; simpler descriptions can be found in solid state textbooks such as Kittel (1971)). A schematic diagram of the arrangement used to excite a surface plasmon is shown in Fig. 6.6(a). The interface between the two transparent media is coated with a thin layer (typically around 50 nm) of a metal such as silver. The metal layer is sufficiently thin to allow some of the light energy to penetrate through; therefore for angles less than the critical angle there is incomplete reflection from the metal surface. Above the critical angle all light is reflected except for a range of angles where the momentum-matching conditions of the light are such that a surface electromagnetic wave mode (surface plasmon) of the interface between the metal and the lower refractive index medium is excited. The details of the effect are given in a number of texts (e.g. Agranovich and Mills, 1982) and will only be described qualitatively here. Since the metal layer is lossy at optical frequencies (i.e. the refractive index is complex), the surface electromagnetic wave is rapidly damped and as a consequence the observed reflectivity of the metal drops to a low level. The effect is maximized when the component of the propagation vector of the incident light along the interface is exactly equal to the propagation vector of the surface plasmon, given by the dispersion equation

$$\frac{2\pi}{\lambda}n_1 \sin \theta_{sp} = k_{sp} = \frac{2\pi}{\lambda}\left(\frac{1}{\varepsilon_2}+\frac{1}{\varepsilon_m}\right)^{1/2}$$

where n_1 is the refractive index of the substrate material, λ is the free-space wavelength of the light, θ_{sp} is the angle of incidence of the light at resonance, k_{sp} is the wavevector of the surface plasmon, ε_m is the real part of the dielectric constant of the metal and ε_2 is the dielectric constant of the material with the lower refractive index (Raether, 1977). At angles adjacent to θ_{sp} the coupling

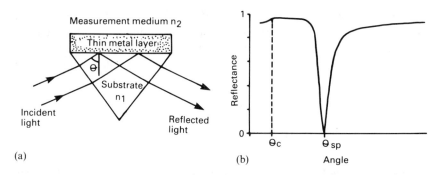

Fig. 6.6 Surface plasmon resonance. (a) The launching configuration consists of a thin metal film on the surface of a substrate with a relatively high refractive index n_1. The surface plasmon at the interface between the metal and the measurement medium, which has a relatively lower refractive index n_2, can be excited optimally at a particular angle of incidence θ_{sp} of the light. (b) The angular reflectance of a 50 nm silver film deposited on a glass prism and immersed in water. The reflectance at θ_{sp} drops to near zero, whilst at other angles greater than the critical angle θ_c it is close to unity.

will be incomplete and therefore the reduction in the reflectivity will be less marked. Figure 6.6(b) shows the type of reflectivity response that is obtained for a 50 nm silver film on the surface of a glass prism immersed in water.

The surface plasmon electric field decays into the lower refractive index medium in an exponential fashion in the same way as an evanescent field and with a similar penetration depth. The surface intensity of the field, however, is typically an order of magnitude or more higher than for the equivalent evanescent field arrangement. This means that the interaction between the light and the surface chemical or refractive index effects can be much stronger, and hence the sensitivity to surface changes is higher. The arrangement has been used to detect single layers of large proteins (Liedberg et al., 1983) by monitoring the change in the resonance angle caused by the deposition of the protein on a thin silver film.

All published work to date has made use of the surface plasmon resonance phenomenon on prisms or rectangular waveguides. There is no problem in principle with the use of the effect on a naked fiber core. However, the losses involved in the interaction are substantial, so that in practice only a short length of the fiber will be coated with the metal film if reasonable light transmission is to be maintained.

6.9 Materials aspects of complete fiber systems

The emphasis of this chapter has been on the various interaction processes taking place in the materials used in optical fiber sensor systems. In addition to these important transducing aspects of the materials it must be recognized that the ultimate performance of any practical system or commercial product will also depend on the way in which the materials of construction have been chosen to match both the operating environment and the likely mode of usage. In this section some comments will be made on the types of materials constraints that may be encountered.

6.9.1 Choice of fiber

A large variety of optical fibers is available from commercial manufacturers, but fundamentally these can be divided into the following basic types.

(1) **All-polymer fibers** have relatively high attenuation particularly for shorter wavelengths. They are only suitable for operation near room temperature and over short distances, but they have the advantage of ruggedness and low breakage.

(2) **Silica fibers** are of course the principal fibers used for communications purposes and are usually doped with germania, phosphorus pentoxide or boric oxide in order to produce the necessary refractive index differences for light guiding. They are advantageous in many intrinsic optical fiber sensors, but for extrinsic sensor work the core diameters are often unnecessarily small. Pure silica core fibers, however, are very useful in some fluorescence systems since they will propagate light in the near-ultraviolet. These wavelengths are needed to pump some fluorescent materials, notably proteins. In addition the fibers can withstand high temperatures provided that they are packaged in appropriate materials.

(3) **Plastic-coated silica (PCS) fibers** have most of the advantages of silica fibers for short distances and it is possible to expose the core of the fiber relatively easily, thus enabling the realization of evanescent sensors. It is also possible to incorporate a number of sensing reagents within the silicone cladding material to provide evanescent field sensing with the fiber.

(4) **Glass fibers** are similar to silica fibers but usually have higher losses and larger core diameters. They can be suitable for both illuminating and reading out from extrinsic sensors.

(5) **Fiber bundles** consist of many glass or polymer fibers grouped together. They have the advantage of ease of light launching and the collection of light over large areas. The main disadvantage is that the exact performance is not easy to predict and is likely to vary from bundle to bundle as a result of variability in the manufacturing process and breakages. A bifurcated arrangement is often chosen for sensor systems so that a light source and a detector system can be connected to a common sensor region without the need for ancillary optics.

6.9.2 Choice of sensing material

The range of materials which have been used or could be used within the sensing element of a fiber system is very extensive. The exact criteria for choosing a particular sensing material will depend on the application; however, there are some general rules which need to be adhered to.

(1) Ideally, the sensor material should only change its properties in response to the variable of interest. In physical sensors this is usually relatively easy to achieve, but for a chemical sensor there is invariably some cross-reactivity. Thus the approach is either to make sure that the measurement environment is highly unlikely to contain the cross-reacting species in significant quantity or to contain the sensing chemical within an environment inside the measurement cell which enhances the specificity. An example of the latter approach is the use of an indicator dye for pH measurements, where the dye is held within a measurement cell at relatively high ionic strength in order to minimize the sensitivity to ionic strength variations in the measurement environment. If neither of these arrangements is feasible, it may be possible to design a sensor system which has several output signals (e.g. monitors light at several different wavelengths) and electronically processes them to obtain an output proportional only to the parameter of interest.

(2) The lifetime of the sensor material should be commensurate with that of the sensor. For chemical sensors in particular, it is important that the reagent phase does not leak from the measurement cell, decompose or, in the case of a fluorescent label, bleach after a period of time. Problems of this type are minimized by careful choice of the immobilization chemistry, the design of the measurement cell (e.g. the use of opaque materials to exclude ambient light), and the level and duration of the sensor illumination (e.g. the use of flash or periodic pulse illumination rather than continuous illumination).

(3) The sensor materials have to be compatible with the operating environment. Thus the use of toxic chemicals within an *in vivo* medical sensor or an on-line sensor for food process control is unacceptable. Specialized polymer materials also need to be used *in vivo* to avoid the build-up of layers of proteins, notably fibrin, on the optical surfaces. These layers not only disturb the measurements but may also endanger the patient.

(4) The overall sensor has to be mechanically and thermally stable. This means that the materials used need to be sufficiently rugged for the environment and also that the thermal expansion properties of different materials are sufficiently well matched to avoid reagent leakage or breakages.

6.10 Conclusion

Materials factors are central to both the sensing means and the practical implementation of most optical fiber sensor systems. However, there is often a danger that these aspects will be neglected in the design of experimental systems. Some of the important materials interaction areas relevant to optical fiber sensors have been explored in this chapter. The way in which these interactions are used in specific sensors will be described in subsequent chapters, notably Chapter 16.

References

Agranovich, V. M. and Mills, D. L. (eds) (1982). *Surface Polaritons: Electromagnetic Waves at Surfaces and Interfaces*, North-Holland, Amsterdam.

Carniglia, C. K., Mandel, L. and Drexhage, K. H. (1972). Absorption and emission of evanescent photons, *J. Opt. Soc. Am.*, **62** (4), 479–486.

Glazer, A. N. and Stryer, L. (1984). Phycofluor probes, *Trends Biochem. Sci.*, pp. 423–427, October.

Guilbault, G. G. (1973). *Practical Fluorescence: Theory, Methods and Techniques*, Marcel Dekker, New York.

Harrick, N. J. (1967). *Internal Reflection Spectroscopy*, Harrick Scientific Corporation, Ossining, NY.

Kirkbright, G. F., Narayanaswamy, R. and Welti, N. A. (1984). Fibre-optic pH probe based on the use of an immobilised colorimetric indicator, *Analyst*, **109**, 1025–1028.

Kittel, C. (1971). *Introduction to Solid State Physics* (4th edn), Wiley, New York.

Lee, E., Benner, R. E., Fenn, J. B. and Chang, R. K. (1979). Angular distribution of fluorescence from liquids and monodisperse spheres by evanescent wave excitation, *Appl. Opt.*, **18** (6), 862–868.

Liedberg, B., Nylander, C. I. and Lundstrom, I. (1983). Surface plasmon resonance for gas detection and biosensing, *Sensors Actuat.*, **4**, 299–304.

Peterson, J. I. and Vurek, G. G. (1984). Fibre-optic sensors for biomedical applications, *Science*, **224**, 123–127.

Peterson, J. I., Goldstein, S. R. and Fitzgerald, R. V. (1980). Fibre-optic pH probe for physiological use, *Anal. Chem.*, **52**, 864–869.

Peterson, J. I., Fitzgerald, R. V. and Buckhold, D. K. (1984). Fibre-optic probe for *in vivo* measurement of oxygen partial pressure, *Anal. Chem.*, **56**, 62–67.

Place, J. F., Sutherland, R. M. and Dahne, C. (1985). Opto-electronic immunosensors: a review of optical immunoassay at continuous surfaces, *Biosensors*, **1** (4), 321–353.

Raether, H. (1977). Surface plasmon oscillations and their applications, *Phys. Thin Films*, **9**.

Schultz, J. S., Mansouri, S. and Goldstein, I. J. (1982). Affinity sensor: a new technique for developing implantable sensors for glucose and other metabolites, *Diabetes Care*, **5** (3), 245–253.

Sutherland, R. M., Dahne, C., Place, J. F. and Ringrose, A. S. (1984). Optical detection of antibody–antigen reactions at a glass–liquid interface, *Clin. Chem.*, **30** (9), 1533–1538.

Tai, H., Tanaka, H. and Yoshino, T. (1987). Fibre-optic evanescent-wave methane-gas sensor using optical absorption for the 3.392 µm line of a He–Ne laser, *Opt. Lett.*, **12** (6), 437–439.

Van de Hulst, H. C. (1957). *Light Scattering by Small Particles*, Wiley, New York.

Weber, G. and Teale, F. W. (1957). *Trans. Faraday Soc.*, **53**, 646.

Wickersheim, K. A. and Alves, R. B. (1979). Recent advances in optical temperature measurement, *Ind. Res. Dev.*, 82–89, December.

Wolfbeis, O. S. (1985). Fluorescence optical sensors in analytical chemistry, *Trends Anal. Chem.*, **4** (7), 184–188.

Chapter 7

Fiber Optic Components

M. J. F. DIGONNET AND B. Y. KIM

7.1 Introduction

The development of single-mode fiber optic components, which has taken place in the last 10 years, has been motivated not only by telecommunications requirements but also to a large extent by the emerging fiber sensor technology. A wide range of functions has been investigated so far to meet these requirements, including directional couplers, polarizers and modulators which form the keystone of intensely studied sensors such as the gyroscope. Several considerations stand behind the need for all-fiber components as a replacement for their bulk optic counterparts. The most important factor is probably the increased mechanical and thermal stability one would expect from circuits built with all-fiber components in which the signal never leaves the confinement of the fiber core. Another factor is the very low intrinsic loss and scattering of single-mode fibers, which initially suggested that all-fiber components should exhibit superior properties. As we shall see, these factors appeared to play a decisive role in fiber device development as today several fundamental all-fiber components perform far better than either their bulk optic or integrated optic counterparts.

The intent of this chapter is to provide a broad description of the different types of components relevant to sensor technology. They have been somewhat arbitrarily divided into seven groups, addressing directional couplers, wavelength-division multiplexers and filters, polarization controllers, polarizers, phase modulators, frequency shifters and finally amplifiers and sources. In the context of this volume, and for the reasons described above, the emphasis has been placed exclusively on all-fiber components, omitting other types such as micro-optic and multimode devices. The general motivation is to provide the reader with the basic physical principles underlying the major components developed to date as well as a critical review of the current component technologies and a comparative analysis of component properties.

7.2 Fiber couplers

The ability to transfer optical signals between fibers to perform the functions of traditional beam splitters was recognized at an early stage as one of the prime requirements for the successful development of all-fiber interferometric sensors. This function is performed by a fiber coupler, represented conceptually in Fig. 7.1, which is a four-port device which ideally splits the input signal (port A) into two channels (the throughput port B and the coupled port C). The primary parameter which characterizes a coupler is its coupling ratio (the fractional amount of light coupled to port C (see the Appendix)). Its required value varies according to the sensor application, ranging from a few per cent or less in distributed sensors to 50% (3 dB) in fiber gyroscopes and close to 100% in resonator sensors. Its insertion loss should preferably be lower than the few decibels typical of LiNbO$_3$ integrated optics couplers. For many sensor schemes, it is desirable to minimize backscattering (into ports A and D), for example to avoid feedback into a narrowband source placed at port A. These and other coupler properties are discussed in the following sections.

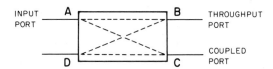

Fig. 7.1   Conceptual diagram of a bidirectional optical coupler.

7.2.1 Coupler principle

The basic principle prevailing in most fiber couplers is that under appropriate conditions light transfer can occur between adjacent fiber cores via a mechanism called evanescent wave coupling. As represented in Fig. 7.2(a) (location A), when two fiber cores are in close proximity the evanescent field of the signal traveling in the throughput fiber reaches into and excites the mode of the coupled fiber. When the modes of the two fibers exhibit the same phase velocity, resonant interaction takes place and total energy transfer occurs after some interaction length referred to as the coupling length (distance AB in Fig. 7.2(a)). If the interaction is allowed to continue beyond this point, the fiber roles are reversed and the signal is coupled back into the throughput fiber until the entire signal resides in the throughput fiber after two coupling lengths (location C in Fig. 7.2(a)). This situation is generally referred to as "overcoupling". If the length of the coupling region is sufficient, the process repeats itself in a cyclical manner along the length of the coupler.

This mechanism can be described by the well-known coupled-mode theory (Vanclooster and Phariseau, 1970; Marcuse, 1971; McIntyre and

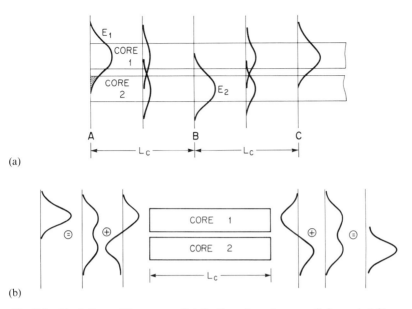

Fig. 7.2 Evolution of the energy distribution along two parallel coupled fiber cores, according to (a) the coupled-mode concept and (b) the normal mode theory.

Snyder, 1973). The mode field equation of the waveguide formed by the two adjacent cores is written as a linear superposition of the normal mode field of each individual isolated fiber. The energy distribution after some interaction length z is given by the relationship (McIntyre and Snyder, 1973)

$$\eta = \left\{1+\left(\frac{\Delta\beta}{2\chi}\right)^2\right\}^{-1/2} \sin^2\left[\left\{\chi^2+\left(\frac{\Delta\beta}{2}\right)^2\right\}^{1/2} z\right] \qquad (7.1)$$

where $\Delta\beta = \beta_2 - \beta_1$ is the propagation constant mismatch between the two modes and χ is the coupling coefficient. This coefficient is described in terms of a spatial overlap integral between the two normalized electric field modes E_1 and E_2 of the isolated fibers (Vanclooster and Phariseau, 1970; Marcuse, 1971; McIntyre and Snyder, 1973):

$$\chi \approx \int \Delta n\, E_1\, E_2{}^*\, dA \qquad (7.2)$$

coupler
cross-section

Δn is the index perturbation resulting from the introduction of a second fiber. For two identical fibers, Δn is equal to the difference between the core index and the cladding index in the core and is zero elsewhere, and the integral in eqn (7.2) only needs to be carried out over the fiber core.

For matched fibers ($\Delta\beta = 0$) the coupling ratio is simply given by $\eta = \sin^2(\chi z)$ (see eqn (7.1)). As z increases the signal energy is coupled back and forth between the two fiber cores. Total energy transfer is expected after a coupling length $L_c = \pi/2\chi$. The closer are the two cores, the stronger is the evanescent field E_2 in eqn (7.2) (see Fig. 7.2(a)) and the larger is the coupling coefficient. For typical fiber parameters and signal wavelengths, the coupling length can be as small as a fraction of a millimeter (Digonnet and Shaw, 1982). For $z \neq mL_c$, where m is an integer, $0 < \eta < 1$, so that in principle the coupling ratio can be set to any value by proper control of the interaction length.

The signal suffers a 90° phase shift upon transfer to the coupled fiber. Full coupling ($\eta = 1$) is possible only because of this phase shift; the coupled signal is 90° out of phase with the throughput signal and 180° out of phase when coupled back to the throughput port, where it interferes destructively with the throughput signal unless of course the latter carries no energy (i.e. $\eta = 1$). This phase shift is often important in sensor circuits, in particular in reciprocal fiber loops, as it affects interference between guided waves.

Alternatively, coupling between fibers can be physically understood by considering the two adjacent cores as a single waveguide (Eyges and Wintersteiner, 1981; Feit and Fleck, 1981). This waveguide supports two normal modes, the symmetric and antisymmetric modes, with propagation constants β_s and β_a respectively (see Fig. 7.2(b)). Intuitively, for identical cores the difference $\Delta\beta_{as} = |\beta_a - \beta_s|$ decreases monotonically as the core spacing h is increased, with $\Delta\beta_{as} = 0$ when h becomes infinite (isolated waveguides). As shown in Fig. 7.2(b), a signal launched into core 1 can be decomposed into (very nearly) equal amounts of these two modes (Eyges and Wintersteiner, 1981). As they travel along the waveguide, they accumulate a phase difference $\Delta\beta_{as}z$. After a length L_c such that $\Delta\beta_{as}L_c = \pi$ they have opposite phases, and interference between them is fully constructive in core 2 and fully destructive in core 1 (see Fig. 7.2(b)), i.e. the energy has been fully transferred to core 2.

Comparison between coupled-mode theory and the nearly exact normal mode theory shows that the former is quite accurate far enough from the cut-off of the antisymmetric mode (sufficiently high V numbers) and/or for relatively well separated cores (Eyges and Wintersteiner, 1981). For very close or contacting cores the error in the prediction of the coupling coefficient is less than 20% (Yeh et al., 1978). The coupled-mode description has therefore often been preferred to the more cumbersome normal mode theory.

7.2.2 Fiber couplers: description

In general, the optical signal traveling inside a single-mode fiber is confined to a very narrow core region surrounded by a thick cladding. Light transfer from one fiber to another therefore requires a physical modification of this situation to bring the core regions within a short distance of each other, typically of the order of one signal wavelength. To this end three basic methods have been developed, implementing etching, fusing and mechanical polishing techniques, each of which is reviewed in the following sections.

7.2.2.1 Etched fiber couplers

In etched fiber couplers the cores are brought in close proximity to each other after removal of most of the cladding region by controlled chemical etching (Sheem and Giallorenzi, 1979; Liao and Boyd, 1981). The fibers are twisted around each other and chemically etched inside a container. Coupling can be adjusted by modifying the fiber spacing by control of the amount of either twisting (Sheem and Giallorenzi, 1979) or tension (Liao and Boyd, 1981). Potting of the thin etched fibers in RTV or a solgel is necessary to reduce the scattering loss (less than 0.5 dB) and increase the thermal and mechanical stability (Koo et al., 1981). The refractive index of the potting material needs to be carefully selected, as it affects the evanescent fields of the structure and therefore its coupling ratio (Liao and Boyd, 1981). The properties of this and other types of couplers are summarized in Table 7.1.

7.2.2.2 Polished fiber couplers

Polished fiber couplers rely on partial removal of the fiber cladding by controlled mechanical polishing along one side of the fiber (Bergh et al., 1980a; Parriaux et al., 1981c). The fibers are first mounted individually in a fused silica substrate where they are bonded in a curved groove (Fig. 7.3(a)). The substrate and fiber are then ground and polished until the desired cladding thickness remains at the apex of the fiber curve (Bergh et al., 1980a). Two such fiber substrates are then mated to form a coupler (Fig. 7.3(b)). As shown in the cross-sectional view (Fig. 7.3(c)), a thin layer of index liquid is inserted between the substrates to match the two surfaces optically. To fabricate a coupler with a specific coupling ratio (at a given wavelength) both the radius of curvature R of the groove and the spacing h_0 between the fibers at their apex (Fig. 7.3(d)), i.e. the amount of cladding material to be removed, must be specified. These values are accurately predicted by a simple model based on the coupled-mode theory (Digonnet and Shaw, 1982). One of the merits of this scheme is that the relative lateral position of the mated fibers can be adjusted with micrometers to control the coupling ratio (Digonnet and Shaw, 1982). This tunability greatly reduces the fabrication tolerance on h_0.

As will become apparent in later sections, polished substrates have found applications in several other types of device which all require close monitoring of the substrate parameters during fabrication. In practice R is controlled by the curvature of the substrate groove (Fig. 7.3(d)). h_0 can be obtained by measuring either the length of the polished fiber cross-section (Bergh et al., 1980a; Digonnet and Shaw, 1982) or the optical attenuation of each substrate in the presence of a liquid of known refractive index, providing accuracies greater than 0.1 μm (Digonnet et al., 1985; Leminger and Zengerle, 1987).

Because the polishing method minimizes physical perturbation of the

Table 7.1 Summary of the optical properties of fiber directional couplers (low birefringence)

Coupler type	Extinction ratio	Insertion loss	Directivity	Polarization dependence	Temperature dependence
Etched		$<0.5\,\text{dB}^a$	$<-25\,\text{dB}^b$		$1\%\,°\text{C}^{-1}$ (potted)[a]
Polished	$-50\,\text{dB}^c$	$0.005\,\text{dB}^d$	$-70\,\text{dB}^c$	$-30\,\text{dB}^c$	$6\%\,°\text{C}^{-1}$ (liquid)[c] $<0.2\%\,°\text{C}^{-1}$ (cemented)[e]
Fused	$-30\,\text{dB}^f$	$<0.05\,\text{dB}^e$		$<-23\,\text{dB}^g$	$0.1\%\,°\text{C}^{-1}$ (air)[e] $<0.02\,\text{dB}$ over $100\,°\text{C}$ (packaged)[g]
D-shaped fiber		$<3\,\text{dB}^h$	$-60\,\text{dB}^h$	$<-10\,\text{dB}^h$	
Two-core fiber		$<0.2\,\text{dB}^i$			$10^{-5}\,°\text{C}^{-1}$ [j]

[a] Koo et al., 1981.
[b] Liao and Boyd, 1981.
[c] Digonnet and Shaw, 1982.
[d] Yu and Hall, 1984.
[e] Beasley et al., 1983.
[f] Bilodeau et al., 1987.
[g] Bricheno and Fielding, 1984.
[h] Schöner et al., 1982.
[i] Murakami and Sudo, 1981.
[j] Meltz et al., 1983.

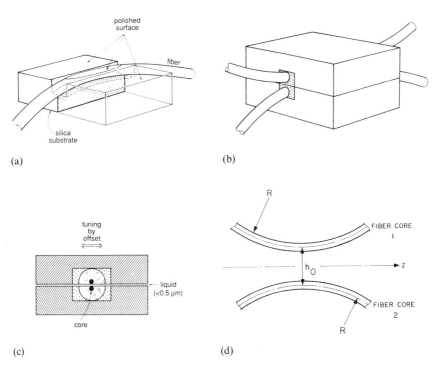

Fig. 7.3 Polished fiber coupler: (a) polished fiber substrate; (b) directional coupler formed by mating two polished substrates; (c) cross-section of the coupler at the center of the coupling region; (d) fiber geometry in the vicinity of the coupling region.

fiber, polished fiber couplers can exhibit very low backscattering in the fourth port ($-70\,$dB directivity (see the Appendix)) (Digonnet and Shaw, 1982) and their insertion loss may be as low as 0.005 dB (Yu and Hall, 1984) (these values apply to couplers with $R = 25\,$cm). Variations in coupling ratio with temperature of about $6\%\,°C^{-1}$ have been observed in adjustable couplers in which a liquid layer (high $\partial n/\partial T$) is involved (Digonnet and Shaw, 1982). A temperature coefficient below $0.2\%\,°C^{-1}$ has been achieved in fixed couplers with cemented substrates (Beasley et al., 1983).

7.2.2.3 Fused couplers

Despite their excellent properties, polished fiber couplers involve a time-consuming fabrication process. An alternative approach which relies on a simpler and faster process is the fused coupler, which is fabricated by slightly twisting two fibers around each other and then heating and drawing them down (Kawasaki et al., 1981; Villarruel and Moeller, 1981; Slonecker, 1982). Several types of heat source have been used for this process, including miniature electrical heating elements (Villarruel and Moeller, 1981), but a flame (Slonecker, 1982) appears to be the preferred source. In practice, the coupling ratio is monitored during fabrication and adjusted by control of the drawing process. In the resulting bitapered region (Fig. 7.4(a)) the core dimension is too small to support a guided mode practically. The signal is coupled to the two lowest-order modes (symmetric and antisymmetric) of the fused region which acts as a new composite waveguide. It is beating between these modes (as opposed to the core modes) which leads to energy exchange (Bures et al., 1983; Lamont et al., 1985).

The refractive index of the external medium surrounding the fused region affects the relative phase velocity of the interacting modes and therefore the coupling ratio (Lamont et al., 1985; Payne et al., 1986). This effect can result in a relatively strong temperature dependence if the external medium exhibits a large $\partial n/\partial T$ coefficient, as is the case for many polymeric materials. This is coupled to the observation that in fused couplers light propagation is highly sensitive to the cross-sectional shape of the fused region (Payne et al., 1986; Zheng and Snyder, 1987). The dependence on external refractive index can be dramatically reduced by using a "dumb-bell" shape of appropriate relative dimensions as opposed to rectangular or elliptical shapes (Fig. 7.4(b)) (Payne et al., 1986; Zheng and Snyder, 1987). This shape, and therefore the susceptibility of the device to temperature, can be controlled in practice by adjusting the degree of fusion applied to the fibers during fabrication (Payne et al., 1986).

The coupling ratio is also affected by bends and strains applied to the bitapered region. Some form of packaging is required for stabilization as well as to prevent corrosion of the bare glass surface. A particular design involved attaching the taper to a silica rod mounted in an Invar container and potting in silicone resin (Bricheno and Fielding, 1984). This design made full use of the inherently high temperature stability of the fused silica fibers as it provided a coupling ratio which was stable to better than 0.5% between $-20\,°C$ and $+100\,°C$ (Bricheno and Fielding, 1984) compared with a variation of 0.1% $°C^{-1}$ for devices in air (Villarruel and Moeller, 1981). Other designs have been proposed to reduce the sensitivity to pressure for undersea sensor applications (Villarruel et al., 1987).

Despite these improvements, fusion still appears to induce more perturbation to the fiber structure than polishing does, and provides somewhat higher insertion losses and poorer signal extinction between output ports (see the Appendix). The best reported values for these quantities in fused couplers are 0.05 dB (Beasley et al., 1983) and -30 dB (Bilodeau et al., 1987) respectively.

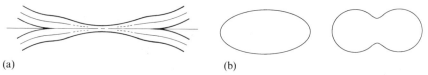

(a)   (b)

Fig. 7.4 Cross-sectional views of a fused fiber coupler: (a) longitudinal; (b) models of the transverse view for various degrees of fusion.

7.2.2.4 Couplers made of nonstandard fibers

Other types of couplers based on nonstandard single-mode fibers have been demonstrated. These have not yet emerged in significant commercial numbers but may find future sensor applications. One such type involves the side-by-side mating of two so-called D-shaped fibers, with a cladding of semicircular cross-section and an eccentric core located just beneath the flat surface of the cladding. In one design (Schöner et al., 1982) liquid polysiloxane provided optical matching between the fibers and was hardened into a protective coating after fiber alignment. The coupling ratio was adjustable by bending the fibers, thereby inducing a propagation constant mismatch (see eqn (7.1)).

Another type is the two-core fiber coupler, which is made of a single fiber containing two parallel cores. It is fabricated by standard preform drawing technology (Schiffner et al., 1980; Murakami and Sudo, 1981; Meltz et al., 1983) and is ideally suited for large-scale manufacturing. Devices with full coupling over lengths as short as $L_c = 240\,\mu m$ have been demonstrated (Meltz et al., 1983). Merits include high temperature stability, calculated to be as high as $0.001\%°C^{-1}$ (Meltz et al., 1983), coupling tunability by bending (Schiffner et al., 1980; Murakami and Sudo, 1981) and a low insertion loss (0.2 dB was reported by Murakami and Sudo) which can potentially be made negligible in practice. However, as for the D-shaped fiber coupler, further work is needed in the area of interfacing to standard single-mode fibers (via butt-coupling or splicing) which is made difficult by the eccentric geometry of the fibers.

7.2.3 Performance comparison

The properties of the different coupler types are summarized in Table 7.1. These figures are taken from a variety of sources, and in general it cannot be assumed that they all apply simultaneously to the same device. The suitability of a coupler type to sensor application depends strongly on the particular sensor requirements. For fiber gyroscopes, attention is generally paid to directivity and stability to environmental parameters, whereas in all-fiber resonator sensors the insertion loss is also a critical parameter. Other considerations include ease of manufacturing. In this respect, fused couplers have taken the lead in popularity because of their relative simplicity of fabrication and high temperature and mechanical stability, while polished couplers continue to exhibit superior properties on most counts (see Table 7.1). Both types are now available from a variety of manufacturers.

7.2.4 Polarization effects in couplers

7.2.4.1 Low birefringence fiber couplers

Two types of polarization effect are of interest in fiber couplers: the dependence of the coupling ratio on the signal polarization, and the effect of the coupling region on the state of polarization (SOP) of the signal. In a coupler made of perfectly nonbirefringent fibers, the coupling ratio is approximately the same for an input signal with polarization parallel or perpendicular to the polished surface, even for contacting cores (Vanclooster and Phariseau, 1970). The polarization dependence of the coupling ratio was measured to be typically 0.1% (-30 dB) in a polished coupler tuned anywhere between 50% and 100% coupling, in accord with theory (Digonnet and Shaw, 1982). Polishing the fiber introduces some birefringence depending on the amount of cladding removed, which in turn can cause polarization coupling (Stolen, 1986). However, since the induced birefringence axes are defined by the polished surface, a signal polarized in or perpendicular to this plane should remain relatively unaffected. A maximum birefringence of $\Delta n = 10^{-4}$ has been measured in a particular fiber substrate (Stolen, 1986). However, the effect of the polished coupler on the SOP has not been directly measured.

In fused couplers an additional polarization dependence arises from birefringence due to anisotropic stresses in the fused region. This dependence was measured to be 0.5% (-23 dB) in a standard 3 dB fused coupler (Bricheno and Fielding, 1984)—as expected somewhat higher than in polished couplers. In fused couplers many coupling lengths long, i.e. highly overcoupled, this effect can be used to form polarization beam splitters (Villarruel et al., 1983).

7.2.4.2 High birefringence fibers

For fiber sensors to benefit fully from the polarization-holding characteristics of high birefringence (HB) fibers, directional couplers for use with such fibers must preserve the signal polarization to a degree comparable with that of the fiber. Since couplers made of standard fibers fail to meet this requirement, a sizable effort has been made to fabricate couplers using HB fibers (Kawachi et al., 1982; Dyott and Bello, 1983; Nayar and Smith, 1983; Pleibel et al., 1983; Stolen et al., 1985; Yataki et al., 1985a; Carrara et al., 1986; Yokohama et al., 1986). Because the two eigenpolarizations of the fiber have different propagation constants, significant power transfer between fibers can occur only for identical polarization modes (see eqn (7.1)). In order to achieve high polarization isolation (see the Appendix) and high coupling, the birefringence axes of the two fibers must be well aligned, to better than $0.5°$ for an isolation of -35 dB (Dyott and Bello, 1983). Reproducible alignment is the most significant difficulty in the fabrication of HB fiber couplers.

The polishing method can be used in combination with visual alignment of the fiber axis with respect to the polishing surface. This method was used with elliptical core fibers to produce an isolation between -35 and -42 dB and an insertion loss of lower than 0.5 dB (Nayar and Smith, 1983). A simple probe was also developed to provide a more reproducible fiber alignment, based on the principle that pressure causes polarization coupling only when applied along an axis different from a fiber polarization axis (Carrara et al., 1986). This work reproducibly led to isolations lower than -28 dB. To simplify the alignment requirement further, D-shaped (Dyott and Bello, 1983; Pleibel *et al.*, 1983) and rectangular (Stolen *et al.*, 1985) fibers were developed with eigenpolarizations aligned with respect to the major and minor fiber axes. During assembly of the fiber substrates the eigenpolarizations are self-aligned with respect to the fiber bend and the polishing surface (Fig. 7.4) (Pleibel *et al.*, 1983; Stolen *et al.*, 1985). This method is appealing in its simplicity and produces low loss devices (less than 0.2 dB according to Dyott and Bello (1983)), but it requires special fibers and has so far produced couplers with only about − 20 dB isolation (Dyott and Bello, 1983; Pleibel *et al.*, 1983).

With the fusion method, the HB fibers need to be mated without twisting to preserve the alignment of their axes prior to fusion. This has been accomplished by optical microscope alignment, followed by either symmetrical flame heating (Yokohama *et al.*, 1986) or sealing by chemical vapor deposition to allow fusion of aligned fibers (Kawachi *et al.*, 1982). Polarization isolation of the order of − 32 dB was achieved for both output ports (Yokohama *et al.*, 1986). Mode coupling to the fiber stress members in the tapered region can contribute to excessive insertion loss. This loss was reduced to the 0.03–0.1 dB range by matching the refractive index of the members to that of the surrounding cladding (Yokohama *et al.*, 1986).

7.3 Wavelength-division multiplexing and filters

In the following, we differentiate between two types of wavelength-filtering devices, namely filters (devices with two or more ports) and multiplexers (devices with three or more ports) which also act as filters. Both types have a broad range of potential applications in fiber sensors. Wavelength-division multiplexing (WDM) is desirable to multiplex two (or more) signals of different wavelengths onto the same fiber carrier, for example when either a reference signal (e.g. in intensity sensors) or a pump signal (e.g. in active sensors) is required. The most important devices are described below.

7.3.1 Wavelength-division multiplexing in directional couplers

In fiber directional couplers, as in most waveguide couplers, the coupling coefficient depends on the signal frequency as a result of fiber mode dispersion. Over most of the practical guiding range of a fiber, longer wavelength signals exhibit stronger evanescent fields and therefore larger coupling coefficients (Digonnet and Shaw, 1983). This effect has been used to develop WDM in fiber couplers, as illustrated in Fig. 7.5. In a coupler with an interaction length L, two signals of different wavelengths exhibiting coupling coefficients χ_1 and χ_2 respectively will be exactly multiplexed when the coupling ratio $\eta = \sin^2(\chi_i L)$ is unity for one signal and zero for the other. The minimum length L required to satisfy this condition is $L = \pi/2|\chi_2 - \chi_1|$. The channel separation $\Delta\lambda$, which

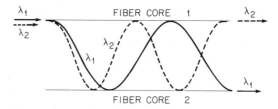

Fig. 7.5 Principle of fiber wavelength-division multiplexing: energy exchange along the length of two coupled fibers at two wavelengths λ_1 and λ_2, selected to be demultiplexed onto fibers 1 and 2 respectively.

is defined as the minimum wavelength spacing that two signals should have to be exactly multiplexed, is therefore (Digonnet and Shaw, 1983)

$$\Delta\lambda = \frac{\pi}{2}\left(\frac{\partial\chi L}{\partial\lambda}\right)^{-1} \tag{7.3}$$

and is inversely proportional to the interaction length.

Because of their long interaction lengths, two-core fibers are ideally suited for good wavelength discrimination. A separation of 0.25 nm was demonstrated in the 530–650 nm range in a device 40 cm long (Meltz et al., 1983). In polished couplers the channel separation can be adjusted via the curvature R (i.e. the interaction length) and/or the minimum fiber spacing h_0 (see eqn. (7.3)) (Parriaux et al., 1981a, c; Digonnet and Shaw, 1983). These predictions were verified experimentally with a smallest channel separation of 35 nm in a coupler with $R = 8$ m ($L \approx 6$ mm) (Digonnet and Shaw, 1983). Furthermore, the center operating wavelength can be tuned over a broad range by adjusting the lateral offset y between the fibers, which relaxes fabrication constraints.

In all-fiber couplers the finite thermal expansion and index dependence on temperature make the coupling ratio increasingly sensitive to temperature as the interaction length is increased. The temperature and wavelength dependences of the phase $\varphi = \chi L$ are proportional (Meltz et al., 1983) so that channel separation is traded for temperature stability. For example in the 0.25 nm bandwidth two-core fiber multiplexer of Meltz et al. (1983) a temperature change of only 80 °C is required to change the coupling ratio from zero to 100%.

The wavelength selectivity can be enhanced by involving fibers with dissimilar dispersion curves, in which case strong power exchange occurs only in the wavelength region where the mode propagation constants of the two fibers are identical. Parriaux et al. (1981a) used this principle to generate a variety of interesting narrow bandpass filters. A channel separation as small as 15 nm was observed with a 20 dB extinction ratio in dissimilar-fiber polished couplers with $R = 5$ m compared with 35 nm in a device with $R = 8$ m made of similar fibers (Digonnet and Shaw, 1983). The same principle is applicable to fused couplers, relying on the dispersion between the two lowest-order modes of the fused region (Whalen and Walker, 1985). In a particular implementation, 1.32 and 1.55 μm signals were multiplexed with channel isolations of 43 and 30 dB respectively (Georgiou and Boucouvalas, 1986).

7.3.2 Wavelength filters

Among the simplest fiber filters are low and high pass filters based on wavelength rejection by absorption caused by a core dopant. For example, high rejection ratios (see the Appendix) of the order of $10^3–10^4$ dB km^{-1} in the sharp absorption bands and low transmission losses elsewhere (a few decibels per kilometer) can be achieved with rare earth dopants such as holmium (Farries *et al.*, 1986) and neodymium (Poole *et al.*, 1985).

Narrowband filtering can be achieved in bitapered fibers, which are fabricated by heating and slightly drawing a short length of fiber. In the tapering region the power is coupled back and forth between the fundamental core and cladding modes. This mechanism is wavelength dependent, and the transmitted signal varies almost sinusoidally with wavelength with a half-period (or linewidth) which is a function of the taper length (Boucouvalas and Georgiou, 1985). The filter rejection ratio decreases as the taper length is increased. It was measured to be 41 dB for a linewidth of 165 nm, while the smallest reported linewidth is 20 nm with a poorer rejection ratio (Boucouvalas and Georgiou, 1985). Twists applied to the taper permit fine tuning of the center wavelength, while the addition of controlled longitudinal strain reduces the residual and twist-induced birefringence and therefore the polarization dependence of the response (Boucouvalas and Georgiou, 1987).

The filter response of normal couplers is sinusoidal. However, filters with different linewidths can be concatenated to generate a variety of optical filters with reduced sideband magnitude. The filter linewidth is set by and is comparable with the smallest linewidth of the filter series, and the sideband magnitude is controlled by the number of couplers and their individual phases. With this principle a 95% transmission filter with a full width at half-maximum (FWHM) of 20 nm was demonstrated with a series of two fused couplers (Yataki *et al.*, 1985b). This principle was also used with bitapered fibers and produced similar filter responses (5.8 nm linewidth with a peak transmission of 50% near 750 nm) (Lacroix *et al.*, 1986).

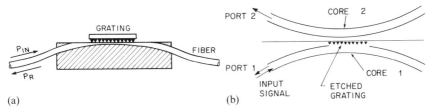

Fig. 7.6 Evanescent field grating devices: (a) tuned back-reflector; (b) back-reflecting directional coupler (see text).

Evanescent field filters have been made in polished fiber substrates where the evanescent field interacts with an optical grating located at the polished surface (Fig. 7.6(a)) (Sorin and Shaw, 1985; Whalen et al., 1986b). The signal back-reflected into the input fiber has a peak wavelength $\lambda_b = 2 n_{eff} \Lambda$, where n_{eff} is the effective index of the fiber mode and Λ is the grating period (Sorin and Shaw, 1985), and an FWHM bandwidth $\Delta\lambda/\lambda = \Lambda/L$ where L is the effective interaction length (Bennion et al., 1986). For values of Λ in the submicrometer range, subnanometer filter bandwidths can be readily achieved with standard fiber substrates ($L = 1$ mm). With the addition of a second coupler on the input lead, these devices can also be used for WDM.

In the simplest implementation an external metallic grating was placed against the substrate with a thin intermediate layer of index-matching liquid, and a 38% back-reflection with a 2.8 Å bandwidth was produced (Sorin and Shaw, 1985). Whalen et al. (1986b) used a grating with a spatially varying period in one direction which was translated across the fiber to tune the peak wavelength of the back-reflected signal. A maximum back-reflection efficiency of about -10 dB over a tuning range of 1.46–1.54 µm was achieved. Much larger efficiencies were obtained by depositing the grating directly on the substrate or etching it into the fiber polished surface. In one implementation the grating was prepared using a conventional photolithography technique and was then coated with a thin film of a high index material (Al_2O_3) and a layer of index-matched material to increase the spatial overlap between the evanescent field and the grating (Bennion et al., 1986). It provided a high back-reflection efficiency of 92% near 1300 nm and a narrow bandwidth of 1.8 nm.

A similar principle was applied to the region between the substrates of a polished coupler to produce very narrow filters (Fig. 7.6(b)) (Whalen et al., 1986a). Depending on its wavelength, an input signal at port 1 is either partially back-reflected into port 1 or Bragg reflected and coupled to the second fiber in the backward direction (port 2). The center wavelengths of the two back-reflections are different (and the device acts as a filter) when the fibers have different propagation constants. Whalen et al. (1986a) used identical fibers and induced slight differences in their propagation constants by polishing the substrates to different depths. Standard masking and reactive ion etching techniques were used to produce grooves 40 nm deep in one of the substrates. The device exhibited FWHM bandwidths of 0.45 nm and 0.6 nm for the direct and coupled signals respectively and a 25% peak wavelength efficiency for the latter.

Despite a less than ideal performance, filters have already found interesting applications as high resolution spectrometers (Russell and Ulrich, 1985) and for narrowing the linewidth of semiconductor lasers below 100 kHz (Brinkmeyer et al., 1986; Park et al., 1986). Polished multiplexing couplers have been successfully implemented in several fiber systems requiring moderate channel separations, in particular recirculating delay lines (Desurvire et al., 1985) and re-entrant active fiber gyroscopes (Desurvire et al., 1988).

7.4 Polarization controllers

In optical fiber sensors utilizing non-polarization-maintaining (non-PM) fibers, the SOP at the receiving end fluctuates due to thermal and mechanical perturbations of the fiber. When polarization-sensitive elements are present, these fluctuations result in undesirable intensity noise and signal fading. The fiber community has responded to this problem by developing PM and single-polarization (SP) fibers. However, such fibers are still costly, and at least for some time fiber polarization controllers will be a strong alternative.

Polarization controllers are devices which transform any given input SOP into an arbitrary output SOP. Since an SOP has two degrees of freedom, this function requires at least two control elements. As polarization variations usually have a thermal origin, slow active control is generally sufficient. In applications requiring a precise (linear) polarization at a given location along the fiber, the controller can be followed by a polarizer. The general function of a controller is therefore usually limited to bringing the SOP to approximately the desired value. Several noninvasive fiber polarization controllers have been demonstrated to date, in which birefringence is induced through squeezing (Johnson, 1979), bending (Lefèvre, 1980) or the Faraday effect (Okoshi, 1985) to form the fiber equivalent of fractional wave plates or rotators. Many controllers exhibit a limited tuning range, so that resetting, which causes a momentary loss of signal, is generally required during active control (Ulrich, 1979). Endless polarization control is a condition which avoids this difficulty and provides continuous control of the SOP.

Polarization control can be achieved by applying lateral pressure to the fiber in well-defined directions. The pressure and directions set the local birefringence strength and axis. The first implementation of this concept, illustrated in Fig. 7.7(a), involved a succession of electromagnetic squeezers at relative angular directions of 45° (Johnson, 1979; Ulrich, 1979). This arrangement forms the most general polarization controller.

A simpler passive device is made of a fiber which is coiled to induce asymmetric radial strains and birefringence (Lefèvre, 1980). The two eigen-polarizations are parallel and perpendicular to the plane of the coil. The coil radius of curvature R is selected so that the phase retardation between them is either 90° ($\lambda/4$ plate) or 180° ($\lambda/2$ plate). The coil axes define the principal axes of the equivalent fractional wave plate, so that the output SOP is adjusted by simply modifying the angular orientation of the coil about the AB axis (see Fig. 7.7(b)). Two $\lambda/4$ plates in series form the most general controller (Lefèvre, 1980). The insertion loss is primarily due to bending loss in the fiber and can be made arbitrarily small by selecting a sufficiently large bend radius and correspondingly increasing the number of loops in the coil (Matsumoto and Kano, 1986). A few simple mechanical configurations, including the interesting crank geometry shown in Fig. 7.7(c) (Okoshi, 1985), enable endless control, i.e. the possibility of rotating each loop about itself in the same direction

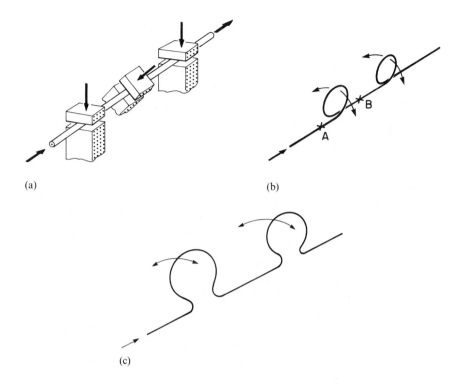

Fig. 7.7 Fiber polarization controllers: (a) squeezer scheme; (b) birefringent coil scheme; (c) endless control crank scheme.

indefinitely without cumulative twisting of the fiber (Matsumoto and Kano, 1986).

The last scheme involves two Faraday rotators separated by a quarter-wave fiber coil (Okoshi, 1985). Each rotator is made of a length of fiber placed in the field of a permanent magnet and relies on the Faraday effect to induce a phase shift between left and right circularly polarized light in the fiber (or rotation of a linear input polarization). The Faraday effect in silica is relatively weak but is significant enough to produce the required birefringence in a few tens of meters of fiber subjected to the magnetic field produced by a reasonably small current coil. The first rotator transforms the input SOP into a vertical elliptical SOP, which is then transformed into a linear SOP by the birefringent coil and finally rotated to the desired orientation by the second rotator. The fiber coil is stationary, so that this scheme is free from mechanical fatigue.

Another form of polarization control is depolarization followed by polarization filtering. It is a more limited form of control as it only provides a linear output SOP and contributes to a 3 dB signal loss, but it does not require active feedback. For narrowband sources it was proposed to divide the signal equally between the two eigenpolarizations of a linearly birefringent fiber and modulate their relative phase to distribute the instantaneous output SOP evenly and cancel the time-averaged degree of polarization (Kersey and Dandridge, 1987). A fiber implementation of the Lyot depolarizer, which transforms different spectral components of a polarized signal into different SOPs so that the output signal averaged over its spectrum appears unpolarized, is applicable for broadband sources (Böhm et al., 1983). In an example of a fiber Lyot depolarizer, in which two strands of 4 mm beat length HB fiber at 45° replaced the conventional birefringent plates, the relative amount of polarized intensity at the output was 1.4×10^{-2} (Böhm et al., 1983). With the best polarization-holding fibers now available, this value would be improved by one order of magnitude. A potential application for depolarizers is in fiber gyroscopes as a means of reducing signal fading and nonreciprocal phase error (Böhm et al., 1981; Fredricks and Ulrich, 1984).

The various features of these controllers are compared in Table 7.2, following the parameters introduced by Okoshi (1985). All devices exhibit low insertion losses, in the range of 0.1 dB or less. Endless control is available only with the coil scheme. The Faraday rotator scheme is the only one which features a fast response time and the absence of mechanical wear. Clearly no scheme fully meets all the requirements of sensor applications. In applications requiring no active feedback and in laboratory sensor models where signal SOPs vary slowly, birefringent coils have been widely used owing to their simplicity of implementation.

7.5 Fiber polarizers

Interferometric fiber sensors utilizing standard single-mode fibers are strongly affected by the presence of two polarization modes in the fiber as they can cause signal fading. Also, in fiber gyroscopes the selection of a single polarization at some point along the fiber is required to avoid nonreciprocal phase errors. To illustrate the importance of this device, it is usually considered that a polarizer extinction ratio (see the Appendix) greater than 100 dB is desirable if gyroscopes of inertial navigation grade are to be achieved. In an attempt to meet this goal several approaches have been investigated, including the development of PM and SP fibers (described in Chapter 8) as well as a large number of invasive and noninvasive fiber polarizers.

Invasive devices require access to the evanescent field of the guided mode to induce preferential attenuation of one of the polarization components. The first reported polarizer of this nature was based on the principle of metal-clad planar waveguides in which the light signal is coupled to the electric current it induces in the metal and suffers a propagation loss via ohmic losses (Eickhoff, 1980). The TM_0 mode has its electric field perpendicular to the metal surface and is more strongly attenuated than the TE_0 mode. Directly coating the

Table 7.2 Comparison of the general performance of in-line fiber polarization controllers

Type of device	Endless control	Temporal response	Mechanical fatigue	Reference
Fiber squeezers	No	Medium	Yes	Johnson, 1979
Rotatable coils	Yes	Slow	Yes	Lefèvre, 1980; Okoshi, 1985; Matsumoto and Kano, 1986
Faraday rotators	No	Fast	No	Okoshi, 1985

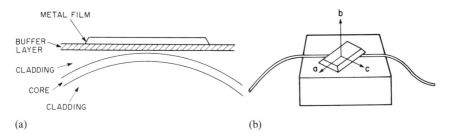

Fig. 7.8 (a) Cross-section of the metal film fiber polarizer; (b) general view of the birefringent crystal fiber polarizer (note crystal orientation). Both are fabricated with a polished fiber substrate.

surface of a polished fiber substrate with a thin layer of aluminum or gold led to sizable losses and moderate differential attenuations (Eickhoff, 1980). This device was refined by recognizing that attenuation can be greatly improved by matching the group velocities of the optical and electrical (plasmon) surface waves, in practice by adding a buffer layer between the polished surface and the metal coating (Fig. 7.8(a)) (Parriaux *et al.*, 1981b). With an evaporated CaF_2 film as a buffer layer and a thin aluminum overlay, an extinction ratio in excess of 45 dB and TE_0 attenuation of 1 dB were demonstrated at 0.85 μm (Gruchmann *et al.*, 1983). The same principle was recently applied to D-shaped fibers, providing a 39 dB extinction ratio and an insertion loss of only 0.2 dB (for low loss polarization) (Dyott *et al.*, 1987).

High performance fiber polarizers have been made by placing a birefringent crystal on a polished fiber substrate, as shown in Fig. 7.8(b). The interaction occurs between the evanescent field of the guided mode and the new birefringent cladding (Bergh *et al.*, 1980b). If, for one of the two linear eigenpolarizations, the refractive index of the birefringent cladding is larger than the effective index of the guided wave, this polarization is coupled out of the core into the crystal and experiences a strong loss. In addition, if for the other polarization the refractive index of the cladding is equal to or slightly lower than the effective index of the guided wave, this polarization is expected to suffer virtually no attenuation. This is realized in practice by a proper choice of crystal and a fine tuning of its axis orientation with respect to the fiber (Fig. 7.8(b)) (Bergh *et al.*, 1980b). This principle was first put into practice with a crystal of potassium pentaborate which yielded extinction ratios in excess of 60 dB (the best figure that could be measured using conventional techniques) and an insertion loss of a few per cent (Bergh *et al.*, 1980b). Record extinction ratios as high as 90 dB were inferred for this type of polarizer by indirect measurements (Bergh *et al.*, 1981). Such high performance is attributed to the achievement of very low levels of scattering and cross-coupling and illustrates one of the primary merits of all-fiber components compared with their bulk optic and integrated optic counterparts.

A last type of invasive device is the cut-off polarizer, initially demonstrated by Eickhoff (1980) and refined by Feth and Chang (1986). It involves a fiber substrate polished into the fiber core such that both polarization modes are below cut-off. A thin metal film deposited on the polished surface then acts as a bridge for the TM_0 mode, which is first converted into a plasmon wave at the input of the interaction region and then converted back to the TM_0 wave at the end of the interaction region. Efficient coupling between the two waves is again achieved by placing a buffer layer between the fiber and the metal film. With a 5 nm silver or gold film and a liquid buffer layer, a TM_0 insertion loss of 1 dB and an extinction ratio of 47 dB were reported (Feth and Chang, 1986).

The above devices rely on the careful removal of prescribed amounts of fiber cladding and share fairly stringent fabrication requirements. Consequently, parallel efforts have been made to develop polarizers requiring simpler fabrication techniques. Among them are noninvasive devices utilizing HB fibers and operating on a cut-off principle. The basic principle of HB fibers is that, through geometrical or stress-induced index anisotropy, one of the polarization modes is more weakly guided than the other. As a result, the two linear polarization modes of HB fibers experience different attenuations at low V numbers. The two modes become leaky at different wavelengths, i.e. there is a narrow window in which polarization filtering occurs (Varnham *et al.*, 1983). At a given wavelength, differential polarization loss can be induced by simply bending the fiber with a prescribed radius to cause a high loss for one mode and yet retain efficient transmission for the other. Polarizers utilizing a bow tie fiber have been demonstrated with less than 2 dB loss for the desired mode and an extinction ratio as high as 62 dB (Varnham *et al.*, 1984a).

The performance of fiber polarizers is summarized in Table 7.3. Extinction ratios in excess of 45 dB have been achieved with the metal overlay, cut-off and crystal polarizers, as well as with the bent HB fiber polarizer. The lowest loss and highest extinction were achieved in the crystal polarizer. However, these extinction values may not be directly comparable as they were measured with input SOPs which were not always matched to the exact polarizer eigenpolarizations. For example, the input polarization is usually linear whereas the electric field lines of the fiber eigenpolarization modes are somewhat curved (Varnham *et al.*, 1984b). As a result, some degree of polarization coupling may have been present and reduced the measured extinction value. This effect was demonstrated for the bent HB fiber polarizer, which exhibited -20 dB of polarization coupling (Varnham *et al.*, 1984a). Consequently, when fiber polarizers are involved in fiber sensors, in particular gyroscopes, care must be taken in relating these values to the system accuracy.

7.6 Phase modulators

Fiber optic phase modulators are widely used for coherent fiber optic systems such as interferometric sensors. They provide a means of either

Table 7.3 Summary of the optical properties of all-fiber polarizers

Type	α_{TM_0} (dB)	α_{TE_0} (dB)	λ (nm)	Reference
Metal film	25	11	680	Eickhoff, 1980
Liquid buffer and metal film	22	5	633	Parriaux et al., 1981b
CaF$_2$ and metal film	>45	1	850	Grunchmann et al., 1983
Cut-off	1	47	820	Feth and Chang, 1986
Crystal	~90	<0.1	633	Bergh et al., 1980b, 1981
D-shaped	39	0.2	820	Dyott et al., 1987
Bent bow tie	62	2	820	Varnham et al., 1983

stabilizing the interferometer against various environmental perturbations or heterodyning for the sensitive and linear detection of optical phase shift. Phase modulation in optical fibers is achieved by an external modulation of the physical length of a section of fiber and/or the effective index of the guided mode. External perturbations which can produce phase modulations include axial elongation, radial stress and temperature. Owing to the inherently slow nature of the latter, most of the phase modulators developed to date have relied on the first two and involve acoustic transducers. In this section two major categories of fiber optic phase modulators, namely lead zirconate titanate (PZT) ring devices and fibers with coaxial piezoelectric transducers, will be discussed.

7.6.1 PZT ring phase modulators

The simplest and most popular form of fiber phase modulator for laboratory use is a piezoelectric cylinder with several turns of fiber wrapped around it under a small tension (Davies and Kingsley, 1974; Kingsley, 1978) as shown in Fig. 7.9(a). When a voltage is applied across the wall of a radially poled PZT cylinder, the circumference of the cylinder changes owing to the strain induced in its wall thickness, height and circumference, resulting in a change in the fiber length. The induced phase shift is given by (Yoshino et al., 1982; Bergh, 1983)

$$\Delta\varphi = \frac{2\pi}{\lambda}(n\,\Delta l + l\,\Delta n) \tag{7.4}$$

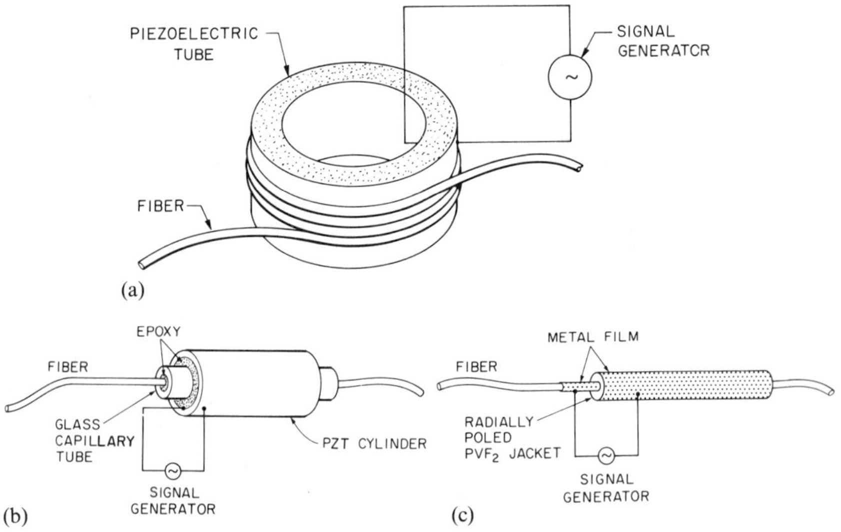

Fig. 7.9 Fiber phase modulators: (a) PZT ring; (b) coaxial PZT transducer scheme; (c) fibers with a piezoelectric jacket.

In a single-mode silica fiber at 633 nm, $\Delta\varphi \approx 0.78(2\pi/\lambda)n\,\Delta l$. This is a little less than the effect of the length increase Δl alone because the refractive index of the fiber decreases under axial strain owing to the photoelastic effect. If PZT-5H ceramic cylinders operated at frequencies well below the lowest mechanical resonance frequency (d.c. to a few kilohertz) are used, a 2π rad phase shift can be realized with an applied voltage–turn product of about 70 V turns (Davies and Kingsley, 1974; Kingsley, 1978) to 100 V turns (Jackson et al., 1980) at $\lambda = 633$ nm. This figure depends on the PZT material, the thickness and diameter of the cylinder, and the electrode configuration. Details of the amplitude response of the PZT modulators to applied voltage are given by Martini (1987).

The modulation amplitude can be increased by several orders of magnitude by operating the modulator at one of the acoustic resonance frequencies of the cylinder. These frequencies are determined by the dimensions of the cylinder, the material and the type of acoustic resonant mode. The most commonly used acoustic resonance in a hollow cylinder with a thin wall is the hoop mode, which corresponds to a symmetrical expansion of the circumference. The resonance frequency is inversely proportional to the diameter of the cylinder, with a frequency constant of about 100 kHz cm depending on the PZT type (*Engineering Databook*). Therefore its upper limit in the hoop mode, typically 100 kHz, is set by the minimum bend radius which can be applied to the fiber without introducing excessive loss. For a given diameter, this resonance frequency can be doubled by changing from a thin-walled cylinder to a solid PZT disk.

Other acoustic resonance modes associated with the height and wall thickness of the cylinder can be used, since expansion in these dimensions is associated with a circumference change. This mode of operation is particularly interesting because a relatively high frequency can be generated in a cylinder of reasonable size. The resonance frequency constants for PZT-5H are about 140 kHz cm for the height-expanding mode and 200 kHz cm for the wall-thickness-expanding mode (*Engineering Databook*). As an example, the height resonance mode of a PZT cylinder with a diameter of 5 cm and a height of 8 mm was used to produce phase modulation at 174 kHz in a fiber gyroscope (Bergh et al., 1981). By using these acoustic resonance modes with properly selected dimensions, efficient phase modulation can be achieved over a wide frequency range up to a few hundred kilohertz. However, for a given PZT cylinder, the frequency bandwidth is limited. Phase modulation with arbitrary waveforms (such as sawtooth and rectangular waveforms) is not generally possible except at a very low frequency (typically less than 1 kHz) as it requires a uniform frequency response for the significant harmonic frequency contents of the waveform.

This type of modulator exhibits a small amount of polarization modulation through modulation of the birefringence induced by tension coiling of the fiber (Bergh, 1983; Martini, 1987). Also, a small amount of nonlinearity may be observed in the response of the phase modulator to the applied voltage. Although these undesirable characteristics are not detrimental for most applications, care has to be taken for extremely sensitive phase measurements such as fiber gyroscopes. Despite such shortcomings and the relatively large size and fiber length requirement (typically 0.1–10 m), this type of phase modulator is by far the most popular for low frequency laboratory and experimental field applications because of its structural simplicity and the large phase modulation amplitude it provides.

7.6.2 Fibers with coaxial piezoelectric transducers

For higher frequency phase modulation a number of approaches have been proposed, including the use of a piezoelectric polymer coating and lateral or radial squeezing of the fiber. One particular implementation (Fig. 7.9(b)) consists of a fiber positioned along the axis of a cylindrical PZT transducer. Acoustic contact between the fiber and the transducer is provided by either a solid or a liquid material (Kingsley, 1975; Carome and Adamovski, 1981; Nosu et al., 1983b). The acoustic wave generated by the thin wall of the cylinder at the resonance frequency of the thickness mode is focused at the center of the cylinder where the core of the fiber is located. This acoustic wave produces a stress modulation in the fiber, which in turn modulates its refractive index through the elasto-optic effect. The typical operational frequency of this type of phase modulator is in the range of a few megahertz for a wall thickness smaller than 1 mm. For example, 0.058 rad V^{-1} cm^{-1} at 6.02 MHz has been obtained with a wall thickness of 0.51 mm (Nosu et al., 1983b). The modulation amplitude is limited by thermal dissipation and relatively short interaction lengths (a few centimeters to remain practical). This type of device has additional resonance peaks originating from the dimensions of the various substructures as seen in Fig. 7.9(b). In order to achieve broadband operation, these additional resonances have to be suppressed, which generally results in a reduced modulation efficiency. One of the advantages of this modulator is that, owing to the symmetry of the applied stress, it is free from polarization modulation provided that the fiber core is located exactly at the center of the cylinder and the fiber itself is cylindrically symmetrical (Nosu et al., 1983b).

7.6.3 Fibers with piezoelectric jackets

Another form of phase modulator operating with a similar principle is an optical fiber with a jacket made from a piezoelectric plastic such as polyvinylidene fluoride (PVF$_2$) as shown in Fig. 7.9(c) (Donalds et al., 1982; DePaula and Moore, 1984; Jarzynski, 1984; Imai et al., 1987). In response to an applied electric field, this jacket modulates the fiber refractive index and, depending on the frequency, the length of the fiber. At frequencies such that the extensional acoustic wavelength is longer than the interaction region, both effects contribute to the phase modulation. At higher frequencies the change in the refractive index dominates. This device can have a relatively long interaction length, as a standard extrusion technique can be used to apply the plastic jacket over long lengths of fiber (Donalds et al., 1982; Jarzynski, 1984). The polymeric jacket should be poled in a high d.c. electric field of the order of $0.5 \, MV \, cm^{-1}$ in order to induce a piezoelectric effect in the material. Both transverse (Donalds et al., 1982) and radial (Jarzynski, 1984; Imai et al., 1987) poling have been used. A uniform frequency response with a phase modulation coefficient of $0.01 \, rad \, V^{-1} \, m^{-1}$ was demonstrated over a very wide frequency range (30 kHz to 2.5 MHz) using a radially poled PVF_2 polymer jacket 120 μm thick (Jarzynski, 1984). An order-of-magnitude improvement in this modulation efficiency is theoretically predicted by orienting the polymer molecules on glass fibers (DePaula and Moore, 1984; Jarzynski, 1984), but this has yet to be practically demonstrated.

More recently, even higher frequency phase modulators, which use a piezoelectric thin film directly deposited on a short section of fiber (a few millimeters) have been studied (Heffner et al., 1986; Godil et al., 1988). The preferred choice of piezoelectric material is a thin film of oriented zinc oxide (ZnO). With a transducer film thickness of 5.5 μm and an interaction length of 3 mm, relatively broadband operation near 450 MHz modulation has been achieved with up to 2 rad of modulation amplitude for 2 W of input electrical power (Godil et al., 1988). The maximum available phase modulation amplitude was again limited by thermal dissipation and the short interaction length. The fundamental upper frequency limit is determined by the condition that half the acoustic wavelength in the fiber should be longer than the diameter of the optical mode. This corresponds to about 600 MHz for a typical mode size of 5 μm. Deposition of a ZnO film with the proper orientation on a cylindrical surface is one of the major difficulties of this technology. In the particular implementations mentioned above (Heffner et al., 1986; Godil et al., 1988) the oriented ZnO film transducer covered only a portion of the fiber circumference. As a result, this device exhibited a dependence on input polarization by a factor of about 2.5 in the relative phase modulation of the two orthogonal polarization modes.

High frequency phase modulators are still in their development stage and it may be important to make a comparison with electro-optic phase modulators, which are already well developed. Integrated optic channel waveguide modulators utilizing the electro-optic effect in materials such as $LiNbO_3$ exhibit a uniform response over an extremely wide range of modulation frequencies, with adequate modulation amplitude for moderate driving voltage (typically of the order of 10 V for a 2π phase modulation in $LiNbO_3$). For applications requiring high frequency and/or very broadband phase modulations, no fiber optic version of this device is currently available. However, in comparison with integrated optic $LiNbO_3$ modulators, the potentially important features of fiber optic phase modulators include negligible optical losses, much higher optical power-handling capabilities and trivial integration into single-mode fiber optic systems. Further research is needed in this area.

7.7 Frequency shifters

Single-sideband frequency shifters are used in fiber optic sensors and signal processing for heterodyne detection and switching. One of the special applications of fiber optic frequency shifters that justifies close attention is closed-loop operation of fiber gyroscopes. Bulk optic frequency shifters such as standard Bragg cells are difficult to implement in fiber optic circuits because they are difficult to align and lack mechanical stability. The frequency shifters discussed here will be limited to the types that keep the optical wave guided in the fiber.

The parameters of importance for frequency shifters vary depending on the application. For gyroscope applications, a high suppression of carrier and image sideband (better than 60 dB for inertial navigation) and a frequency tuning range of 1–2 MHz are required. For optical switching applications, a fast switching speed and a high on–off ratio are desirable. In all cases a high conversion efficiency is a necessary requirement for a practical frequency shifter.

7.7.1 Principles

In a standard Bragg cell a traveling acoustic wave forms a moving refractive index grating in a crystal induced by the elasto-optic effect. Light of frequency ω_0 passing through this region at a specified angle with respect to the acoustic wave propagation direction is diffracted by this index grating, as shown in Fig. 7.10(a). At the same time its frequency is shifted by the acoustic frequency ω_a. The angle of diffraction θ from the incident angle is determined by the optical and acoustic wavelengths λ_0 and λ_a via the relationship $\sin \theta = \lambda_0/2\lambda_a$. An angle-dependent spatial filter can be used to separate the diffracted beam from the original carrier, and this device operates as a single-sideband frequency shifter. The typical operating frequency range is 40–1000 MHz.

In optical fibers a similar acousto-optic interaction can be achieved, with the additional requirement that the carrier at frequency ω_0 and the shifted wave at frequency $\omega_0 + \omega_a$ or $\omega_0 - \omega_a$ must be guided modes of the fiber. The acoustic wavelength λ_a must satisfy the relationship $\Delta\beta = 2\pi/\lambda_a$, where $\Delta\beta$ is the difference in propagation constant between the carrier and the frequency-shifted modes. This condition uniquely specifies the acoustic frequency $\omega_a = 2\pi v_a/\lambda_a$ (v_a is the acoustic wave velocity) and the frequency shift. The two types of mode used for this purpose have been either the two orthogonal

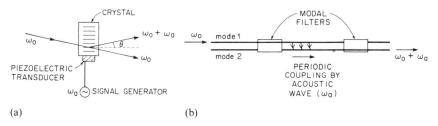

Fig. 7.10 Principle of acousto-optic frequency shifting (a) in a bulk optic form (Bragg cell) and (b) in an optical fiber.

polarization modes of HB fibers or the two transverse spatial modes (LP_{01} and LP_{11} modes) of two-mode fibers.

Figure 7.10(b) shows schematically the operation of a fiber frequency shifter. The optical wave excited in mode 1 interacts with the traveling acoustic wave and is coupled to mode 2 as its frequency is shifted by the acoustic frequency. The first modal filter ensures that any initial energy in mode 2 does not enter the interaction region. Further down the fiber, the frequency-shifted component resides in mode 2 and is separated from mode 1, which carries the original unshifted frequency component, by the second modal filter. When the acoustic wave is traveling in the same direction as the optical wave, optical coupling from the fast mode (smaller propagation constant) to the slow mode (larger propagation constant) results in a frequency up-shift. A frequency down-shift occurs either when coupling from the slow mode to the fast mode or when reversing the propagation direction of the acoustic wave.

The tuning range $\Delta\omega_a$ of the acoustic frequency, and thus of the frequency shift, around the optimum value ($\omega_a = v_a \Delta\beta$) is limited by either that of the acoustic transducer or the number N of acoustic wavelengths in the interaction length ($\Delta\omega_a/\omega_a < 1/N$). The switching speed is limited by the transit time of the acoustic wave through the interaction length.

7.7.2 Birefringent fiber frequency shifters

When a birefringent fiber is under lateral stress in a direction other than that of its birefringent axis, optical power coupling takes place between the two original normal polarization modes owing to the additional stress-induced birefringence. Efficient optical power coupling can be achieved by separating the stress (or coupling) points by one polarization mode beat length (typically 1–2 mm), in which case coherent addition of coupled optical power occurs. This form of static polarization coupling has been achieved by applying a periodic lateral pressure at an angle of 45° with respect to the fast and slow axes of a birefringent fiber (Youngquist et al., 1983). The same principle can be applied for frequency shifter applications provided that this periodic pressure pattern is propagating along the fiber.

A particular approach consisted in using an array of piezoelectric transducers oscillating at the same frequency and with a proper relative phase to simulate a traveling acoustic wave (Nosu et al., 1983a). This device required a fiber with a long beat length and exhibited poor carrier suppression. Another implementation involved interaction between the fiber and a surface or bulk acoustic wave generated on a fused quartz substrate (Risk et al., 1984) as shown in Fig. 7.11. The fiber is sandwiched between a surface acoustic wave substrate and a silicon backing plate. The acoustic wave travels on the substrate and exerts a propagating pressure wave on the fiber. The operational frequency is adjustable over a wide range by forming an angle between the propagation direction of the acoustic wave and the fiber axis (Tarng and Chang, 1985; Risk et al., 1986; Chen, 1987) or by using a ridge backing with a period shorter than the beat length (Risk and Kino, 1986). An optical coupling efficiency of about 4% per watt of electrical input power (a 95% maximum conversion in pulsed operation) at 4.4 MHz was demonstrated in a device with a polarization beat length of 1.7 mm and an interaction length of 32 mm (Risk et al., 1986). Suppression of spurious frequency components was about 25–35 dB. Another example used an acoustic shear wave at 245 MHz and produced a coupling efficiency of $7\% \, \mathrm{W}^{-1}$ (a maximum of 35% conversion in continuous-wave (CW) operation) and a bandwidth of 20 MHz (Tarng and Chang, 1985). The conversion efficiency of these devices is currently limited by thermal dissipation.

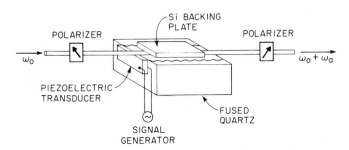

Fig. 7.11   Birefringent fiber frequency shifter using either bulk or surface acoustic waves to induce polarization coupling at a shifted frequency.

The suppression of the carrier and image sidebands is determined by several parameters, including the coupling efficiency, the alignment of the axes of the input and output polarization filters with respect to the fiber birefringence axes, and the extinction ratios of the filters. For example, in order to achieve a 40 dB suppression in the case of 50% coupling efficiency, the accuracy of the angular alignment of each polarizer should be better than 0.6°. Another limiting factor is the static pressure applied to the fiber which induces polarization coupling (without change in frequency) and gives rise to unwanted frequency components, in particular at the carrier frequency and at the frequency of the unwanted sideband (e.g. $\omega_o - \omega_a$ for frequency up-conversion).

7.7.3 Two-mode fiber frequency shifter

In the two-mode fiber optic frequency shifter the coupled modes are the LP_{01} and LP_{11} fiber modes (typical beat length, 50–500 µm) (Blake *et al.*, 1986a; Kim *et al.*, 1986), and the mode-coupling mechanism is the periodic bending of the fiber provided by a traveling acoustic flexural wave (Taylor, 1984; Blake *et al.*, 1986b, 1987). A schematic diagram of the device is shown in Fig. 7.12(a). The flexural acoustic wave is excited by a PZT transducer through a vitreous silica acoustic horn whose thin end is bonded to the optical fiber and produces a vibration orthogonal to the fiber axes.

The all-fiber configuration of this frequency shifter involves two different modal filters which transmit either only the LP_{01} mode or only the LP_{11} mode (Fig. 7.12(b)). An LP_{01} transmission filter is realized by simply coiling the two-mode fiber with a small bend radius to induce a large bending loss for the LP_{11} mode and no significant loss for the fundamental mode. The LP_{11} mode transmission filter can be a directional coupler involving a two-mode fiber and a single-mode fiber, which provides unity coupling of the LP_{11} mode to the single-mode fiber yet negligible coupling of the LP_{01} mode (Sorin *et al.*, 1986). The requirement for these two conditions to be met is that the propagation constant of the guided mode in the single-mode fiber must equal that of the LP_{11} mode in the two-mode fiber. Alternative configurations for the modal filters include a symmetric bitaper as a second-order mode stripper, and an intermodal coupler (Blake *et al.*, 1986b) followed by an LP_{01} transmission filter as a fundamental mode stripper. A high mode selectivity is essential for high suppression of the carrier and the image sideband. Also, the use of a two-mode fiber with a highly elliptical core to improve the LP_{11} mode stability has been proposed (Kim *et al.*, 1987).

A near-unity coupling efficiency at 8 MHz with a 35 dB suppression of both the carrier and the image sideband has been demonstrated using 100 mW electrical input power and an interaction length of 7.5 cm (Blake *et al.*, 1986a;

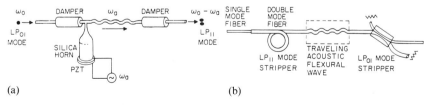

(a)   (b)

Fig. 7.12 Two-mode fiber frequency shifter: (a) schematic diagram of the frequency shifter principle showing the acoustic horn transducer with respect to the optical fiber; (b) general diagram showing the input and output mode filters.

Kim *et al.*, 1986). A much longer interaction length is possible since the acoustic wave is guided in the fiber without experiencing significant loss. The acousto-optic interaction is very efficient because of the confinement of acoustic energy in a very small region. Compared with the birefringent fiber devices, the two-mode frequency shifter does not require extremely accurate angular alignments. The requirement now resides in the modal filters which must exhibit a mode selectivity higher than currently demonstrated (about 25–30 dB (Sorin *et al.*, 1986)) to achieve better suppression of spurious frequency components.

7.7.4 Serrodyne frequency shifter

Another type of fiber frequency shifter, called a serrodyne frequency shifter, is based on phase modulation with a time-dependent sawtooth waveform. When a phase ramp $\varphi = at$ is applied to an optical wave $A \exp(\omega t)$, the frequency of the output optical wave $A \exp\{(\omega + a)t\}$ is changed by the slope a of the phase ramp. This effect can be achieved in practice by periodically resetting the applied phase ramp by 2π (sawtooth modulation). The frequency of the applied phase modulation corresponds to the frequency shift. Since the waveform contains many harmonic frequency components, this type of frequency shifter requires a phase modulator with a uniform response over a wide frequency range. This requirement makes electro-optic modulators a logical choice. However, for small frequency shifts (less than 100 kHz) the PZT cylinder fiber optic phase modulator described in the previous section of this chapter could be used with additional mechanisms to damp the mechanical ringing caused by the rapid reset of the waveform (Dakin *et al.*, 1985). This also allows the use of feedback control to ensure that the PZT dimensional changes follow the sawtooth drive waveform.

7.8 Amplifiers and sources

Fiber amplifiers and sources have been investigated for some time for a broad range of telecommunications and sensor applications. Amplifiers are desirable to provide signal enhancement in recirculating fiber gyroscopes. Both narrowband and broadband fiber sources would find applications in fiber sensors. Miniature versions of these devices already exist in the form of semiconductor laser diodes and superluminescent diodes. However, because of mode mismatch and astigmatism they generally couple poorly to single-mode fibers and consequently provide marginal power to the fiber or poor optical gain to the signal. In contrast, a fiber source or amplifier can be perfectly mode matched and permanently attached to the system fiber, thereby offering optimum performance and improved mechanical stability. Also, a fiber amplifier can be optically pumped from a remote location through one end of the fiber circuit without involving additional electrical connections as for semiconductor amplifiers.

Single-mode fiber sources and amplifiers may rely on any of essentially three different physical processes: amplification by active ions (e.g. a rare earth) incorporated in the fiber core material, nonlinear optical processes in conventional fiber materials, and evanescent coupling to an active material (a layer of laser dye). In all cases the fiber is end-pumped with an optical beam with energy and wavelength characteristics dependent on the process used. As in any active waveguide device, for a given pump power the gain increases with the degree of confinement of the interacting waves, i.e. essentially as the reciprocal of the fiber core area (Digonnet and Gaeta, 1985). Consequently large gains (in amplifiers) and low thresholds (in oscillators) can be accomplished in fibers with minimal excitation energy.

7.8.1 Nonlinear amplifiers and sources

The two nonlinear processes most widely used to form optically pumped amplifiers are Raman and Brillouin stimulated scattering (SRS and SBS) (Stolen, 1980). Other optical parametric processes such as stimulated four-photon mixing can be very useful for light amplification, but for conciseness we refer the reader to Stolen (1980) for further details. SRS is a process by which a pump photon is scattered by optical phonons associated with vibration modes of the host matrix, generating a spontaneous photon at a frequency down-shifted by an amount corresponding to the phonon energy. Stimulated emission forms the basis for optical amplification in both directions with respect to the pump. In silica SRS produces a broad gain curve (FWHM, about $300 \, \text{cm}^{-1}$) centered about $450 \, \text{cm}^{-1}$ from the pump frequency (Stolen, 1980). One of the appeals of this mechanism is that the gain center wavelength can be tuned by adjusting the pump frequency. The Raman gain factor at line center is of the order of $10 \, \text{dB} \, \text{W}^{-1} \, \text{km}^{-1}$ in a single-mode silica fiber near 1 μm (Stolen, 1980; Desurvire et al., 1983).

A wide range of fiber Raman amplifiers has been investigated both theoretically and experimentally. Large gains have been observed at moderately high pump levels (45 dB near 1.24 μm with a 2 W peak power pump (Desurvire et al., 1983)). Fiber oscillators have also been produced in a variety of configurations with relatively low thresholds (Stolen, 1980). The addition of dopants can potentially contribute to increasing the gain (e.g. germanium (Lin et al., 1977)) or increasing the Raman shift to attain longer operating wavelengths (e.g. hydrogen or deuterium (Chraplyvy et al., 1983)). However, the large Raman bandwidth inevitably means a low gain per unit pump power, so that all applications reported to date suffer from high pump power requirements.

In contrast, SBS is characterized by a narrow linewidth and the highest gains of all the nonlinear processes occurring in silica fibers, approximately

300 times that of the Raman process (Stolen, 1980). SBS has produced submilliwatt threshold oscillators in fiber ring resonators involving a single-frequency pump laser (Stokes et al., 1982). For SBS to be practical a stringent pump frequency stability is required, and this has so far limited its practical application in optical fibers.

7.8.2 Evanescent field amplifiers

The basic concept of evanescent field amplification involves placing an active material in the evanescent field of the guided mode of a single-mode fiber. In the only device of this kind reported to date, a polished fiber substrate was used to gain access to the fiber mode and a drop of laser dye solution was placed on top of it (Lamouroux et al., 1983; Sorin et al., 1983). The dye was excited by an argon ion laser end-coupled to the fiber. The solution refractive index was adjusted by proper selection of solvent to be slightly below the effective mode index and to optimize the penetration of the evanescent fields into the active medium. A net gain of about 13 dB was observed at 633 nm (Lamouroux et al., 1983; Sorin et al., 1983). However, the gain and intrinsic attenuation of these devices are very sensitive to the index of the dye solution (Lamouroux et al., 1983), and consequently to the temperature and possibly to pump-induced heating. A solid amplifying medium would certainly reduce this sensitivity, but most solid gain media are poorly index matched to the silica fiber. These devices have therefore not shown much practical promise so far, and the direct incorporation of amplifying dopants into the core, which is described in the next section, appears to be a more attractive alternative.

7.8.3 Rare-earth-doped fibers

The potential of rare-earth-doped fibers was first demonstrated with a neodymium-doped glass fiber amplifier (Koester and Snitzer, 1964). In this early implementation the fiber was wound around a flashlamp and produced a very large net single-pass gain of 65 dB. Only in recent years has this principle been applied to modern single-mode fiber technology (Poole et al., 1985). Work has focused so far on dopants from the lanthanide series, in particular neodymium and erbium ions, which provide gain and oscillation in the 0.9, 1.06, 1.4 μm and 1.55 μm ranges respectively. Dopant incorporation to the core of a few hundreds of parts per million using a standard modified chemical vapor deposition technique results in very low additional loss at these laser wavelengths (Poole et al., 1985). The inherently low solubility of these ions in silica can be overcome by co-doping. It has produced more heavily doped fibers with similar loss characteristics at these laser wavelengths, e.g. with up to 1 wt% Nd_2O_3 (Po et al., 1986), for shorter and compact devices.

In its simplest form, a fiber oscillator is composed of a strand of fiber (a few centimeters to a few meters) with its ends either butt-coupled to external

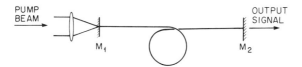

Fig. 7.13   Basic schematic diagram of an optically end-pumped fiber laser: M_1, high reflector at the laser wavelength; M_2, output coupler.

reflectors or directly coated with high reflectors (Fig. 7.13). This structure is optically end-pumped by an optical beam focused into the fiber through one of the reflectors. It has been demonstrated with both types of ions in a variety of configurations and pump sources including krypton ion lasers (Po *et al.*, 1986), dye lasers (Alcock *et al.*, 1986) and laser diodes (Jauncey *et al.*, 1986; Po *et al.*, 1986). Nd:silica fiber lasers were brought to oscillation with as little as 90 μW of absorbed pump power (Po *et al.*, 1986). Sub-angstrom output bandwidths were reported with external reflectors made of a narrowband fiber grating filter (Jauncey *et al.*, 1986). Wavelength tunability (over 80 nm with neodymium and 25 nm with erbium (Reekie *et al.*, 1986)) and Q-switching (Alcock *et al.*, 1986; Mears *et al.*, 1986) were also accomplished by incorporating bulk optic components in the cavity. Novel devices making use of the fiber geometry were also reported, in particular ring resonator lasers (Reekie *et al.*, 1986) and lasers with end-reflectors made of a reciprocal fiber loop (Miller *et al.*, 1987). Fiber lasers can produce several milliwatts of output power in the low loss wavelength windows of silica fibers, and offer improved wavelength stability with temperature compared with semiconductor sources. The pump bands of Er^{3+} and Nd^{3+} in the silica host are sufficiently broad that the fiber laser output power is relatively insensitive to the pump wavelength, which is of interest when pumping with an inherently temperature-sensitive laser diode.

Nd:silica fibers exhibit a gain near 1.06 μm of the order of 0.47 dB per milliwatt of absorbed pump power (Po *et al.*, 1986). This value is sufficient for amplifier applications requiring a few decibels of gain with only a few milliwatts of pump power, as is readily available from a single-stripe laser diode. The availability of high gains at relatively low pump levels was used to create a high probability of stimulated emission and reach the onset of superfluorescence in a fiber (Po *et al.*, 1986; Liu *et al.*, 1987). Recently up to 10 mW of 1060 nm superfluorescent signal was generated in a neodymium-doped fiber end-pumped near 820 nm with a CW dye laser (Liu *et al.*, 1987). The large bandwidth (about 17 nm) and potentially high temperature stability of the output make this new source particularly suitable for fiber gyroscopes.

7.9 Conclusions

As pointed out in Section 7.1, this account was not intended to be exhaustive and many devices have not been mentioned. However, the reader will have realized that a surprisingly large number of components, based on a wide range of physical principles, have been developed over a period of less than 10 years. Because of the high quality of the fiber as a waveguiding structure, the performance frequently significantly exceeds that of the bulk optic or integrated optic counterparts. Many of these devices, in particular fused and polished couplers, bending-induced polarizers, absorption filters, amplifiers and sources made of rare-earth-doped fibers, have been commercially available for some time. This availability has dramatically increased the rate of development of all-fiber sensors.

However, at this point in time further efforts are needed in the area of active fiber components. For example, several applications would benefit greatly from the availability of switchable couplers or fast light modulators. Several encouraging attempts have been made in this direction, but they have been inherently limited by the passive nature of the fiber material. As discussed in Sections 7.6 and 7.7, further work is also needed to develop broadband phase modulators and high carrier suppression frequency shifters.

Some of the answers to these requirements may well be provided by improvements in existing technologies. Of particular importance to this effort, as well as to the field of passive components, is what may be called the polished fiber substrate technology. This technology has emerged as a powerful tool to perform a large number of basic functions within the fiber by providing controlled access to its core and hence to the guided wave. It offers a geometry closely related to that of integrated optics circuits and has produced to date an impressive range of devices, often making use of developments in integrated optics components. Because it minimizes the physical perturbation of the core environment, it has led, where applicable, to some of the finest devices demonstrated to date. Its possibilities are far from being exhausted, especially in the area of evanescent interaction with selected materials to produce active components. Also noteworthy is the development of selectively doped fibers, in particular rare-earth-doped silica fibers. This ongoing effort is extending the range of the otherwise rather limited active properties of silica fibers and broadening the spectrum of potential passive and active components.

Appendix

Definition of selected technical terms

To avoid possible confusion in terminology, the definitions of some of the terms used in the text are presented below.

Coupling ratio In a fiber coupler, the coupling ratio is the ratio of coupled output power to the sum of the coupled power and throughput power. In a lossless coupler it is also the ratio of coupled power to input power.

Directivity   In a fiber coupler, the directivity is the ratio of output power at the fourth port to the total (coupled plus throughput) output power (or input power for a lossless coupler).

Extinction ratio   In a polarizer, the extinction ratio is the ratio of transmitted power for the rejected input polarization to the transmitted power for the preferred (or transmitted) input polarization. In a fiber coupler, it characterizes the maximum achievable coupling ratio; it is defined as the ratio of residual throughput signal when the coupler is in the fully coupled state to the total (throughput and coupled) output power.

Isolation   In a fiber coupler, isolation refers to the degree of polarization of the output signal (either throughput or coupled) relative to a linear input polarization.

Rejection ratio   In a fiber filter, the rejection ratio is the ratio of the transmitted power at the rejected wavelength to the transmitted power at the (nearest) peak transmission wavelength.

References

Alcock, I. P., Tropper, A. C., Ferguson, A. I. and Hanna, D. C. (1986). Q-switched operation of a neodymium-doped monomode fibre laser, *Electron. Lett.*, **22** (2), 84–85.

Beasley, J. D., Moore, D. R. and Stowe, D. W. (1983). Evanescent-wave fiber-optic couplers: three methods, *Proc. Optical Fibers Conf. '83, February 1983*, Paper ML5, Optical Society of America, Washington, DC.

Bennion, I., Reid, D. C. J., Rower, C. J. and Stewart, W. J. (1986). High reflectivity monomode-fibre grating filters, *Electron. Lett.*, **22**, 341–343.

Bergh, R. A. (1983). All-fiber gyroscope with optical-Kerr-effect compensation, *Ph.D. Thesis*, Stanford University.

Bergh, R. A., Kotler, G. and Shaw, H. J. (1980a). Single-mode fiber-optic directional coupler, *Electron. Lett.*, **16**, 260–261.

Bergh, R. A., Lefèvre, H. C. and Shaw, H. J. (1980b). Single-mode fiber-optic polarizer, *Opt. Lett.*, **5**, 479–481.

Bergh, R. A., Lefèvre H. C. and Shaw, H. J. (1981). All-single-mode fiber-optic gyroscope with long term stability, *Opt. Lett.*, **6** (10), 502–504.

Bilodeau, F., Hill, K. O., Johnson, D. C. and Faucher, S. (1987). Compact, low loss, fused biconical taper couplers: overcoupled operation and antisymmetric super-mode cutoff, *Opt. Lett.*, **12** (8), 634–636.

Blake, J. N., Kim, B. Y., Engan, H. E. and Shaw, H. J. (1986a). All-fiber acousto-optic frequency shifter using two-mode fiber, *Proc. SPIE*, **719**, 92–100.

Blake, J. N., Kim, B. Y. and Shaw, H. J. (1986b). Fiber-optic modal coupler using periodic microbending, *Opt. Lett.*, **11**, 177–179.

Blake, J. N., Kim, B. Y., Engan, H. E. and Shaw, H. J. (1987). Analysis of intermodal coupling in a two-mode fiber with periodic microbends, *Opt. Lett.*, **12**, 281–283.

Böhm, K., Marten, P., Petermann, K., Weidel, E. and Ulrich, R. (1981). Low-drift fibre gyro using a superluminescent diode, *Electron. Lett.*, **17** (10), 352–353.

Böhm, K., Petermann, K. and Weidel, E. (1983). Performance of Lyot depolarizers with birefringent single-mode fibers, *IEEE J. Lightwave Technol.*, **1**, 71–74.

Boucouvalas, A. C. and Georgiou, G. (1985). Biconical taper coaxial coupler filter, *Electron. Lett.*, **21** (22), 1033–1034.

Boucouvalas, A. C. and Georgiou, G. (1987). Methods for fine-tuning the wavelength response of single-mode optical-fibre taper filters, *Electron. Lett.*, **23** (8), 410–411.

Bricheno, T. and Fielding, A. (1984). Stable low-loss single-mode couplers, *Electron. Lett.*, **20** (6), 230–232.

Brinkmeyer, E., Brennecke, W., Zürn, M. and Ulrich, R. (1986). Fibre Bragg reflector for mode selection and line-narrowing of injection lasers, *Electron. Lett.*, **22**, 134–135.

Bures, J., Lacroix, S. and Lapierre, J. (1983). Analyse d'un coupleur bidirectionnel à fibres optiques monomodes fusionnées, *Appl. Opt.*, **22**, 1918–1922.

Carome, E. F. and Adamovski, G. (1981). High kilohertz frequency fiber optic phase modulators. In Ezekiel, S. and Arditty, H. J. (eds), *Fiber-optic Rotation Sensors and Related Technologies*, pp. 157–162, Springer, Berlin.

Carrara, S. L. A., Kim, B. Y. and Shaw, H. J. (1986). Elasto-optic alignment of birefringent axes in polarization-holding optical fiber, *Opt. Lett.*, **11** (7), 470–472.

Chen, W-H. (1987). Fiber-optic frequency shifter using a grating acoustic scanner, *Opt. Lett.*, **12**, 930–932.

Chraplyvy, A. R., Stone, J. and Burrus, C. A. (1983). Optical gain exceeding 35 dB at 1.56 μm due to stimulated Raman scattering by molecular D_2 in a solid silica optical fiber, *Opt. Lett.*, **8**, 415–417.

Dakin, J. P., Wade, C. A. and Haji-Michael, C. (1985). A fiber optic serrodyne frequency translator based on a piezoelectrically-strained fiber phase shifter, *Proc. Inst. Electr. Eng.*, **132**, 287–290.

Davies, D. E. N. and Kingsley, S. (1974). Method of phase-modulating signals in optical fibers: application to optical-telemetry systems, *Electron. Lett.*, **10**, 21–22.

DePaula, R. P. and Moore, E. L. (1984). Review of all-fiber phase and polarization modulators, *Proc. SPIE*, **478**, 3–11.

Desurvire, E., Papuchon, M., Pocholle, J. P., Raffy, J. and Ostrowsky, D. B. (1983). High-gain optical amplification of laser diode signal by Raman scattering in single-mode fibres, *Electron. Lett.*, **19**, 751–753.

Desurvire, E., Digonnet, M. J. F. and Shaw, H. J. (1985). Raman amplification of recirculating pulses in a reentrant fiber loop, *Opt. Lett.*, **10** (2), 83–85.

Desurvire, E., Kim, B. Y., Fesler, K. and Shaw, H. J. (1988). Reentrant fiber Raman gyro, *IEEE J. Lightwave Technol.*, **6** (4), 481–491.

Digonnet, M. J. F. and Gaeta, C. J. (1985). Theoretical analysis of optical fiber laser amplifiers and oscillators, *Appl. Opt.*, **24** (3), 333–342.

Digonnet, M. J. F. and Shaw, H. J. (1982). Analysis of a tunable single-mode optical fiber coupler, *IEEE J. Quantum Electron.*, **18**, 746–754.

Digonnet, M. and Shaw, H. J. (1983). Wavelength multiplexing in single-mode fiber couplers, *Appl. Opt.*, **22** (3), 484–491.

Digonnet, M. J. F., Feth, J. R., Stokes, L. F. and Shaw, H. J. (1985). Measurement of the core proximity in polished fiber substrates and couplers, *Opt. Lett.*, **10** (9), 463–465.

Donalds, L. J., French, W. G., Mitchell, W. C., Swinehart, R. M. and Wei, T. (1982). Electric field sensitive optical fiber using piezoelectric polymer coating, *Electron. Lett.*, **18**, 327–328.

Dyott, R. B. and Bello, J. (1983). Polarisation-holding directional coupler made from elliptically cored fibre having a D section, *Electron. Lett.*, **19**, 601.

Dyott, R. B., Bello, J. and Handerek, V. A. (1987). Indium-coated D-shaped-fiber polarizer, *Opt. Lett.*, **12** (4), 287–289.

Eickhoff, W. (1980). In-line fiber-optic polariser, *Electron. Lett.*, **16**, 762–764.

Engineering Databook, Vernitron Piezoelectric Division, 232 Forbes Road, Bedford, OH 44146.

Eyges, L. and Wintersteiner, P. (1981). Modes of an array of dielectric waveguides, *J. Opt. Soc. Am.*, **71** (11), 1351–1360.

Farries, M. C., Townsend, J. E. and Poole, S. B. (1986). Very high-reflection optical fibre filters, *Electron. Lett.*, **22** (21), 1126–1128.

Feit, M. D. and Fleck, J. A., Jr. (1981). Propagating beam theory of optical fiber cross coupling, *J. Opt. Soc. Am.*, **71** (11) 1361–1372.

Feth, J. R. and Chang, C. L. (1986). Metal-clad fiber-optic cutoff polarizer, *Opt. Lett.*, **11** (6), 386–388.

Fredericks, R. J. and Ulrich, R. (1984). Phase error bounds of fibre gyro with imperfect polariser/depolariser, *Electron. Lett.*, **20** (8), 330–332.

Georgiou, G. and Boucouvalas, A. C. (1986). High-isolation single-mode-wavelength division multiplexer/demultiplexer, *Electron. Lett.*, **22** (2), 62–63.

Godil, A. A., Patterson, D. B., Heffner, B. L., Kino, G. S. and Khuri-Yakub, B. T. (1988). All-fiber acousto-optic phase modulators using zinc oxide films on glass fiber, *5th Int. Conf. on Optical Fiber Sensors, New Orleans, LA, January 1988*, Paper ThBB4, Optical Society of America, Washington, DC.

Gruchmann, D., Petermann, K., Staudigel, L. and Weidel, E. (1983). Fiber-optic polarizers with high extinction ratio, *Proc. 9th European Conf. on Optical Communications*, p. 305, Elsevier, Amsterdam.

Heffner, B. L., Risk, W. P., Khuri-Yakub, B. T. and Kino, G. S. (1986). Deposition of piezoelectric films on single-mode fibers and applications to fiber modulators, *IEEE Ultrasonics Symp. Proc.*, pp. 709–713, IEEE, New York.

Imai, M., Shimizu, T., Ohtsuka, Y. and Odajima, A. (1987). An electric-field-sensitive fiber with coaxial electrodes for optical phase modulation, *IEEE J. Lightwave Technol.*, **5**, 926–931.

Jackson, D. A., Priest, R., Dandridge, A. and Tveten, A. B. (1980). Elimination of drift in a single-mode optical fiber interferometer using a piezoelectrically stretched coiled fiber, *Appl. Opt.*, **19**, 2926–2929.

Jarzynski, J. (1984). Frequency response of a single-mode optical fiber phase modulator utilizing a piezoelectric plastic jacket, *J. Appl. Phys.*, **55**, 3243–3250, and references cited therein.

Jauncey, I. M., Reekie, L., Mears, R. J., Payne, D. N., Rowe, C. J., Reid, D. C. J. and Edge, C. (1986). Narrow-linewidth fibre laser with integral fibre grating, *Electron. Lett.*, **22**, 987–988.

Johnson, M. (1979). In-line fiber-optical polarization transformer, *Appl. Opt.*, **18** (9), 1288–1289.

Kawachi, M., Kawasaki, B. S., Hill, K. O. and Edahiro, T. (1982). Fabrication of single-polarization single-mode-fibre couplers, *Electron. Lett.*, **18** (22), 962–964.

Kawasaki, B. S., Hill, K. O. and Lamont, R. G. (1981). Biconical-taper single-mode fiber coupler, *Opt. Lett.*, **6**, 327–328.

Kersey, A. D. and Dandridge, A. (1987). Monomode fibre polarisation scrambler, *Electron. Lett.*, **23** (12), 634–636.

Kim, B. Y., Blake, J. N., Engan, H. E. and Shaw, H. J. (1986). All-fiber acousto-optic frequency shifter, *Opt. Lett.*, **11**, 389–391.

Kim, B. Y., Blake, J. N., Huang, S. Y. and Shaw, H. J. (1987). Use of highly elliptical core fibers for two-mode fiber devices, *Opt. Lett.*, **12**, 729–731.

Kingsley, S. A. (1975). Optical-fiber phase modulator, *Electron. Lett.*, **11**, 453–454.

Kingsley, S. A. (1978). Fiberdyne systems for passive or semipassive fiber-optic sensors, *Electron. Lett.*, **14**, 419–422.

Koester, C. J. and Snitzer, E. (1964). Amplification in a fiber laser, *Appl. Opt.*, **3** (10), 1182–1186.

Koo, K., Tran, D. C., Sheem, S. K., Villarruel, C. A. and Moeller, R. P. (1981). *Proc. Integrated Optics and Optical Fiber Communication, April 1981*, Paper TUJ-2, Optical Society of America, Washington, DC.

Lacroix, S., Gonthier, F. and Bures, J. (1986). All-fiber wavelength filter from successive biconical tapers, *Opt. Lett.*, **11**, 671–673.

Lamont, R. G., Johnson, D. C. and Hill, K. O. (1985). Power transfer in fused biconical-taper single-mode fiber couplers: dependence on external refractive index, *Appl. Opt.*, **24**, 327–332.

Lamouroux, B. F., Orszag, A. G., Prade, B. S. and Vinet, J. Y. (1983). Continuous laser amplification in a monomode fiber longitudinally pumped by evanescent field coupling, *Opt. Lett.*, **8**, 504–505.

Lefèvre, H. C. (1980). Single-mode fiber fractional wave devices and polarisation controllers, *Electron. Lett.*, **16** (20), 778–780.

Leminger, O. and Zengerle, R. (1987). Determination of the variable core-to-surface spacing of single-mode fiber-coupler blocks, *Opt. Lett.*, **12** (3), 211–213.

Liao, F. J. and Boyd, J. T. (1981). Single-mode fiber coupler, *Appl. Opt.*, **20** (15), 2731–2734.

Lin, C., Cohen, L. G., Stolen, R. H., Tasker, G. W. and French, W. G. (1977). Near infrared sources in the 1–1.3 µm region by efficient stimulated Raman emission in glass fibers, *Opt. Commun.*, **20**, 426–428.

Liu, K., Digonnet, M., Shaw, H. J., Ainslie, B. J. and Craig, S. P. (1987). 10 mW superfluorescent single-mode fiber source at 1060 nm, *Electron. Lett.*, **23**, 1320–1321.

Marcuse, D. (1971). The coupling of degenerate modes in two parallel dielectric waveguides, *Bell. Syst. Tech. J.*, **50**, 1791–1816.

Martini, G. (1987). Analysis of a single-mode optical fiber piezoceramic phase modulator, *Opt. Quantum Electron.*, **19**, 179–190.

Matsumoto, T. and Kano, H. (1986). Endlessly rotatable fractional-wave devices for single-mode-fibre optics, *Electron. Lett.*, **22** (2), 78–79.

McIntyre, P. D. and Snyder, A. W. (1973). Power transfer between optical fibers, *J. Opt. Soc. Am.*, **63** (12), 1518–1527.

Mears, R. J., Reekie, L., Poole, S. B. and Payne, D. N. (1986). Low-threshold tunable CW and Q-switched fibre laser operating at 1.55 µm, *Electron. Lett.*, **22**, 159–160.

Meltz, G., Dunphy, J. R., Morey, W. W. and Snitzer, E. (1983). Cross-talk fiber-optic temperature sensor, *Appl. Opt.*, **22**, 464–477.

Miller, I. D., Mortimore, D. B. Urquhart, P., Ainslie, B. J., Craig, S. P., Millar, C. A. and Payne, D. B. (1987). A Nd^{3+}-doped CW fiber laser using all-fiber reflectors, *Appl. Opt.*, **26**, 2197–2201.

Murakami, Y. and Sudo, S. (1981). Coupling characteristics measurements between curved waveguides using a two-core fiber coupler, *Appl. Opt.*, **20** (3), 417–422.

Nayar, B. K. and Smith, D. R. (1983). Monomode-polarization-maintaining fiber directional couplers, *Opt. Lett.*, **8**, 543–545.

Nosu, K., Rashleigh, S. C., Taylor, H. F. and Weller, J. F. (1983a). Acousto-optic frequency shifter for single-mode fibers, *Electron. Lett.*, **19**, 816–818.

Nosu, K., Taylor, H. F., Rashleigh, S. C. and Weller, J. F. (1983b). Acousto-optic phase modulator for single-mode fibers, *Electron. Lett.*, **19**, 605–607.

Okoshi, T. (1985). Polarization-state control schemes for heterodyne or homodyne optical fiber communications, *IEEE J. Lightwave Technol.*, **3** (6), 1232–1237.

Park, C. A., Rowe, C. J., Buus, J., Reid, D. C. J., Carter, A. and Bennion, I. (1986).

Single-mode behaviour of a multimode 1.55 µm laser with a fibre grating external cavity, *Electron. Lett.*, **22**, 1132–1134.

Parriaux, O., Bernoux, F. and Chartier, G. (1981a). Wavelength selective distributed coupling between single mode optical fibers for multiplexing, *J. Opt. Commun.*, **2**, 105–109.

Parriaux, O., Gidon, S. and Cochet, F. (1981b). Fiber-optic polarizer using plasmon-guided wave resonance, *European Conf. on Optical Communications, September 1981*, Paper P6, Peter Peregrinus, Stevenage, UK.

Parriaux, O., Gidon, S. and Kuznetsov, A. A. (1981c). Distributed coupling on polished single-mode optical fibers, *Appl. Opt.*, **20**, 2420–2423.

Payne, F. P., Finegan, T., Yataki, M. S., Mears, R. J. and Hussey, C. D. (1986). Dependence of fused taper couplers on external refractive index, *Electron. Lett.*, **22**, 1207–1209.

Pleibel, W., Stolen, R. H. and Rashleigh, S. C. (1983). Polarisation-preserving coupler with self aligning birefringent fibres, *Electron. Lett.*, **19**, 825–826.

Po, H., Hakimi, F., Mansfield, R. J., McCollum, B. C., Tumminelli, R. P. and Snitzer, E. (1986). Neodymium fiber laser at 0.905, 1.06 and 1.4 µm, *Proc. Optical Society of America Meet., Seattle, WA, October 1986*, Optical Society of America, Washington, DC.

Poole, S. B., Payne, D. N. and Fermann, M. E. (1985). Fabrication of low-loss optical fibres containing rare-earth ions, *Electron. Lett.*, **21** (17), 737–738.

Reekie, L., Mears, R. J., Poole, S. B. and Payne, D. N. (1986). Tunable single-mode fiber lasers, *IEEE J. Lightwave Technol.*, **4** (7), 956–960.

Risk, W. P. and Kino, G. S. (1986). Acousto-optic fiber-optic frequency shifter using periodic contact with a copropagating surface acoustic wave, *Opt. Lett.*, **11**, 336–338.

Risk, W. P., Youngquist, R. C., Kino, G. S. and Shaw, H. J. (1984). Acousto-optic frequency shifting in birefringent fiber, *Opt. Lett.*, **9**, 309–311.

Risk, W. P., Kino, G. S. and Shaw, H. J. (1986). Fiber-optic frequency shifter using a surface acoustic wave incident at an oblique angle, *Opt. Lett.*, **11**, 115–117.

Russell, P. St. J. and Ulrich, R. (1985). Grating-fiber coupler as a high-resolution spectrometer, *Opt. Lett.*, **10**, 291–293.

Schiffner, G., Schneider, H. and Schöner, G. (1980). Double-core single-mode optical fiber as directional coupler, *Appl. Phys.*, **23**, 41–45.

Schöner, G., Klement, E., Shiffner, G. and Douklias, N. (1982). Novel method for making single-mode optical fibre directional couplers, *Electron. Lett.*, **18**, 566–568.

Sheem, S. K. and Giallorenzi, T. G. (1979). Single mode fiber-optical power divider: encapsulated etching technique, *Opt. Lett.*, **4**, 29–31.

Slonecker, M. H. (1982). Single-mode fused biconical taper coupler, *Proc. Optical Fiber Conf. '82, April 1982*, Paper WBB7, Optical Society of America, Washington, DC.

Sorin, W. V. and Shaw, H. J. (1985). A single-mode fiber evanescent grating reflector, *IEEE J. Lightwave Technol.*, **3**, 1041–1043.

Sorin, W. V., Jackson, K. P. and Shaw, H. J. (1983). Evanescent amplification in a single-mode optical fibre, *Electron. Lett.*, **19**, 820–822.

Sorin, W. V., Kim, B. Y. and Shaw, H. J. (1986). Highly selective evanescent modal filter for two-mode optical fibers, *Opt. Lett.*, **11**, 581–583.

Stokes, L. F., Chodorow, M. and Shaw, H. J. (1982). All-fiber stimulated Brillouin ring laser with submilliwatt pump threshold, *Opt. Lett.*, **7**, 509–511.

Stolen, R. H. (1980). Fiber Raman lasers, *Fiber Integ. Opt.*, **3**, 21–51.

Stolen, R. H. (1986). Polishing-induced birefringence in single-mode fibers, *Appl. Opt.*, **25** (3), 344–347.

Stolen, R. H., Pleibel, W. and Simpson, J. R. (1985). High birefringence fibers by preform deformation, *IEEE J. Lightwave Technol.*, **2**, 639–641.

Tarng, S. S. and Chang, I. C. (1985). High frequency acousto-optic modulation in single-mode fiber, *IEEE Ultrasonic Symp. Proc.*, pp. 429–431, IEEE, New York.

Taylor, H. F. (1984). Bending effects in optical fibers, *IEEE J. Lightwave Technol.*, **2**, 617–628.

Ulrich, R. (1979). Polarization stabilization on single-mode fiber, *Appl. Phys. Lett.*, **35** (11), 840–842.

Vanclooster, R. and Phariseau, P. (1970). The coupling of two parallel dielectric fibers, Parts I and II, *Physica*, **47**, 485–514.

Varnham, M. P., Payne, D. N., Birch, R. D. and Tarbox, E. J. (1983). Single-polarisation operation of highly birefringent bow-tie optical fibres, *Electron. Lett.*, **19** (7), 246–247.

Varnham, M. P., Payne, D. N., Barlow, A. J. and Tarbox, E. J. (1984a). Coiled-birefringent-fiber polarizers, *Opt. Lett.*, **9**, 306–308.

Varnham, M. P., Payne, D. N. and Love, J. D. (1984b). Fundamental limits to the transmission of linearly polarised light by birefringent optical fibres, *Electron. Lett.*, **20** (1), 55–56.

Villarruel, C. A. and Moeller, R. P. (1981). Fused single mode fiber access couplers, *Electron. Lett.*, **17**, 243–244.

Villarruel, C. A., Abebe, M. and Burns, W. K. (1983). Polarisation preserving single-mode-fibre coupler, *Electron. Lett.*, **19**, 17–18.

Villarruel, C. A., Abebe, M., Dandridge, A., Greenblatt, A. S. and Schuette, L. (1987). Pressure tolerant single-mode fiber coupler, *Appl. Opt.*, **26** (10), 1824–1826.

Whalen, M. S. and Walker, K. L. (1985). In-line optical-fibre filter for wavelength multiplexing, *Electron. Lett.*, **21**, (17), 724–725.

Whalen, M. S., Divino, M. D. and Alferness, R. C. (1986a). Demonstration of a narrowband Bragg-reflection filter in a single-mode fibre directional coupler, *Electron. Lett.*, **22**, 681–682.

Whalen, M. S., Tennant, D. M., Alferness, R. C., Koren, U. and Bosworth, R. (1986b). Wavelength-tunable single-mode fibre grating reflector, *Electron. Lett.*, **22**, 1307–1308.

Yataki, M. S., Payne, D. N. and Varnham, M. P. (1985a). All-fibre polarising beamsplitter, *Electron Lett.*, **21** (6), 249–251.

Yataki, M. S., Payne, D. N. and Varnham, M. P. (1985b). All-fiber wavelength filters using concatenated fused-taper couplers, *Electron. Lett.*, **21**, 248–249.

Yeh, C., Manshadi, F., Casey, K. F. and Johnston, A. (1978). Accuracy of directional coupler theory in fiber or integrated optics applications, *J. Opt. Soc. Am.*, **68** (8), 1079–1083.

Yokohama, I., Kawachi, M., Okamoto, K. and Noda, J. (1986). Polarisation-maintaining fibre couplers with low excess loss, *Electron. Lett.*, **22**, 929–930.

Yoshino, T., Kurosawa, K., Itoh, K. and Ose, T. (1982). Fiber-optic Fabry-Perot interferometer and its sensor applications, *IEEE J. Quantum Electron.*, **18**, 1624–1633.

Youngquist, R. C., Brooks, J. L. and Shaw, H. J. (1983). Birefringent fiber polarization coupler, *Opt. Lett.*, **8**, 656–658.

Yu, M. H. and Hall, D. B. (1984). Low loss fiber ring resonator, *Proc. SPIE—Fiber Optic and Laser Sensors II*, **478**, 104–108.

Zheng, X. H. and Snyder, A. W. (1987). Fused couplers: condition for insensitivity to external refractive index, *Electron. Lett.*, **23** (5), 182–184.

Chapter 8

Optical Fibers for Sensors

W. A. GAMBLING AND S. B. POOLE

8.1 Introduction

Optical fibers have been developed to a high degree of sophistication for applications in long distance transmission. Silica-based fibers have attenuations close to the theoretical minimum at wavelengths of 0.85, 1.3 and 1.55 µm, and the bandwidth of single-mode fibers can be made almost infinite, for all practical purposes, at wavelengths greater than 1.3 µm. However, although the great majority of experimental and commercial intrinsic fiber sensors currently employ telecommunications grade fibers, largely as a result of their ready availability, this policy frequently leads to a design compromise and in some cases makes the performance marginal, or even untenable, owing to excessive environmental sensitivity. Consequently, attention is now being given to the design of special sensor fibers with enhanced (or depressed) sensitivity to specific measurands.

Few special fibers are currently commercially available. Perhaps the best known is the highly birefringent fiber (Dyott et al., 1979), in both polarization-maintaining (Birch et al., 1982) and polarizing (Varnham et al., 1983a) form. Such fibers are extensively applied to polarization control in fiber gyroscopes and other sensors, and are also under investigation for use in coherent communications systems (Smith et al., 1983). The pace of development is increasing, however, and a large number of other fiber designs tailored to specific applications have been reported. For example, the unusual propagation properties of circularly birefringent fibers (Varnham et al., 1985; Li et al., 1986a) make them very suitable for magnetic field sensing. Work is also under way on metal–glass composite fibers for the production of polarizers (Li et al., 1986b) and Kerr modulators (Li et al., 1986c).

Considerable scope exists for modifying the properties of silica fibers by incorporating suitable dopants to enhance a given effect. Thus the acousto-optic, magneto-optic, nonlinear and electro-optic coefficients, which are small in pure silica, can be increased by adding various transition metal and rare earth ions (Poole et al., 1985). Such effects are being studied in several

249

laboratories (Po *et al.*, 1986; Millar *et al.*, 1987; Shimizu *et al.*, 1987). However, it should be noted that, in general, the greatest improvements in sensors, modulators and other devices can be obtained by abandoning silica altogether as a host material and employing compound glasses, infrared (e.g. chalcogenide) glasses or even polymers. The increase in loss which may result from the use of alternative glasses is not normally a problem, since an improvement of several orders of magnitude in device sensitivity is attainable and only a few meters of fiber are usually required.

Perhaps the most exciting recent development has been the demonstration of lasing action in single-mode fibers at wavelengths of 1.06, 1.08 and 1.536 μm by doping with Pr^{3+}, Nd^{3+} and Er^{3+} respectively (Mears *et al.*, 1985, 1986; Reekie *et al.*, 1986a, b). The losses at the lasing wavelength in these fibers are so low that it has been possible to construct lasers up to 1400 m long. Apart from the obvious application of the fibers as sources and amplifiers for communication and sensor systems, the availability of a multipass resonant active device suggests a number of sensor possibilities. Both ring resonator and Fabry–Pérot laser devices have been built, with finesses of up to 300. Consequently, a sensitivity enhancement of the same order to acoustic radiation, for example, should be possible. In addition, the availability of low loss rare-earth-doped fibers with controlled absorption and fluorescence characteristics provides further opportunities for distributed sensing by monitoring the variation in these parameters with temperature (Farries *et al.*, 1986a).

It is clear that fiber fabrication technology is now able to offer a number of attractive solutions to the unique problems presented by fiber sensors. A wide range of possibilities is available, including modified telecommunications fibers which are bend resistant, metal-coated (Dandridge *et al.*, 1980) and special polymer-coated (Koo and Sigel, 1982) fibers, fibers with liquid cores (Hartog, 1983) or claddings (Scheggi *et al.*, 1983), spun low birefringence fibers (Barlow *et al.*, 1981) and twin-core fibers (Snitzer *et al.*, 1982).

The fabrication of fibers with novel design features and materials is described in this chapter. It is intended to be tutorial rather than definitive and illustrates some of the wide range of options available to the designers of fiber sensors.

8.2 Fibers with modified polarization properties

8.2.1 Introduction to birefringence

In single-mode fibers the fundamental HE_{11} mode is linearly polarized. Thus, in theory, if an ordinary single-mode fiber is perfectly constructed so that it is circularly symmetric and laid in a straight line, linearly polarized light launched at the input will maintain this state along the whole length of the fiber to the output. In practice, however, such ideal conditions are not possible. Fibers cannot be made as perfect cylindrical structures so that intrinsic imperfections, as well as external factors such as bends, stress and changes of temperature, produce optical azimuthal inhomogeneities. Linearly polarized input light can be decomposed into linearly polarized orthogonal components with different phase velocities. Thus coupling between the two orthogonal components and random variations in the relative phase velocity cause the state of polarization to vary along the length of the fiber in an unpredictable way.

In many sensor designs, however, the state of polarization of the modes in a fiber must be strictly controlled. For example, a stable state of linear polarization is required in fibers for interferometric sensors. Conversely, a Faraday rotation sensor requires the fiber to have either very low linear birefringence or a high circular birefringence in order to observe the small field-induced polarization rotation. These disparate requirements lead to a number of special fiber designs with differing degrees and types of birefringence.

8.2.2 Fibers with negligible birefringence

The detection of magnetic fields and electric currents through the Faraday effect requires fibers with very low inherent linear birefringence to allow the observation of the small field-induced polarization rotation. This is particularly important in the fiber current sensor, where several turns of fiber are wrapped around a current-carrying conductor. The angle through which the plane of polarization is rotated is proportional to the integral of the magnetic field in the axial direction along the fiber.

Initially, the approach taken was to reduce noncircularity by improved fabrication methods and to minimize asymmetric stress by forming the core and cladding from materials with equal thermal expansion coefficients. The task was by no means easy since calculations indicated that even for a relative index difference as low as 3.4×10^{-3} the noncircularity must be no greater than 0.06% in order to achieve a retardance of $3° \text{m}^{-1}$. This approach was partially successful and retardances as low as $2.6° \text{m}^{-1}$ were achieved, some three orders of magnitude smaller than in a typical fiber (Norman et al., 1979). However, the fabrication process was difficult, giving a low yield with usable lengths limited to about 100 m.

Another possibility is to average out the linear birefringence in a fiber by twisting it (Ulrich and Simon, 1979). Unfortunately the fiber breaks before the effect becomes useful (i.e. at beat lengths (see Section 8.2.3) of about 10 cm) and in any case strongly twisted fibers are not easy to handle. However, it has been demonstrated that fibers with almost zero internal birefringence can be made by rotating the preform of a conventional fiber about its longitudinal axis during drawing (Barlow et al., 1981). Spinning rates of several thousand revolutions per minute are possible, with the result that any azimuthal inhomogeneities rotate along the length of the fiber with a very short pitch length. Linearly polarized light is unable to follow this rapid rotation of the birefringence axes, so that the core appears to be circularly symmetric as far as the propagating mode is concerned. The inherent linear birefringence and polarization mode dispersion can thus be reduced to negligibly low levels (Payne et al., 1982).

External effects, such as bends, pressure etc., can re-introduce birefringence which is not affected by the spun core. This forms a practical limit to the sensitivity of Faraday rotation sensors fabricated with low birefringence fibers, and a better solution where high sensitivity is required is to employ circularly or elliptically birefringent fibers (see Sections 8.2.4 and 8.2.5). Nevertheless, spun fibers are particularly useful for the measurement of magnetic fields and electric currents, provided that the externally induced birefringence is kept small.

8.2.3 Linearly birefringent fibers

As discussed previously, a stable state of linear polarization is required for many fiber sensors. To achieve this, it is necessary to reduce the amount of coupling between the two mode components by introducing strong linear birefringence into the fiber.

One method of doing this is to make the core noncircular in shape so that the refractive index distributions in the two principal directions are different (Fig. 8.1(a)) (Dyott et al., 1979). In these form-birefringent fibers the difference between the refractive indices of the core and the cladding must be large, since the birefringence B is proportional to Δn^2, which means in turn that in order to maintain single-mode propagation the core diameter must be very small. (Typical parameters for $B \approx 4 \times 10^{-4}$ are a core size of $1\,\mu m \times 2\,\mu m$ and $\Delta n = 0.03{-}0.04$.) This gives rise to problems of fabrication and jointing of the fiber. However, bending-induced losses are reduced and coupling to the noncircular active emission spot of a semiconductor laser is eased; a simple butt connection to a laser diode can have a loss of only 1.9 dB (Dyott, 1984). The transmission loss of this type of fiber has been reduced to $9\,dB\,km^{-1}$ at $0.85\,\mu m$ and $2.5\,dB\,km^{-1}$ at $1.3\,\mu m$ (Dyott, 1987).

A more common method of producing linear birefringence is to introduce asymmetric stress over the core of the fiber, either by means of an elliptical cladding or, more commonly, by fabricating the fiber with two regions of highly doped glass located on opposite sides of the core, as in the well-known "bow tie" (Birch et al., 1982) or PANDA (Sasaki et al., 1982) fibers (Figs 8.1(b) and 8.1(c)). Linear birefringence is now induced elasto-optically by the different thermal contractions of the doped regions combined with the asymmetric fiber cross-section. Of the various designs of stress-birefringent fibers, the one producing the largest birefringence is the bow tie structure in

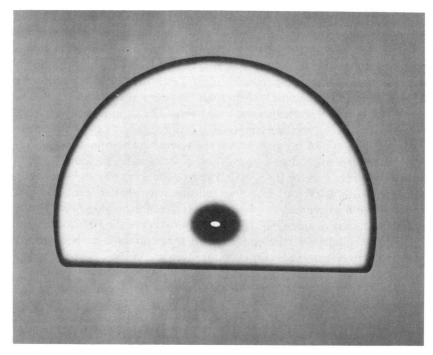

(a)

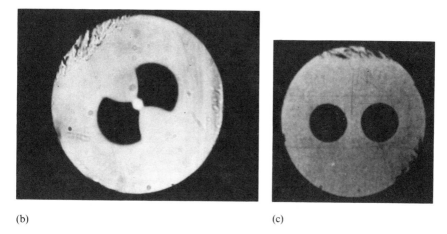

(b)   (c)

Fig. 8.1   (a) Photomicrograph of D-shaped elliptical-core fiber; (b) photomicrograph
of bow tie fiber; (c) photomicrograph of PANDA fiber.

which the shape of the stress-producing sectors has been optimized to produce
the maximum degree of birefringence.

Bow tie fibers are fabricated by an adaptation of the modified chemical vapor deposition (MCVD) process (Fig. 8.2). After the normal buffer layer has been deposited on the inside of the deposition tube to prevent the diffusion of water into the core and cladding regions, a layer of stress-producing material (e.g. borosilicate glass) is deposited. The tube rotation is then stopped and the stress-producing glass is etched away on opposite sides of the preform tube. The tube is again rotated and layers of cladding followed by core glass are deposited in the usual way. The deposited tube is then collapsed into a solid rod preform. During the collapse process the cusp-like regions of stress-producing glass in the tube assume the bow tie shape.

It is possible to produce a high degree of stress in the preform, typically around $20\,\text{kg}\,\text{mm}^{-2}$ in the B_2O_3-doped stress-producing regions but even up to the breakdown level of glass, thus causing it to shatter. Provided that shattering has not occurred, the preform rod is then drawn into a fiber. During cooling from the drawing temperature of approximately $2000\,^\circ\text{C}$, where the stresses are completely relieved, to room temperature a high degree of asymmetric stress is once again introduced owing to the different thermal

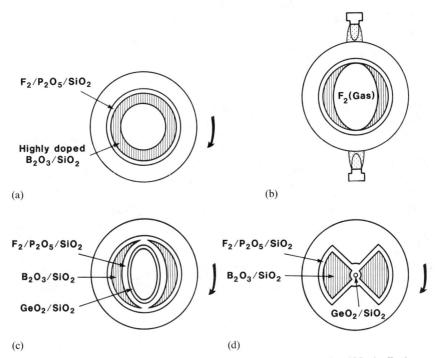

Fig. 8.2 Fabrication of bow tie fiber: (a) deposition of an F_2–P_2O_5–SiO_2 buffer layer and a B_2O_3–SiO_2 stress-producing layer in a rotating tube; (b) etching of a deposited B_2O_3–SiO_2 layer with fluorine gas in a stationary tube; (c) conventional deposition of cladding and core layers; (d) controlled collapse under pressure to give the distinctive bow tie shape of stress-producing sectors.

expansion coefficients of the borosilicate sectors and the silica substrate. The fiber, as distinct from the preform, is mechanically strong and is no more likely to break than a conventional fiber. On the contrary the compressive stress at the fiber surface tends, if anything, to increase the practical fiber strength and reduce static fatigue (Sammut and Chu, 1985).

An alternative technique is that employed in the fabrication of the so-called PANDA (polarization-maintaining and absorption-reducing) fiber. Here, a symmetrical pair of holes is drilled on each side of the core in a VAD (vapor phase axial deposition) preform and a boron-doped MCVD preform is inserted into each hole. This composite preform is then drawn in the usual way to produce a solid fiber in which the stress-producing sectors are formed by the boron-doped MCVD preforms. Similar techniques using rods doped with Al_2O_3 (Marrone et al., 1984) and B_2O_3–GeO_2 to provide the stress-inducing regions have also been reported.

In all stress-birefringent fibers the stress-producing sectors should be as near to the core as possible to obtain maximum birefringence. However, too close a proximity may cause an increased attenuation by interaction with the evanescent field in the cladding. Furthermore, there is a slight temperature dependence of the birefringence, as the applied stresses will vary with temperature. The properties of fibers produced by the various fabrication processes are summarized in Table 8.1.

Table 8.1   Characteristics of polarization-maintaining fibers

Fiber type	Modal birefringence B ($\times 10^4$)	Polarization-holding parameter h ($\times 10^{-6}\,m^{-1}$)	Minimum loss (dB km^{-1})	Minimum loss wavelength (μm)
Elliptical core[a]	4.0	10	2.5	1.3
Bow tie[b]	4.8	1	<1	1.55
PANDA[c]	3.15	0.16	0.22	1.55

[a] Dyott, 1987.
[b] Birch et al., 1982.
[c] Kikuchi et al., 1986.

In all highly birefringent fibers, the degree of birefringence can easily be assessed by observing the light scattered sideways from the fiber when the input (from an He–Ne laser for example) is linearly polarized at an angle of 45° to the principal transverse axes. Because of their different phase constants the two propagating polarization modes run into and out of phase at a rate determined by the birefringence, thus producing a periodic variation in the transmitted polarization state from linear to circular and back again. The radially scattered intensity, which depends on the polarization of the transmitted light, therefore fluctuates with the same periodicity.

If the phase constants of the two polarization modes are β_1 and β_2, the "beat length" L measured in this way is given by

$$L = \frac{2\pi}{\beta_1 - \beta_2} = \frac{\lambda}{B} \qquad (8.1)$$

where λ is the optical wavelength and B is the normalized birefringence which is related to the refractive indices by the formula

$$B = n_1 - n_2 = \frac{\lambda}{2\pi}(\beta_1 - \beta_2) \qquad (8.2)$$

Beat lengths as low as 0.55 mm ($B = 10^{-3}$) have been measured (Birch *et al.*, 1982).

The ultimate linear polarization-holding ability of a highly birefringent fiber is limited by Rayleigh scattering, which continuously feeds a small amount of power into the unwanted polarization, and by the fact that the fiber mode is not truly linearly polarized but exhibits field curvature. It therefore has both a major and a minor (orthogonally polarized) field component (Varnham *et al.*, 1984). The polarization-holding limits are shown in Fig. 8.3, where the polarization crosstalk is plotted as a function of fiber length. It can be seen that for short fiber lengths the mode-field curvature limits the transmission of linearly polarized light to an extinction ratio of about −40 dB, whereas for a length of 100 km the Rayleigh scattering limit is −30 dB. (The

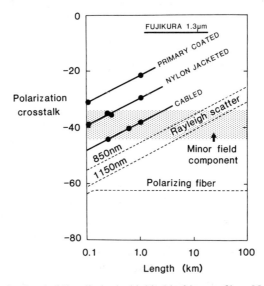

Fig. 8.3 Polarization-holding limits in highly birefringent fiber. Note that in short fiber lengths the crosstalk is dominated by the minor field component, whilst in long lengths Rayleigh scatter is the limiting component. The effect of different fiber coating designs is shown by the three full lines.

limitations due to minor field components which are present when the extinction in a short length of fiber is measured with conventional bulk optics can be overcome by the use of fiber devices to remove the minor field components. For instance, a short length of conventional monomode fiber will filter the minor field components spatially (to $-70\,dB$) prior to the polarization analyzer, or alternatively a fiber polarizer (see below) can be used to replace the bulk optic analyzer in the measurement.) For comparison, experimental results (Kikuchi $et\ al.$, 1986) for long lengths of PANDA fiber are also shown. We see that the current status of polarization-holding ability is some 15 dB worse than the theoretical limit.

This polarization-holding ability of a highly birefringent fiber is normally characterized by the so-called h parameter (Rashleigh, 1983), which is defined as the fractional power transfer per meter of fiber length. The h parameter for the PANDA fiber above is $1.6 \times 10^{-7}\,m^{-1}$, corresponding to an output extinction ratio of $-38\,dB$ after 1 km. Note, however, that this figure is dependent on the fiber configuration and packaging and will be worse when the fiber is wound in tight coils or sheathed in badly designed cables. Therefore for practical applications the h parameter alone may not be a sensible parameter for describing birefringence in fibers.

Recent theoretical work (Payne $et\ al.$, 1987) has shown that the previous interpretation of the h parameter is incorrect, since no account was taken of the role of the fiber birefringence in suppressing bend-induced mode coupling. It can be shown that, for significant mode coupling to occur, the correlation length of the applied perturbation must be comparable with the fiber beat length, typically a few millimeters. The currently observed levels of polarization crosstalk cannot therefore be due to imperfections within the fiber. They are a consequence of uneven fiber coating and externally applied stresses and bends arising from winding onto a drum. This interpretation is supported by recent measurements on the effects of different fiber coatings on the h parameter (Kikuchi $et\ al.$, 1986).

8.2.3.1 Polarization-maintaining fibers

A fiber exhibiting a high degree of linear birefringence can operate in two quite distinct ways. In the first of these the two orthogonal modes have a low transmission loss and propagate with roughly equal attenuation. If an equal amount of light is launched into each of the modes, as described above, the state of polarization changes periodically along the length of the fiber from linear to circular to linear and so on. However, if only one of the modes is launched, the light remains linearly polarized along the entire length of the fiber because the large difference in phase constants of the modes greatly reduces the coupling between them that might be caused by bends, microbends, kinks, twists and so on. In the presence of strong external distortion some of the original polarization couples into the orthogonal mode and continues to propagate in that mode to the output. The intensity of light in the coupled mode can provide a measure of the external parameter. Thus the characteristic of polarization-maintaining fiber is that the attenuations of the two polarization modes are equal but the phase constants are very different.

8.2.3.2 Polarizing fibers

Another method of operating a linearly birefringent fiber is to introduce attenuation preferentially into one of the modes. Light launched into the low loss mode will continue in that mode to the end of the fiber. Any light coupled into the orthogonal, i.e. high loss, mode is rapidly attenuated and the output remains linearly polarized despite the mode coupling. Such a fiber is termed a "polarizing" fiber because, for any state of input polarization, only linearly polarized light emerges (Varnham et al., 1983a).

Many designs for such a fiber have been proposed (Okoshi and Oyamoda, 1980, 1982; Eickhoff, 1982; Birch et al., 1983; Varnham et al., 1983a), although the only practical devices currently available are based on introducing a preferential loss into one mode by either winding the fiber into a coil or fabricating the fiber with an absorbing metal sector aligned to one of the birefringent axes (see Section 8.3.3). In the former, the different refractive index distributions in the two principal transverse planes cause the bending loss edges of the two modes to occur at different wavelengths, so that there is a wavelength region where the attenuation of the two modes is very different. The steepness of the bending edges, their positions and their separation can be changed by the fabrication conditions, the radius of bend and microbends (Varnham et al., 1983b). The wavelength region in which polarizing action occurs can also be controlled. The spectral variation in attenuation (decibels per kilometer) for the x- and y-polarized modes of a typical polarizing fiber is shown in Fig. 8.4. The fiber was 500 m long and had a beat length of 1.2 mm at

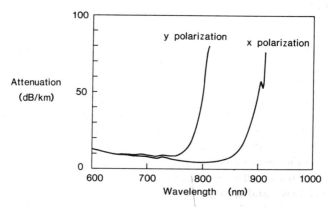

Fig. 8.4 Spectral variation of the extinction ratio of x- and y-polarized modes in polarizing fiber.

633 nm and a second-order mode cut-off ($V = 2.405$) at 600 nm. Extinction ratios of 60 dB have been obtained over a wide (more than 400 nm) wavelength range (see also Section 8.3.3).

8.2.4 Circularly birefringent fibers

Fibers exhibiting a high degree of circular birefringence can find application in the monitoring of magnetic fields and hence electric current. As distinct from spun fibers, they are relatively unaffected by internal or external perturbations.

Probably the simplest method of producing circular birefringence is by twisting a conventional optical fiber about its longitudinal axis (Ulrich and Simon, 1979). It is then found that the propagation constants of modes polarized in the left-hand and right-hand circular directions are different. However, this method is limited since, as indicated earlier, the fiber will break if attempts are made to produce beat lengths shorter than about 10 cm.

A much more effective method is to produce a fiber in which the core does not lie along the longitudinal fiber axis but follows a helical path about it (Birch, 1987). Such fibers are fabricated by inserting a normal MCVD preform containing core and cladding into an off-axis hole drilled in a silica rod. As the silica rod containing the offset core–cladding preform is being drawn into fiber it is rotated about its longitudinal axis. The core of the resulting fiber is in the form of a tight helix with a pitch length of a few millimeters (Fig. 8.5). The

Fig. 8.5 Side view of a helical-core fiber.

degree of circular birefringence is more than an order of magnitude greater than can be obtained by twisting the fiber, and beat lengths down to 5 mm (corresponding to a modal birefringence B of 1.3×10^{-4}) and less have been produced (Fig. 8.6).

An interesting consequence of this method of fabrication is that the bend loss of the second- and higher-order modes is greatly increased compared with that of the fundamental mode, so that the fiber can be operated at high normalized frequencies, e.g. $V = 25$, whilst effectively maintaining single-mode operation. The core diameter can thus be much larger than normal.

The helical-core fiber is stable and its birefringence is relatively unaffected by external effects. It is therefore robust, in polarization terms, and can be looped around a conductor for current measurement with ease. Since the rotation of the plane of polarization is proportional to the line integral of the magnetic field, the position of the coil is of no consequence and it can be close to the conductor or some distance from it. Clearly the measurement is

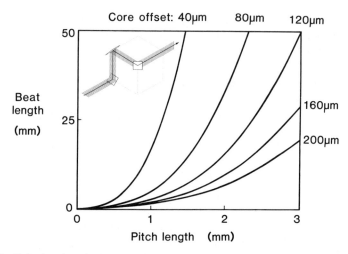

Fig. 8.6 Calculated optical rotation (beat) lengths in a circularly birefringent helical-core fiber as a function of pitch length for various values of core offset. The inset shows a schematic illustration of the rotation of a linearly polarized wave in a helical guiding structure of the type found in these fibers.

unaffected by stray magnetic fields, including those created by nearby currents which are not enclosed by the coil. However, the fiber has a larger diameter than normal (about 500 μm), because the degree of circular birefringence increases rapidly with helix diameter, and is therefore stiff, restricting applications to coils of 30 cm radius or more. Furthermore, the mode axis is at an angle to the fiber axis so that launching is more difficult than with a conventional fiber. Nevertheless the helical-core fiber is otherwise well suited to measurements on power lines.

8.2.5 Elliptically birefringent fibers

An elliptically birefringent fiber can be fabricated by spinning a fiber with high linear birefringence (e.g. a bow tie fiber) during drawing. The resulting fiber has a permanent frozen-in rotation of the birefringent axes. The polarization eigenmodes are elliptically polarized, and the elliptical birefringence is dependent on the linear birefringence of the unspun fiber and the rate of twist. The beat length L_p' between the elliptically polarized modes of the spun fiber is given in terms of the beat length L_p of the unspun fiber by (Li *et al.*, 1986a)

$$L_p' = \frac{L_p L_t}{(4L_p^2 + L_t^2)^{1/2} - 2L_p} \qquad (8.3)$$

where L_t is the spin pitch.

The beat length L_p' is a measure of the resistance to external pertur-

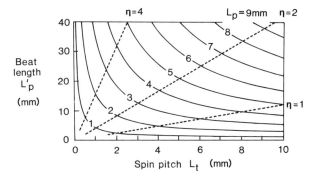

Fig. 8.7 Elliptical mode beat length in a spun bow tie fiber as a function of the spin pitch for various values of the unspun beat length L_p. The broken lines represent constant values of $\eta = 2L_p/L_t$.

bations and should normally be less than 10 mm. The elliptical mode beat length is shown in Fig. 8.7 as a function of the spin pitch L_t for various values of the unspun beat length L_p. Curves for values of the ratio $\eta = 2L_p/L_t$ from 1 to 4 are also shown, and it can be seen that, provided that the spin pitch is not less than the unspun beat length, an acceptable increase in fiber beat length of four times results from the spinning process. A bow tie fiber thus remains highly (elliptically) birefringent. The ellipticity (ratio of the minor to the major axis) of the eigenmodes is given by

$$\varepsilon = \tan\left\{\frac{1}{2}\tan^{-1}\left(\frac{2L_p}{L_t}\right)\right\} \tag{8.4}$$

At high spin rates $(2L_p/L_t > 2)$ the ellipticity approaches unity, and the modes are therefore predominantly circularly polarized. Hence little quenching of the Faraday effect occurs and the sensitivity (Faraday rotation angle less than 20°) differs little from the perfect isotropic fiber $(2L_p/L_t = 0)$ for values of $2L_p/L_t$ greater than about 2 (corresponding to a resultant elliptical beat length L_p' equal to $4.24L_p$). Thus, to ensure a sufficiently large elliptical birefringence $(L_p' < 10 \text{ mm})$ the unspun beat length L_p must be less than about 3 mm. Beat lengths as short as 7.2 mm have been produced by this technique, which is sufficient to overcome all but the worst packaging effects.

Current sensors constructed from these fibers give excellent performance and are relatively insensitive to external perturbations caused by temperature and pressure fluctuations. For instance, a fiber coil with 100 turns and a diameter of 25 mm has been demonstrated which, when using reflection techniques and a broad spectrum source to compensate for temperature effects, has a current range of 500 A and is detector shot-noise limited to 1 mA (r.m.s.) $Hz^{-0.5}$ (Laming $et\ al.$, 1988). It is anticipated that this could be improved to give a sensitivity of 100 µA (r.m.s.) $Hz^{-0.5}$ by a suitable choice of light source and optical coupling.

8.3 Evanescent field devices

8.3.1 Introduction

In some kinds of sensor it is necessary to have direct access to the propagating optical field in and near the core. Examples embrace Raman spectroscopy, chemical and biological sensing and resonant absorption. There are several methods of exposing the evanescent field near the core. These include grinding off and polishing the cladding, tapering the fiber to cause field expansion beyond the reduced cladding, grinding the preform prior to drawing to give a D-shaped fiber and creating a longitudinal aperture inside the fiber at a controlled distance from the core during the fabrication process. The techniques for polishing (Bergh et al., 1980) and tapering (Kawasaki et al., 1981) fibers are described elsewhere and we will thus concern ourselves only with the modified fiber designs for D-fibers and hollow-section fibers.

8.3.2 D-fibers

If the substrate and cladding are removed from one side of a single-mode fiber preform, for instance by planar grinding and polishing of the preform surface, the resulting D-shaped preform can be pulled into a fiber which maintains the same D-shape as the preform (Dyott and Schrank, 1982) (Fig. 8.1(a)). The drawing temperature must be low in order to prevent the glass from flowing and reverting to a circular cross-section. The drawing process has the effect of fire-polishing the ground surface of the glass to give an extremely smooth low scatter surface at which interaction can be obtained. By selecting the thickness of the material left on the preform (Millar et al., 1986) or by subsequently removing part of the remaining cladding (Dyott et al., 1987), access can be gained to the evanescent field within the fiber to form fiber couplers and polarizers.

8.3.3 Hollow-section fibers

In their simplest form, hollow-section fibers are a development of the D-fibers described above and have a single longitudinal aperture at a fixed distance from the fiber core. They are fabricated by grinding and polishing a flat on the starting preform (as for a D-fiber) and then sleeving the preform within a close-fitting jacketing tube. The fiber drawing conditions are then chosen to ensure that the preform and jacketing tube fuse together, leaving a hole corresponding to the ground section of the preform along one side of the core. This again fire-polishes the ground surface of the glass to give an extremely smooth low scatter surface.

A particular application has been to metal–glass fiber polarizers (Li et al., 1986b) in which a metal is incorporated directly into the fiber close to the core,

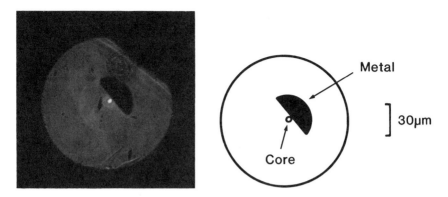

Fig. 8.8   Photograph and schematic diagram of a composite metal–glass polarizer. Note the proximity of the metal insert to the fiber core.

as shown in Fig. 8.8. The result is a high performance metal–glass fiber polarizer produced in continuous lengths and having an extinction ratio which can be selected by cutting to a given length. The acrylate-coated fiber illustrated in Fig. 8.8 had a numerical aperture (NA) of about 0.16, a cut-off wavelength of about 1.25 μm and a distance between the core and the hollow section of about 3 μm. The fiber was bonded to a stainless steel syringe containing a 48% Sn–52% In alloy (melting point about 120 °C). The syringe and the fiber were heated to about 130 °C and a gas pressure of about 4 bar was introduced above the metal through a stainless steel tube. Filling a length of 2 m took about 1 min. The resultant composite metal–glass fiber can be handled, cleaved and spliced in a similar manner to a conventional fiber. The extinction ratio of a 5 cm length of polarizer fiber is around 40 dB over a wide spectral window from 1300 to 1600 nm (Fig. 8.9). The temperature stability of these devices has also been measured and they have been shown to be temperature insensitive over the temperature range −40 to +100 °C. The maximum operating temperature is limited by the melting point of the alloy (in

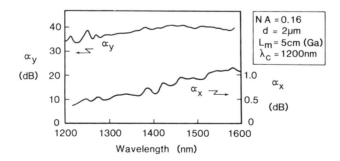

Fig. 8.9   Spectral variation of the extinction ratio α_y and the insertion loss α_x of a 5 cm length of a composite glass–metal polarizer.

this case to about 120 °C), but higher temperature operation can be obtained by using alternative alloys.

Both the extinction ratio and the insertion loss are proportional to the length, and it is theoretically possible to design a polarizer with a virtually unlimited extinction ratio at the expense of increased insertion loss. This is important because in many applications, particularly the fiber gyroscope, a large extinction ratio is essential whereas an insertion loss of 1 or 2 dB is acceptable. The fiber polarizer reported here allows this choice to be made by simply cutting the fiber to the required length. Moreover, the fiber can be designed to provide the required extinction ratio for lengths varying from a few centimeters to several meters simply by adjusting the core–metal separation. The ultimate limit to the extinction ratio attainable in these fibers is set by Rayleigh scattering as in a highly birefringent fiber (see Section 8.2.3). However, as the polarizer can be designed to be very short (1 cm or less), the maximum extinction ratio is expected to be in excess of 100 dB.

As indicated above, other liquids and gases can be introduced into the cavity for sensor applications. By providing longitudinal metal sectors, symmetrically placed on each side of the core (Li et al., 1986c), even a moderate voltage can produce a strong electric field across the core. Modulation of the propagating wave can then occur via the optical Kerr effect. The device could be applied to the measurement of voltage or, more usefully, as a modulator. In the latter mode, a bandwidth of several megahertz with an applied half-wave voltage of only a few tens of volts has been reported.

A further application of the twin side-pit fiber is as a pressure sensor (Xie et al, 1986). Here the holes are filled with the fluid whose pressure is to be monitored and any changes in the fluid pressure are translated into a change in the polarization state at the output of the fiber. Response times as short as 1 ms have been reported.

8.4 Fibers made from modified materials

8.4.1 Introduction

To maintain low transmission losses in the near-infrared wavelength region, it is necessary to reduce all but the essential glass constituents of optical fibers to an absolute minimum. However, the number of potential sensor applications for fibers can be increased if the appropriate fiber properties can be introduced, or enhanced, without appreciably increasing the attenuation at the low loss wavelengths. In the methods discussed so far, the purity of both core and cladding is maintained and the propagating wave is modulated by externally applied forces such as mechanical strain, electric field, magnetic field, change of temperature and so on. Another method of modifying the fiber properties is by altering the materials from which the fiber is fabricated, for instance by using non-silica-based glasses, or by introducing small quantities of suitable materials into the core or cladding.

8.4.2 Multicomponent glass fibers

Fibers fabricated from multicomponent glasses of low silica content may find many applications when the ultralow loss of telecommunications fiber is not required. Such applications include fiber sensors and nonlinear devices, where the increased performance obtainable in nonsilica glasses is more critical than the fiber loss, particularly since only a few meters of fiber are usually required. This is important since the use of nonsilica glasses, combined with the rod-in-tube fabrication technique, usually leads to higher losses than in conventional fibers. Nevertheless, it is possible to obtain single-mode fibers with many desirable properties. Indeed, the Verdet constant and nonlinear coefficient $\chi^{(3)}$ can be an order of magnitude higher in soft glasses than in silica. Furthermore, since, for example, the Verdet constant is related to absorption losses in the material, it is possible to optimize the fiber design by a suitable choice of glass to obtain sensors with a very high bandwidth owing to the short length of fiber required.

Examples of soft-glass fibers fabricated at Southampton University are shown in Fig. 8.10, from which it can be seen that many fiber designs are possible. Single-mode soft-glass fibers produced by the rod-in-tube technique have losses of less than $400\,\mathrm{dB\,km^{-1}}$. In addition, high birefringence fibers have been obtained with beat lengths of less than 7 mm.

Soft-glass fibers may prove highly attractive for the generation of nonlinear effects because a small core diameter is associated with the large $\varDelta$ available. This results in high power densities which, combined with high nonlinear coefficients, should lead to considerably reduced thresholds for the generation of Raman or Brillouin spectra for instance (Sudo *et al.*, 1986).

8.4.3 Fibers doped with rare earths

8.4.3.1 Introduction

By introducing rare earth ions into the light-guiding regions of the fiber, many interesting devices can be constructed including

(1) fiber lasers and amplifiers,
(2) distributed temperature sensors based on (a) absorption and (b) fluorescence,
(3) fibers with increased Verdet constant and
(4) fibers with increased Kerr effect and nonlinear optical coefficients.

Until recently, it was thought that incorporation of these dopants would destroy the hard-won low loss characteristics of telecommunications fibers

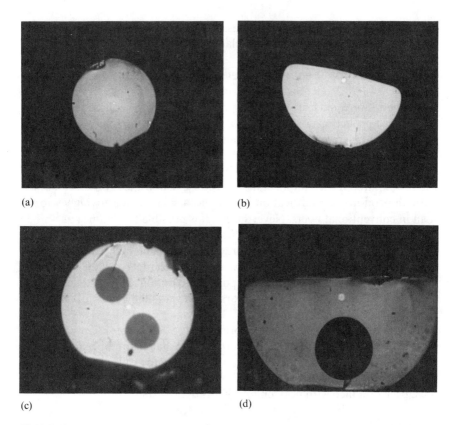

(a)   (b)

(c)   (d)

Fig. 8.10 Examples of soft-glass monomode fibers produced at Southampton University: (a) single-mode fiber; (b) D-fiber; (c) birefringent fiber; (d) birefringent D-fiber.

and render them inoperable as distributed sensors and amplifiers. However, simple and reproducible fiber fabrication techniques have now been developed which do not significantly increase the fiber loss. These processes allow the uniform incorporation of low levels of rare earth ions into the core or cladding of many types of optical fiber. The dopants are not limited to the rare earth elements and can be extended to, for instance, the transition metals.

These various techniques will be illustrated by describing a method based on the MCVD process which was developed at Southampton University (Poole *et al.*, 1985, 1986; Townsend *et al.*, 1987). However, other techniques are also possible (Po *et al.*, 1986; Millar *et al.*, 1987; Shimizu *et al.*, 1987).

8.4.3.2 Fiber fabrication

A major advantage of conventional MCVD fabrication is that the appropriate material halides, which can be obtained in very pure form and are

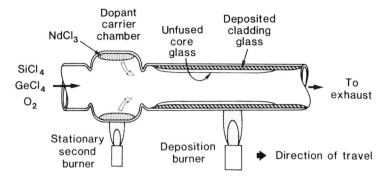

Fig. 8.11 Vapor phase process for fabrication of rare-earth-doped fibers. The second (stationary) burner is used only to purify the dopant precursor and during the core deposition process.

liquid at room temperature, can be used as starting materials. The problems to be overcome in extending this technique to the rare earth halides is that these are solid at room temperature, they have a high melting point and thus a low vapor pressure, and they occur in hydrated form.

One of the methods adopted to overcome these difficulties (Poole et al., 1985) is illustrated in Fig. 8.11. Prior to deposition, a conventional deposition tube is modified and the required dopant, for example $NdCl_3 \cdot 6H_2O$ (99.9% pure, melting point 758 °C), is introduced into a special dopant chamber which is added at the upstream end. The dopant is dried by heating the chamber under a chlorine atmosphere and, at the same time, the anhydrous crystals are fused to the chamber wall. The inside of the deposition tube is then cleaned to remove any dopant which may have been deposited there during the drying process, following which the cladding glass is deposited in the usual way. During the core deposition the dopant chamber is heated to about 1000 °C to produce small quantities of $NdCl_3$ vapor which is carried downstream by the reactant flow where it is oxidized and incorporated into the core. The temperature for core deposition is kept lower than usual so that the core components are initially unfused. Further drying is carried out by heating in a chlorine atmosphere, after which the core is fused into a clear nonporous layer. Subsequent collapse of the deposited tube into a solid rod preform and drawing of the preform into fiber then follows the normal MCVD procedures.

The technique is simple and reproducible, and it can provide single-component or multicomponent doping of a wide range of materials into the core or cladding of both multimode and single-mode optical fibers. Such techniques have been used to fabricate single-mode fibers containing various rare earths (neodymium, erbium, dysprosium, terbium, cerium, europium, thulium, ytterbium and praseodymium) with dopant levels between 0.2 and 3000 ppm (Townsend et al., 1987). Remarkably, all exhibit windows in which losses are comparable with conventional fibers, despite the close proximity of

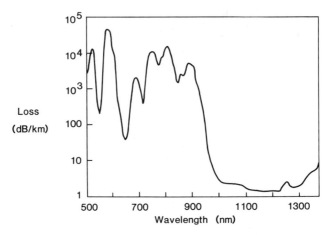

Fig. 8.12 Loss spectrum of fiber doped with 800 ppm Nd^{3+} ions. The absorption bands visible are typical of the Nd^{3+} ion in a glass host. Note the regions of extremely low loss away from the absorption bands.

high loss dopant absorption bands (Fig. 8.12). Measurements using optical time domain reflectometry (OTDR) indicate that the dopant is incorporated uniformly along the length of the fiber. The low fiber losses, combined with the consistency of dopant incorporation along the fiber length, make the fiber suitable for use in distributed sensors, fiber lasers and amplifiers, and nonlinear devices.

8.4.3.3 Rare-earth-doped fiber sensors

Nd^{3+}-doped glass point-temperature sensors based on changes in the absorption spectrum with temperature have been known for many years (Snitzer *et al.*, 1983). However, the application of this technique to distributed sensors required the development of low loss rare-earth-doped fiber as described above. In a distributed sensor of this type, the loss of a fiber at a wavelength on the edge of an absorption band is monitored by interrogating the local fiber absorption by OTDR. The typical temperature dependence of absorption of an Nd^{3+}-doped fiber at a wavelength of 600 nm is shown in Fig. 8.13. Although the fiber contains only 5 ppm Nd^{3+}, a linear change in absorption of $0.2\% \, °C^{-1}$ was found over the temperature range investigated. This represents a $10 \, dB \, km^{-1}$ variation in fiber loss for a 100 °C temperature change. The temperature distribution along this fiber could be determined with an accuracy to 2 °C and a spatial resolution of 15 m (Farries *et al.*, 1986a).

Considerable improvements in performance can be obtained with other rare earth dopants at higher concentrations. This has been demonstrated with fiber containing 1000 ppm Ho^{3+}. In this way a sensitivity of better than 1 °C with a spatial resolution of 3.5 m was obtained over the temperature range −200 to +100 °C (Farries *et al.*, 1987).

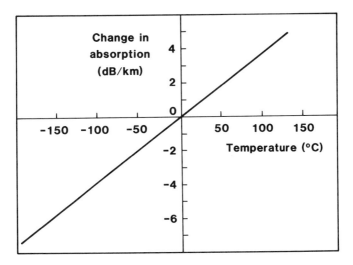

Fig. 8.13   Temperature dependence of the absorption of an Nd^{3+}-doped multimode fiber at 600 nm.

8.4.3.4 Rare-earth-doped fiber filters

The very large sharp absorption bands of rare-earth-doped fibers combined with the low losses attainable away from these absorptions suggest that compact wavelength filters with low insertion losses and extremely high rejection ratios can be fabricated. Typical applications are in wavelength multiplexing and also in spectroscopy, where very high rejection of the exciting laser is required. As a demonstration of such a filter, a short length of Ho^{3+}-doped fiber was able to separate the anti-Stokes spontaneous Raman scattering from the pump wavelength (Farries *et al.*, 1986b). The fiber had a differential attenuation of about 10^9 between the pump laser wavelength (He–Ne at 633 nm) and the anti-Stokes Raman line at 616 nm. The experimental arrangement is shown in Fig. 8.14. A 20 m length of single-mode fiber generated forward-scattered anti-Stokes Raman radiation and a 7 m

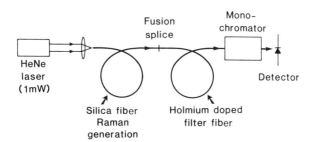

Fig. 8.14   Experimental configuration for a fiber filter. The length of Ho^{3+}-doped filter fiber was 7 m, giving a pump rejection of more than 10^9.

length of Ho^{3+}-doped fiber filtered the unwanted pump signal. The resulting Raman spectrum is shown in Fig. 8.15, in which the anti-Stokes scattering is at 616 nm. There is also a weak emission at 684 nm (corresponding to the 1183^{-1} Raman line in silica). Some pump radiation remains, but greater rejection could be obtained, if required, by simply increasing the fiber length. Thus extremely high rejection ratios are possible in rare-earth-doped fiber filters.

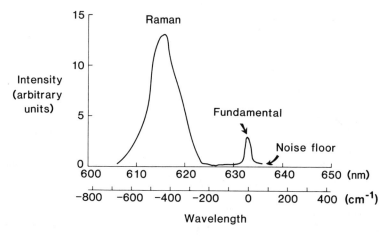

Fig. 8.15   Transmission of a fiber filter showing both pump rejection and Raman transmission.

8.4.3.5 Fiber lasers

A class of active fiber devices compatible with single-mode optical fiber sensor systems is highly desirable to supplement the hybrid semiconductor diode–optical fiber technologies currently in use. As a first step towards this goal, lasing action in rare-earth-doped silica single-mode fiber lasers has been demonstrated. These possess a number of advantages over their bulk counterparts. By virtue of their small active areas, it is possible to achieve very low thresholds and high gains. Since the typical fiber diameter is 125 µm, the thermal effects which plague bulk glass lasers are greatly reduced. Silica, the host material, has good power-handling characteristics; moreover, it broadens the rare earth transitions, enabling compact tunable diode-pumped lasers with various wavelengths to be constructed. Such devices could be of considerable interest as light sources for sensors and measurements. Moreover, it is now possible to construct a wide range of active fiber devices and sensors which exploit the numerous fiber components available, such as four-port couplers, ring resonators, polarizers and filters. The very low loss of the fiber permits the construction of long (1400 m has been demonstrated) amplifiers and lasers, as well as nonlinear devices and distributed active sensors.

A typical fiber laser configuration is shown in Fig. 8.16. For Nd^{3+}-doped fibers, a lasing threshold as low as 100 µW can be obtained by longitudinal

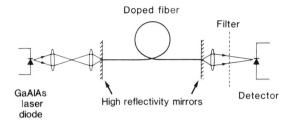

Fig. 8.16 Fabry–Pérot configuration for a diode-pumped fiber laser. The exact mirror reflectivities are chosen to suit the fiber under investigation.

pumping with a semiconductor laser (Mears *et al.*, 1985). In an optimized cavity, an output exceeding 6 mW at a wavelength of 1088 nm with a slope efficiency of 40% has been observed. Tuning of the output wavelength can be accomplished by substituting a grating for one of the mirrors (Reekie *et al.*, 1986b), and a tuning range of 92 nm (from 1062 to 1154 nm) is possible. This is the most extensive tuning range yet obtained in an Nd:glass laser and compares favorably with that of a dye laser.

Erbium-doped fiber lasers operate between 1530 and 1555 nm, i.e. within the important minimum loss window for optical communications. The fluorescence spectrum, with a typical tuning curve for an Er^{3+}-doped fiber laser superimposed on it, is shown in Fig. 8.17. The transition is between the $^4I_{13/2}$ and $^4I_{15/2}$ (ground state) levels and, despite being a three-level laser system, the Er^{3+}-doped fiber laser operates continuously (Mears *et al.*, 1986) and has a threshold of only 1.6 mW (Jauncey *et al.*, 1988). At the time of writing this represented the lowest threshold three-level glass laser reported. The recent demonstration of a diode-pumped Er^{3+} fiber laser (Reekie *et al.*, 1987) will lead to many practical applications of this device. Optical bistability has also been observed in an Er^{3+}-doped fiber laser operating at 1.54 μm (Reekie

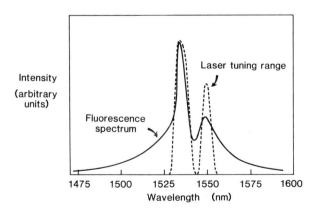

Fig. 8.17 Laser tuning curve and fluorescence spectrum for an Er^{3+}-doped fiber laser.

et al., 1986c). The mechanism is one of saturable absorption and has many potential applications including optical memories, switching and amplification.

Q-switching of fiber lasers with an acousto-optic modulator or rotating chopper is also possible, and peak powers of up to 250 W have been observed in pulses ranging from 50 ns to 1 μs in duration. In particular, it is possible to obtain pulses in excess of 100 W from a diode-pumped Nd^{3+} fiber laser, a performance which will find many applications in fiber sensors.

Recently, a number of optical fiber devices have been integrated into fiber lasers. These include fiber polarizers to give single-polarization operation of the laser (Lin *et al.*, 1987) and fiber gratings to reduce the output linewidth (Jauncey *et al.*, 1986). In addition, a number of novel resonant configurations are possible which obviate the need for dielectric mirrors (Miller *et al.*, 1987; Payne, 1987). Thus the way is open to the creation of all-fiber systems containing no bulk optical components.

Fiber lasers represent a new class of active fiber devices which are fully compatible with existing fiber components. Their low threshold, tunability and high-peak-power pulsed output provides a unique new all-fiber laser technology which will find application in fiber sensors. Immediate potential uses are as a high power source for fiber OTDR measurements and as a broadband emitter for the optical fiber gyroscope.

8.4.3.6 Fiber amplifiers

Optical amplifiers are of interest as wideband in-line repeaters for telecommunications and as signal regenerators or power amplifiers for a variety of sensor applications. Much current research has concentrated on semiconductor laser amplifiers (O'Mahoney *et al.*, 1985) which are difficult to splice to fiber systems. It is clear that an amplifier consisting of a special optical fiber compatible with telecommunications fiber would overcome this problem. An optical fiber amplifier based on an Er^{3+}-doped fiber which has a maximum gain at a wavelength of 1.536 μm has been reported (Mears *et al.*, 1987). The amplifier (shown schematically in Fig. 8.18) is optically pumped and

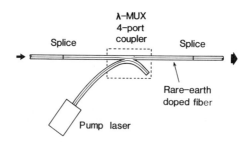

Fig. 8.18   Schematic representation of a doped fiber amplifier. The pump laser and coupler characteristics are chosen to suit the properties of the doped fiber.

a number of different pump sources, including Ar^+ and dye lasers, are available. With a dye laser pump operating at 665 nm, a maximum gain of 32 dB has been obtained at modulation rates of up to 400 MHz (Mears *et al.*, 1988). The input equivalent noise power was measured as -45 dBm in a 140 MHz bandwidth which compares favorably with state-of-the-art avalanche photodiode detectors at 1.54 μm. A maximum output power of $+13$ dBm was achieved before the onset of saturation. These preliminary results show that Er^{3+}-doped fiber amplifiers have excellent gain and noise characteristics which make them attractive as wideband optical amplifiers and repeaters for multichannel optical systems.

8.5 Conclusions

A wide variety of new optical fiber materials and structures are available which may lead to many different types of sensor application. The examples outlined in this chapter are intended to be illustrative and not definitive. The design of novel fiber structures and sensors is in its infancy, and much research remains to be done. The overriding requirements are, as always, for high performance at low cost, and only the future can tell whether and in what systems these targets can be met.

Acknowledgments

The authors would like to pay tribute to the many colleagues whose work they have drawn on in preparing this chapter, and to Dr R. B. Dyott and York VSOP for their contribution of unpublished results.

References

Barlow, A. J., Payne, D. N., Hadley, M. R. and Mansfield, R. J. (1981). Production of single-mode fibres with negligible intrinsic birefringence and polarisation mode dispersion, *Electron. Lett.*, **17**, 725–726.

Bergh, R. A., Kotter, G. and Shaw, H. J. (1980). Single-mode fibre optic directional coupler, *Electron. Lett.*, **16**, 260–261.

Birch, R. D. (1987). Fabrication and characterisation of circularly-birefringent helical fibres, *Electron. Lett.*, **23**, 50–52.

Birch, R. D., Payne, D. N. and Varnham, M. P. (1982). Fabrication of polarisation-maintaining fibres using gas-phase etching, *Electron. Lett.*, **18**, 1036–1038.

Birch, R. D., Varnham, M. P., Payne, D. N. and Okomoto, K. (1983). Fabrication of a stress-guiding optical fibre, *Electron. Lett.*, **19**, 866–867.

Dandridge, A., Tveten, A. B., Sigel, G. H., West, E. J. and Giallorenzi, T. G. (1980). Optical fibre magnetic field sensors, *Electron. Lett.*, **16**, 408–409.

Dyott, R. B. (1984). Personal communication.

Dyott, R. B. (1987). Personal communication.

Dyott, R. B. and Schrank, P. F. (1982). Self-locating elliptically cored fibre with an accessible guiding region, *Electron. Lett.*, **18**, 980–981.

Dyott, R. B., Cozens, J. R. and Morris, D. G. (1979). Preservation of polarisation in optical fibre waveguides with elliptical cores, *Electron. Lett.*, **15**, 380–382.

Dyott, R. B., Bello, J. and Handerek, V. A. (1987). Indium-coated D-shaped-fiber polarizer, *Opt. Lett.*, **12**, 287–289.

Eickhoff, W. (1982). Stress-induced single-polarisation single-mode fiber, *Opt. Lett.*, **7**, 2252–2257.

Farries, M. C., Fermann, M. E., Laming, R. I., Poole, S. B., Payne, D. N. and Leach, A. P. (1986a). Distributed temperature sensor using Nd^{3+}-doped fibre, *Electron. Lett.*, **22**, 418–419.

Farries, M. C., Townsend, J. E. and Poole, S. B. (1986b). Very high rejection optical fibre filters, *Electron. Lett.*, **22**, 1126–1128.

Farries, M. C., Fermann, M. E., Poole, S. B. and Townsend, J. E. (1987). Distributed temperature sensor using holmium-doped optical fibre, *Proc. Optical Fiber Communication Conf., Reno, NV, January 1987*, Paper WI5, Optical Society of America, Washington, DC.

Hartog, A. H. (1983). A distributed temperature sensor based on liquid-core optical fibers, *J. Lightwave Technol.*, **1**, 498–509.

Jauncey, I. M., Reekie, L., Mears, R. J., Payne, D. N., Rowe, C. J., Read, D. C. J., Bennion, I. and Edge, C. (1986). Narrow-linewidth fibre laser with integral fibre grating, *Electron. Lett.*, **22**, 987–988.

Jauncey, I. M., Reekie, L., Poole, S. B. and Payne, D. N. (1988). Extended wavelength operation of an Er^{3+}-doped fibre laser pumped at 808 nm, *Proc. Optical Fiber Communication Conf., New Orleans, LA, January 1988*, Optical Society of America, Washington, DC.

Kawasaki, B. S., Hill, K. O. and Lamont, R. G. (1981). Biconical-taper single-mode fiber couplers, *Opt. Lett.*, **6**, 327–328.

Kikuchi, Y., Himeno, K., Kawakami, N., Suzuki, F. and Fukuda, O. (1986). Ultra-low crosstalk polarisation-maintaining fiber, in a short length operation, *Proc. Optical Fiber Communication Conf., Atlanta, GA, February 1986*, p. 36, Optical Society of America, Washington, DC.

Koo, K. P. and Sigel, G. H. (1982). An electric field sensor utilising a piezo electric polyvinylidene fluoride (PVF2) film in a single-mode interferometer, *IEEE J. Quantum Electron.*, **18**, 670.

Laming, R. I., Payne, D. N. and Li, L. (1988). Compact optical fibre current monitor with passive temperature stabilization, *Proc. Optical Fiber Communication Conf., New Orleans, LA, January 1988*, Optical Society of America, Washington, DC.

Li, L., Qian, J.-R. and Payne, D. N. (1986a). Current sensors using highly-birefringent bow-tie fibres, *Electron. Lett.*, **22**, 129–130.

Li, L., Wylangowski, G., Payne, D. N. and Birch, R. D. (1986b). Broadband metal/glass single-mode fibre polarisers, *Electron. Lett.*, **22**, 1020–1022.

Li, L., Birch, R. D. and Payne, D. N. (1986c). An all fibre electro-optic Kerr modulator, *Proc. IEE Colloq. on Advanced Fibre Waveguide Devices, London, May 1986*, Institution of Electrical Engineers, London.

Lin, J. T., Reekie, L. and Li, L. (1987). Single polarisation operation of a Nd^{3+}-doped single-mode fibre laser, *Proc. Conf. on Lasers and Electro-optics, Baltimore, MD, June 1987*, Optical Society of America, Washington, DC.

Marrone, M. J., Rashleigh, S. C. and Blaszyk, P. E. (1984). Polarization properties of birefringent fibres with stress rods in the cladding, *J. Lightwave Technol.*, **2**, 155–160.

Mears, R. J., Reekie, L., Poole, S. and Payne, D. N. (1985). Neodymium-doped silica single-mode fibre lasers, *Electron. Lett.*, **21**, 738–740.

Mears, R. J., Reekie, L., Poole, S. B. and Payne, D. N. (1986). Low threshold tunable CW and *Q*-switched fibre lasers operating at 1.55 µm, *Electron. Lett.*, **22**, 159–160.

Mears, R. J., Reekie, L., Jauncey, I. M. and Payne, D. N. (1987). Low-noise erbium-doped fibre amplifier operating at 1.54 µm, *Electron. Lett.*, **23**, 1026–1028.

Mears, R. J., Reekie, L., Jauncey, I. M. and Payne, D. N. (1988). Optical fiber amplifiers for 1.5 µm operation, *Proc. Optical Fiber Communication Conf., New Orleans, LA, January 1988*, Paper THD3, Optical Society of America, Washington, DC.

Millar, C. A., Ainslie, B. J., Brierley, M. C. and Craig, S. P. (1986). Fabrication and characterisation of D-fibres with a range of accurately controlled core/flat distances, *Electron. Lett.*, **22**, 322–324.

Millar, C. A., Ainslie, B. J., Miller, I. D. and Craig, S. P. (1987). Concentration and co-doping dependence of the $^4F_{3/2}$ to $^4I_{11/2}$ lasing behaviour of Nd^{3+} silica fibres, *Proc. Optical Fiber Communication Conf., Reno, NV, January 1987*, Paper WI4, Optical Society of America, Washington, DC.

Miller, I. D., Mortimore, D. B., Ainslie, B. J., Urqhart, W. P., Craig, S. P., Millar, C. A. and Payne, D. B. (1987). A new type of all-fibre laser, *Proc. Optical Fiber Communication Conf., Reno, NV, January 1987*, Paper WI3, Optical Society of America, Washington, DC.

Norman, S. R., Payne, D. N., Adams, M. J. and Smith, A. M. (1979). Fabrication of single-mode fibres exhibiting extremely low polarisation birefringence, *Electron. Lett.*, **15**, 309–311.

Okoshi, T. and Oyamoda, K. (1980). Single-polarisation single-mode optical fibre with refractive-index pits on both sides of the core, *Electron. Lett.*, **16**, 712–713.

Okoshi, T. and Oyamoda, K. (1982). Side tunnel fibre; an approach to polarization-maintaining optical waveguiding scheme, *Electron. Lett.*, **18**, 824–826.

O'Mahoney, M. J., Marshall, I. W., Devlin, W. J. and Regnault, J. C. (1985). Low-reflectivity semiconductor laser amplifier with 20 dB fibre to fibre gain at 1500 nm, *Electron. Lett.*, **21**, 501–502.

Payne, D. N. (1987). Special fibres and their applications, *Proc. Optical Fiber Communication Conf., Reno, NV, January 1987*, Paper WI1, Optical Society of America, Washington, DC.

Payne, D. N., Barlow, A. J. and Ramskov-Hansen, J. J. (1982). Development of low- and high-birefringence optical fibers, *IEEE J. Quantum Electron.*, **18**, 477–487.

Payne, F. P., Payne, D. N. and Varnham, M. P. (1987). Cross-talk in polarization-maintaining fibres, *Proc. European Conf. on Optical Communication, Barcelona, September 1987*, pp. 239–242, Telefonica, Barcelona.

Po, H., Hakimi, F., Mansfield, R. J., Tumminelli, R. P. and McCollum, B. C. (1986). Neodymium fiber lasers at 0.905, 1.06 and 1.4 µm, *Ann. Meet. Optical Society of America, Cambridge, MA*, Optical Society of America, Washington, DC.

Poole, S. B., Payne, D. N. and Fermann, M. E. (1985). Fabrication of low-loss optical fibres containing rare-earth ions, *Electron. Lett.*, **21**, 737–738.

Poole, S. B., Payne, D. N., Mears, R. J., Fermann, M. E. and Laming, R. I. (1986). Fabrication and characterization of low-loss optical fibers containing rare-earth ions, *J. Lightwave Technol.*, **4**, 870–876.

Rashleigh, S. C. (1983). Origins of polarization in single-mode fibers, *J. Lightwave Technol.*, **1**, 312–331.

Reekie, L., Mears, R. J., Poole, S. B. and Payne, D. N. (1986a). A Pr^{3+}-doped single-mode fibre laser, *IOP–IEE Symp. on Advances in Solid State Lasers, London*, Institute of Physics, London.

Reekie, L., Mears, R. J., Poole, S. B. and Payne, D. N. (1986b). Tunable single-mode fibre lasers, *J. Lightwave Technol.*, **4**, 956–960.

Reekie, L., Mears, R. J., Poole, S. B. and Payne, D. N. (1986c). Optical bistability at 1.54 μm in an Er^{3+}-doped fibre laser, *Proc. Conf. on Lasers and Electro-optics, San Francisco, CA, June 1986*, Optical Society of America, Washington, DC.

Reekie, L., Jauncey, I. M., Poole, S. B. and Payne, D. N. (1987). Diode laser pumped operation of an Er^{3+}-doped single-mode fibre laser, *Electron. Lett.*, **23**, 1076–1078.

Sammut, R. A. and Chu, P. L. (1985). Axial stress and its effect on relative strength of polarization-maintaining fibers and preforms, *J. Lightwave Technol.*, **3**, 283–287.

Sasaki, Y., Okamoto, K., Hosaka, T. and Shibata, N. (1982). Polarization-maintaining and absorption-reducing fibers, *Proc. Optical Fiber Communication Conf., Phoenix, AZ, January 1982*, Paper ThCC6, Optical Society of America, Washington, DC.

Scheggi, A. M., Brenchi, M., Conforti, C., Falciai, R. and Preti, G. P. (1983). Optical fiber thermometer for medical use, *1st Int. Conf. on Optical Fibre Sensors, London*.

Shimizu *et al.* (1987). High-efficiency Nd-doped fibre lasers using direct-coated dielectric mirrors, *Electron. Lett.*, **23**, 768–769.

Smith, D. W., Harmon, R. A. and Hodgkinson, T. G. (1983). Polarisation stability requirements for coherent optical fibre transmission systems, *British Telecom Tech. J.*, **1** (2), 12–16.

Snitzer, E. *et al.* (1982). In *Fibre Optic Rotation Sensors*, p. 406, Springer, Berlin.

Snitzer, E., Morey, W. W. and Glenn, W. H. (1983). Fiber optic rare-earth temperature sensors, *1st Int. Conf. on Optical Fibre Sensors, London*, pp. 79–81.

Sudo, S., Hosaka, T., Itoh, H. and Okamoto, K. (1986). High-ΔN small-core single-mode fibres for efficient non-linear optical effects, *Electron. Lett.*, **22**, 833–835.

Townsend, J. E., Poole, S. B. and Payne, D. N. (1987). Solution-doping technique for the fabrication of rare-earth-doped optical fibres, *Electron. Lett.*, **23**, 329–331.

Ulrich, R. and Simon, A. (1979). Polarization optics of twisted single-mode fibers, *Appl. Opt.*, **18**, 2241.

Varnham, M. P., Payne, D. N., Birch, R. D. and Tarbox, E. J. (1983a). Single-polarisation operation of highly-birefringent bow-tie optical fibres, *Electron. Lett.*, **19**, 246–247.

Varnham, M. P., Payne, D. N., Birch, R. D. and Tarbox, E. J. (1983b). Bend behaviour of polarising optical fibres, *Electron. Lett.*, **19**, 679–680.

Varnham, M. P., Payne, D. N. and Love, J. D. (1984). Fundamental limits to the transmission of linearly polarised light by birefringent optical fibres, *Electron. Lett.*, **20**, 55–56.

Varnham, M. P., Birch, R. D. and Payne, D. N. (1985). Helical-core circularly-birefringent fibres, *Proc. Integrated Optics and Optical Communication Conf. and European Conf. on Optical Communication, Venice, September 1985*, pp. 135–138.

Xie, H. M., Dabkiewicz, Ph., Ulrich, R. and Okamoto, K. (1986). Side-hole for fiber-optic pressure sensing, *Appl. Opt.*, **11**, 333–335.

Chapter 9

Integrated Optics for Sensors

R. TH. KERSTEN

9.1 Introduction

The history of integrated optics began in December 1969 with a paper published in the *Bell System Technical Journal* (Miller, 1969) where Miller discussed the dream of a new future of integrated circuits which would use photons instead of electrons. In principle this idea was obvious and based on historic experience: today's electronics are possible only because of technological advances in the integration of electronic elements in complicated electronic circuits. In the same manner, the future of optics could be seen in an integration of bulky optics into complicated planar circuits.

Scientists working in the fields of optics, communications and microwaves became euphoric about these predictions and various efforts to realize these new components were initiated worldwide. At that time the main application of this exciting field was seen in optical communications, but the optical computer was also discussed. Optical communications took a large step forward in 1970, when Corning Glass Works announced the first low loss fiber ($20\,dB\,km^{-1}$ at a wavelength of about $800\,nm$) (Kapron *et al.*, 1970). However, it soon became clear that the so-called multimode step-index fibers would not offer the expected properties with respect to bandwidth. Therefore development in optical communications was concentrated on single-mode fibers; this was a real encouragement for integrated optics, because it was already obvious that integrated optics components would offer the most interesting advantages using single-mode technology.

In the middle of the 1970s, however, it was claimed that graded-index multimode fibers would provide the same properties as single-mode fibers but would avoid the adjustment problems because of a much larger core diameter. This was almost the demise of integrated optics; only workers on signal processing survived in the field and the effort in new developments in integrated optics was substantially reduced. Fortunately new bandwidth-limiting effects were discovered with respect to graded-index fibers, and by the end of the 1970s research and development in integrated optics was revitalized.

277

Since then several semicommercial integrated optics elements have been realized, investigated and used in prototypes. In addition, the use of the new fiber optic sensors in optical communications produced new developments in the world of integrated optics, e.g. a gyroscope on a chip (Ezekiel, 1982).

The original proposals for integrated optics components made by Miller in 1969 do not differ very much from today's designs. The question of why these components are still under development and not commercially available in large quantities is quite easy to answer: the technological processes required to produce integrated optics components have not yet reached an economical stage.

9.2 Fundamentals

As in optical fibers light guiding in integrated optics is based on the phenomenon of total internal reflection. Therefore the light is confined to an area of higher refractive index with respect to its surroundings. The materials used for the realization of integrated optics circuits should have low losses at the working wavelength.

9.2.1 Theoretical fundamentals: the slab waveguide

The theoretical approach to a description of integrated optics waveguides uses geometrical ray optics for multimode guides and wave theory for single-mode waveguides. Although integrated optics waveguides can be described in a similar way to optical fibers, complications arise because of the absence of circular geometry. Therefore various numerical methods have been developed.

As an aid to understanding the properties of planar waveguides, we will give a brief description of the theory of the most simple planar waveguide, the slab waveguide, which is shown in Fig. 9.1. It consists of a substrate coated with a thin waveguiding layer of thickness d with $n_1 > n_2$. It is assumed that the surrounding environment (superstrate) is air ($n_3 = 1$), that the substrate and

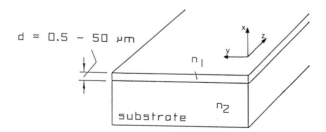

Fig. 9.1   Schematic diagram of a planar slab waveguide; the surrounding environment (superstrate) is assumed to be air ($n_3 = 1$).

waveguide material are ideal (no loss) at the wavelength used and that the substrate–waveguide interface is a perfect plane.

Using Maxwell's equation, we can derive the main equation for this special problem:

$$\frac{\partial^2 E_y}{\partial x^2} + (n_i^2 k_0^2 - \beta^2) E_y = 0 \tag{9.1}$$

where E_y is the electric field in the y direction, n_i is the refractive index of medium i, $k_0 = 2\pi/\lambda_0$ is the propagation constant, λ_0 is the wavelength in a vacuum and β is the propagation constant of the wave in the guide. All the other components can be derived from E_y. If we assume the propagation of a plane wave, i.e.

$$E \approx \exp\{j(\omega t - \beta z)\} \tag{9.2}$$

where ω is the circular frequency and z is the direction of propagation, we can calculate three different solutions for the three media substrate, waveguide and superstrate. By postulating continuity at the interfaces, we obtain the eigenvalue equation for the planar slab waveguide:

$$\frac{2\pi d\gamma}{\lambda_0} - \arctan\left(\frac{q_2\sigma}{\gamma}\right) - \arctan\left(\frac{q_3\alpha}{\gamma}\right) = m\pi \tag{9.3}$$

where

$$\gamma = \{n_1^2 - (\beta/k_0)^2\}^{1/2}$$
$$\sigma = \{(\beta/k_0)^2 - n_2^2\}^{1/2}$$
$$\alpha = \{(\beta/k_0)^2 - n_3^2\}^{1/2} \tag{9.4}$$
$$q_i = \begin{cases} 1 & \text{TE modes} \\ (n_1/n_i)^2 & \text{TM modes} \end{cases} \quad i = 2 \text{ and } 3$$

Obviously there are two different types of waves (or modes) that can propagate in the slab waveguide: transverse electric (TE) modes and transverse magnetic (TM) modes. The two mode types have different polarizations, i.e. TE modes are polarized parallel and TM modes perpendicular to the waveguide surface. Polarization refers to the electric field vector, which is perpendicular to the propagation direction.

Although we have been treating the most simple form of waveguide (the planar waveguide) eqn (9.3) is a transcendental equation which cannot be solved analytically. However, some important information can be obtained from eqn (9.3) which will be used in the field of integrated optics sensors. The solution of eqn (9.3) can only be real if all eqns (9.4) are real, from which it follows that

$$n_1 \geqslant \beta/k_0 \geqslant n_2, n_3 \tag{9.5}$$

Assuming TE modes we can calculate the minimum waveguide thickness d_{min} for the mth-order mode as follows:

$$d_{min} = \frac{m\pi + \arctan[q_3\{(n_2{}^2 - n_3{}^2)/(n_1{}^2 - n_2{}^2)\}^{1/2}]}{k_0(n_1{}^2 - n_2{}^2)^{1/2}} \quad (9.6)$$

If the thickness d becomes smaller than d_{min}, the wave can no longer propagate.

A very important special case is $m = 0$ (the fundamental mode) and $n_2 = n_3$ (i.e. the waveguide is covered with a material of the same refractive index as the substrate). Then d_{min} becomes zero, i.e. the fundamental mode can propagate (theoretically) even if the waveguide becomes infinitely thin. This behavior corresponds to an optical fiber in which the core is surrounded by one material only.

We can obtain the cut-off wavelength λ_{max} for the mth-order mode in a similar way:

$$\lambda_{max} = \frac{2\pi d(n_1{}^2 - n_2{}^2)^{1/2}}{m\pi + \arctan[q_3\{(n_2{}^2 - n_3{}^2)/(n_1{}^2 - n_2{}^2)\}^{1/2}]} \quad (9.7)$$

This corresponds to the cut-off wavelength of an optical fiber.

The eigenvalue equation (9.3) can be solved either numerically or geometrically. If we know the propagation constant β for all propagating

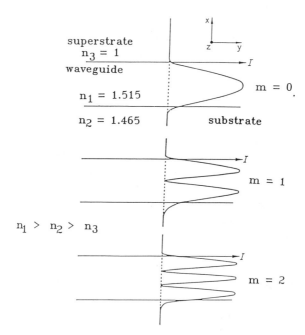

Fig. 9.2 Intensity distribution of modes of order zero to 2 for a slab waveguide in a special configuration.

modes, we can evaluate the electromagnetic fields or, more obviously, the intensity distribution. Examples are given in Fig. 9.2 (note the coordinate system!). From this we obtain the following important information, which we will use later:

(1) the mode order m is identical with the number of intensity minima;

(2) the light intensity is not restricted to the waveguide region only but penetrates into the surroundings;

(3) the smaller the difference between the refractive indices of the waveguide and the surroundings is, the further the light intensity penetrates out of the guide;

(4) the higher the mode order is, the stronger is the intensity penetration out of the guide.

Points (2)–(4) are relevant to evanescent wave sensors (for both fibers and integrated optic waveguides).

We can define a structural constant V for slab waveguides similar to that for a fiber (again assuming $n_2 > n_3$):

$$V = \frac{d\pi}{\lambda_0}(n_1{}^2 - n_2{}^2)^{1/2} \qquad (9.8)$$

This can be used for a rough estimate of the total number M of propagating modes for a slab waveguide:

$$M = \frac{4V}{\pi} \qquad (9.9)$$

9.2.2 Structures

In principle a number of different waveguiding structures have been proposed and realized. In addition to slab waveguides, which have been treated above, channel (or strip) waveguides are important. Unfortunately the nomenclature is still inconsistent: slab waveguides are sometimes called two-dimensional waveguides (light is guided in two dimensions, i.e. transverse and longitudinal) and channel waveguides are known as three-dimensional waveguides (guiding takes place in all three dimensions). While slab waveguides are used for fundamental investigations as well as for optical signal processing, channel waveguides are used in connection with fiber optics.

Various guiding structures have been investigated for channel waveguides (Fig. 9.3). The simplest (Fig. 9.3(a)) is a high index strip, which is generally rectangular, deposited on a low index substrate. As in (9.9) the number of guided modes depends on the dimensions, the refractive indices and the wavelength. Because the guide is not circularly symmetric (like fibers), we have to distinguish between lateral and transverse modes. The larger the

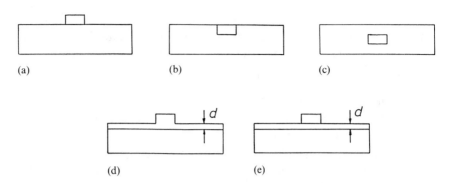

Fig. 9.3 Channel waveguide structures: (a) strip waveguide; (b) embedded waveguide;
(c) buried waveguide; (d) ridge waveguide; (e) strip-loaded waveguide.

dimensions of the guide and the difference between the refractive indices of the
guiding and surrounding material are, the higher will be the number of guided
modes. Therefore one disadvantage of the structure in Fig. 9.3(a) becomes
obvious: despite the presence of the substrate, the whole guide is surrounded
by air and hence the index difference is large. Therefore to obtain a single-
mode waveguide the dimensions have to be reduced to very small values (in the
range of micrometers or even less); this usually results in severe technological
problems.

To avoid this problem the guide can be embedded in the substrate
(Fig. 9.3(b)) so that only one face is adjacent to the surrounding air. However,
there is still a disadvantage with respect to guiding loss as the amount of
scattered light depends on the surface roughness as well as the index difference.
Therefore such guides have to be prepared with high precision to avoid
additional losses: to reduce the additional loss caused by surface roughness to
below $1\,\mathrm{dB\,cm^{-1}}$, the roughness of the guide interface with the air must be less
than 50 nm!

This problem can be avoided by burying the guide well below the
substrate surface (Fig. 9.3(c)). In this case all guide–substrate interfaces have
the same refractive index difference, which is usually small, and the preparation of low loss waveguides is much easier. However, special techniques are
required to prepare such buried guides.

Two other guide structures are important, particularly for integrated
optics using semiconductor materials (i.e. III–V compounds). Figure 9.3(d)
shows the ridge waveguide. First a slab waveguide is deposited on the
substrate, and then the slab thickness d outside the guide is reduced (by
chemical etching for example) below the cut-off thickness of the fundamental
mode. The light is therefore confined to the thicker part of the slab structure.
The strip-loaded channel waveguide (Fig. 9.3(e)) is similar. In this case a slab
structure, which is too thin to guide any mode (i.e. $d < d_{\mathrm{min}}$), is loaded with a

strip of a high index material (usually different from the slab material) so that together they form a channel waveguide.

No standard classification of waveguides is given in the literature. However, to avoid any misunderstanding we will use the classification given in Table 9.1 in the remainder of this chapter.

Table 9.1   Classification of integrated optics waveguides

Passive	Waveguides with fixed properties (e.g. beam splitters, curvatures, crossings etc.)
Passive and dynamic	Waveguides with variable properties (e.g. modulators, switches etc.)
Active	Optically active waveguides (e.g. lasers, amplifiers, parametric oscillators etc.)
	Single mode Multimode

9.2.3 Theory of strip waveguides

It is obvious, in view of the complexity of the theory of slab waveguides, that the treatment of strip waveguides will be complicated. Therefore we will give only a brief description of some of the approaches adopted.

Marcatili (1969) adopted an approach based on slab waveguide theory. Two slab waveguides are assumed to cross at right angles. By looking for one solution for both guides, we should obtain a description of modes propagating in the rectangular area covered by both of them, as can be seen in Fig. 9.4. However, the following problems arise with this simplification: the shaded areas in Fig. 9.4 are not taken into account; because of other approximations,

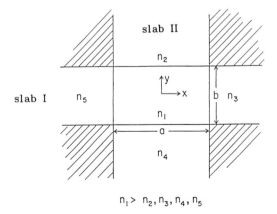

$$n_1 > n_2, n_3, n_4, n_5$$

Fig. 9.4   Schematic diagram of the slab waveguide approach to a description of strip waveguides: slabs I and II cross and form a strip guide (refractive index n_1).

the theory is inaccurate for small dimensions and hence it is generally invalid for single-mode waveguides.

In view of these limitations other approaches have been made. One of the most powerful numerical approaches is the beam propagation (BP) method which is widely used to investigate integrated optical structures. This method (Feit and Fleck, 1978) has been improved, and with today's computer technology programs can be run on personal computers. A detailed discussion of this numerical approach can be found elsewhere (Thylen, 1983). A diagram of a special guiding structure (for details see Section 9.2.5.1) and the corresponding behavior of the fundamental mode with a Gaussian intensity distribution coupled to guide 1 can be seen in Fig. 9.5 (Bernard and Schlaak,

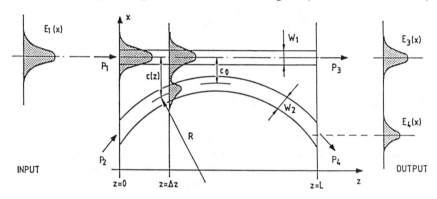

(a)

BPM: relates optical field E $(z=\Delta z)$ to optical field E $(z=0)$

E $(z=\Delta z)$ = $\{$operator$\}$ E $(z=0)$

Operator solution of scalar wave equation

$$\nabla^2 E + k^2 n^2 E = 0$$

$$n^2 = n^2 (x,z)$$

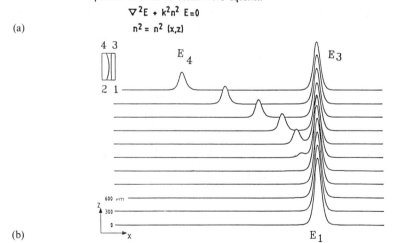

(b)

Fig. 9.5 Example of a BP calculation: (a) schematic diagram of the structure to be evaluated; (b) intensity distribution of the light along the guides if guide 1 is excited.

1984). Figure 9.5(a) shows the arrangement of the waveguides and explains the principle of the BP method. Figure 9.5(b) demonstrates a calculation for the structure given in Fig. 9.5(a) if $P_1 = 1$ and $P_2 = 0$ at $z = 0$. The coupling between the waveguides can be seen (compare Section 9.2.5.1).

A major advantage of the BP method is that almost arbitrary refractive index distributions can be used for the calculation. This is important, because some of the technologies used for the fabrication of integrated optical waveguides provide graded-index rather than step-index waveguides.

9.2.4 Principal structures

Integrated optics circuits are composed of a few fundamental waveguiding structures which are shown in Fig. 9.6. Figure 9.6(a) shows the most simple element: a straight guide which connects other integrated optics elements. It should be noted that curved guides are allowed but corners are not (in contrast with electrical integrated circuits). However, for technological reasons, corners with small angles, i.e. less than 1°, are used; the allowed radius of curvature depends very much on the refractive index difference and is usually large (with respect to the wavelength of light).

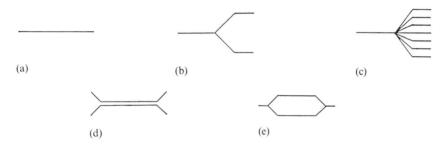

Fig. 9.6 Fundamental integrated optics strip waveguide structures: (a) straight strip guide; (b) Y junction; (c) 1–7 star coupler; (d) directional coupler; (e) Mach–Zehnder interferometer.

Figure 9.6(b) shows a branch or Y junction which is used either to split or to combine the light. A similar but more complicated structure—the 1–7 star coupler—is shown in Fig. 9.6(c). It must be emphasized that the elements shown in Figs 9.6(a)–9.6(c) can be either single-mode or multimode waveguides and that the structures shown are sketches; actual waveguides are usually more complicated.

In the case of multimode waveguides, structures such as those shown in Figs 9.6(b) and 9.6(c) are very difficult to design because every mode behaves individually. Therefore the function depends very much on the mode excitation. This implies that integrated optics is mainly a single-mode technology.

Figures 9.6(d) and 9.6(e) will be discussed in Section 9.2.5.1 and Section 9.2.5.2 respectively.

9.2.5 Combined structures

Because of their importance, two single-mode waveguide structures consisting of a combination of some principal structures discussed earlier will be treated in more detail. These structures are the directional coupler and the Mach–Zehnder interferometer.

9.2.5.1 Directional coupler

A typical directional coupler, shown schematically in Fig. 9.6(d), realized using LiNbO₃ technology (see Section 9.3) is depicted in Fig. 9.7. It consists of two adjacent parallel waveguides and four lead-down–lead-up waveguides. If light is coupled to waveguide 1, it will penetrate into the surroundings and will

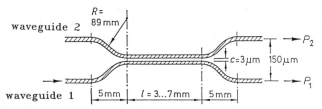

Fig. 9.7   Design of a directional coupler realized in LiNbO₃.

finally "see" guide 2 in the parallel section of the two waveguides. Because of the evanescent field, the light power will couple to guide 2. Under certain circumstances, the light from guide 1 will be completely coupled to guide 2 and then back again and so forth. Using a simple planar slab model, which describes the parallel waveguide section only, we obtain the following formulae for the electric fields in guides 1 and 2:

$$E_1(z) = \exp(-jb_+ z)\left[\left\{\cos(bz) - j\frac{b_-}{b}\sin(bz)\right\}E_1(0) + j\frac{c_{12}}{b}\sin(bz)\,E_2(0)\right] \quad (9.10)$$

$$E_2(z) = \exp(-jb_+ z)\left[\left\{\cos(bz) + j\frac{b_-}{b}\sin(bz)\right\}E_2(0) + j\frac{c_{12}}{b}\sin(bz)\,E_1(0)\right] \quad (9.11)$$

where

$$b = \left(\frac{\beta_1 - \beta_2}{2}\right)^2 + c_{12}{}^2$$

$$b_- = \frac{\beta_1 - \beta_2}{2} \quad\quad\quad (9.12)$$

$$b_+ = \frac{\beta_1 + \beta_2}{2}$$

c_{12} is the coupling coefficient between the two guides and depends on their separation c and geometry, the wavelength and the refractive indices of the whole structure. Usually c_{12} is determined experimentally because it is influenced by unavoidable technological tolerances during the fabrication process.

We are interested in the output powers of guides 1 and 2. By evaluating eqns (9.10) and (9.11) we can plot the light powers P_1 of guide 1 and P_2 of guide 2 as a function of the normalized coupler length $c_{12}z/\pi$. In Fig. 9.8 we have assumed that $\beta_1 = \beta_2$, i.e. waveguides 1 and 2 are completely identical. The periodic power transfer can be seen: the power is completely coupled from guide 1 to guide 2 at $c_{12}z/\pi = 0.5$ and back again at $c_{12}z/\pi = 1$. However, $\beta_1 = \beta_2$ can only be achieved theoretically. Therefore Fig. 9.9 shows similar plots for different values of c_{12} and for $(\beta_1 - \beta_2)/2 = 0.75\,\text{mm}^{-1}$. Two facts are important: 100% coupling no longer occurs, and the coupling periodicity changes with c_{12} and is always less than for $\beta_1 = \beta_2$.

In this approximate theoretical approach the parallel section of the coupler was treated in only a simple way. The connecting waveguides have to be included in the theoretical calculation also, because there is already substantial coupling between the guides before they reach their smallest separation c (see Fig. 9.7).

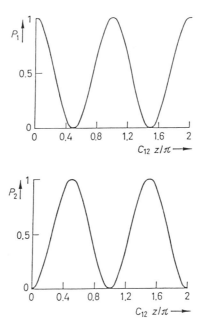

Fig. 9.8 Output powers P_1 and P_2 at guides 1 and 2 respectively as a function of the normalized coupler length $c_{12}z/\pi$ for $\beta_1 = \beta_2$.

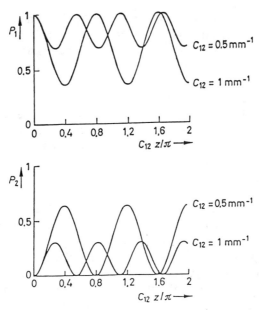

Fig. 9.9 As for Fig. 9.8 but with $(\beta_1 - \beta_2)/2 = 0.75 \, \text{mm}^{-1}$ and various values of c_{12}.

Unusual couplers in which there is no parallel section have been analyzed using the BP method. Such couplers have one very important feature—their behavior seems to be nonreciprocal, i.e. the outputs from ports 3 and 4 when light is launched from port 1 are generally in a different ratio from the outputs from ports 1 and 2 when light is launched from port 4. This is because the output mode shapes are different at the two outputs and the "intermediate" common modes in the coupling region are launched with different overlap integrals depending on the symmetry of the input port. These observations apply to all structures which are not symmetric about the z (propagation) direction.

9.2.5.2 Integrated optics Mach–Zehnder interferometer

The integrated optics Mach–Zehnder interferometer consists of two combined Y junctions as shown schematically in Fig. 9.6(e). Light is coupled to the structure and is divided into two guided waves by the first Y junction. The two guided waves travel along the two arms of the interferometer and are combined by the second Y junction. Because the two waves are excited by the same source, they are coherent and interfere if the difference between the lengths of the two arms is less than the coherence length of the light used.

We can distinguish two different situations at the second Y junction.

(1) The two waves are in phase: they will interfere constructively and will be guided to the output port.

(2) The two waves have a phase difference of π (or an odd multiple of π): they interfere destructively and will form a higher-order mode (Fig. 9.10) which will not be guided by the waveguide. Consequently the light is irradiated into the substrate.

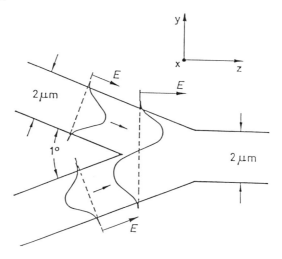

Fig. 9.10 The two fundamental modes with a phase shift of π relative to each other in the two arms of a Mach–Zehnder interferometer are combined destructively at the second Y junction. The mode of order 1 cannot be guided in the single-mode exit waveguide (2 µm) and is irradiated into the substrate.

All other states between these two extremes are possible depending on the phase difference between the two waves guided in the two interferometer arms.

Mach–Zehnder interferometers for special applications can be realized by a combined fiber–integrated optics technology. For example, if a very long interferometer arm is needed, this can be accomplished using a fiber while the two Y junctions are integrated optics circuits (Eberhard and Voges, 1988). All sensing effects in Mach–Zehnder interferometers depend on different influences on the phase velocity of the guided waves in the two interferometer arms. A typical example of a temperature sensor is given by Haruna et al. (1985), and Enokihara et al. (1988) describe a fluid sensor.

9.2.6 Passive dynamic structures

Passive dynamic structures can change their behavior under an external influence, e.g. a Mach–Zehnder interferometer may go from a 100% output to a zero output. A variety of physical effects can be used to achieve this, of which the most important are the electro-optic effect, the acousto-optic effect and the thermo-optic effect. The efficiency of the effect depends on the material. In the early days of integrated optics the use of the electro-optic effect was common because $LiNbO_3$ has a high electro-optic coefficient, i.e. the refractive index changes very significantly if the material is placed in an electric field.

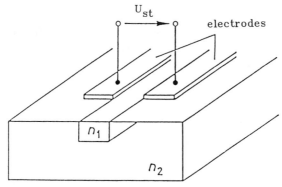

Fig. 9.11 Schematic diagram of a phase modulator: an example of a passive dynamic strip waveguide.

The simplest structure is shown in Fig. 9.11. The guide is placed between two electrodes. If the guide material has a sufficiently high electro-optic coefficient, a voltage U_{st} will cause a phase change φ in the light wave. This phase shift is given by

$$\varphi = \frac{2\pi}{\lambda_0} l \, \Delta n(E, r, \lambda_0, F) \tag{9.13}$$

where l is the electrode length and the change Δn in the refractive index depends on the electric field E (which depends on U_{st} and the electrode configuration), the electro-optic coefficient r of the material (for anisotropic materials the coefficient parallel to the electric field is effective), the wavelength λ_0 of the light and the overlap F between the electric field of the optical wave and the electric field induced by the voltage. The voltage needed to obtain an optical phase shift of $\pi/2$ is known as $V_{\pi/2}$. In the case of LiNbO$_3$ a few volts are sufficient (depending on the configuration). If such a phase shifter is introduced into the two arms of a Mach–Zehnder interferometer, an on–off switch as well as an intensity modulator can be obtained (Fig. 9.12).

As already discussed in Section 9.5.2.1, any change in the waveguide (i.e. in β) of a directional coupler will change the output of the coupler. According to eqns (9.10) and (9.11), for a directional coupler to be in the cross-state (light coupled to guide 1 will be completely coupled to the output of guide 2) the following conditions must be fulfilled:

$$(2s+1)\frac{\pi}{2} = c_{12} l \qquad s = 0, 1, 2, \ldots$$

$$\beta_1 = \beta_2 \tag{9.14}$$

In the case of a directional coupler made from LiNbO$_3$ which satisfies these conditions, an electric field can be used to make β_1 no longer equal to β_2 and change the output. However, a coupler designed for 100% cross-state cannot be realized in practice because of unavoidable technological tolerances. Thus the $\Delta\beta$ coupler (Fig. 9.13) was designed to use this scheme for switching

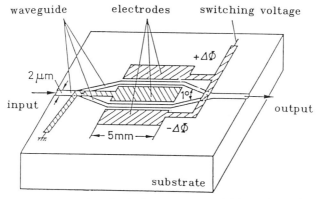

Fig. 9.12   A dynamic Mach–Zehnder interferometer which can be used as an intensity modulator.

purposes. This device consists of two directional couplers in series which can be controlled by two different voltages/electrodes. It has been shown theoretically and experimentally that both the cross-state and the bar-state (all light coupled to guide 1 will emerge from guide 1) can be obtained by using appropriate control voltages (Schmidt and Kogelnik, 1976).

The three principal passive dynamic structures are shown schematically in Fig. 9.14.

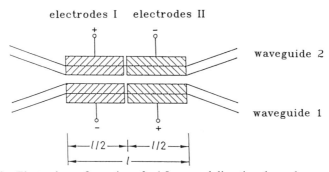

Fig. 9.13   Electrode configuration of a $\Delta\beta$-reversal directional coupler arrangement.

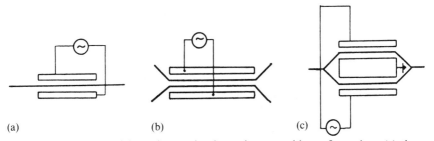

Fig. 9.14   Summary of the major passive dynamic waveguide configurations: (a) phase modulator; (b) directional coupler; (c) Mach–Zehnder interferometer.

9.3 Materials

So far we have discussed the principles of integrated optics without considering the realization of devices. As has already been mentioned, a low loss material which allows for the preparation of waveguides (i.e. structured areas with increased refractive index) is needed. At present three material systems are important with respect to integrated optics technology: glass; dielectric crystals; semiconductors (III–V compounds). A summary of the materials, the technology and the losses for a straight single-mode channel waveguide is given in Table 9.2.

Table 9.2 Materials for integrated optics

Material	Glass	Crystal (LiNbO$_3$)	Semiconductor (InGaAsP)
Technology	Ion exchange Sputtering CVD	Ti in-diffusion Proton exchange	LPE MOCVD MBE
Loss (dB cm^{-1})	0.01	0.1	1

CVD, chemical vapor deposition; LPE, liquid phase epitaxy; MOCVD, metallo-organic chemical vapor deposition; MBE, molecular beam epitaxy.

Whereas ion exchange is the most important technology for glass and titanium in-diffusion is the most important technology for LiNbO$_3$ (a crystal with a high electro-optic constant), there is no preferred technology for InGaAsP. It is likely that metallo-organic chemical vapor deposition (MOCVD) will be the most suitable because it is possible to prepare large substrates which are sufficiently homogeneous.

Obviously glass is used for passive waveguides such as bifurcations or combiners. Therefore it is both a multimode and a single-mode technology. Both LiNbO$_3$ and InGaAsP can be used to build passive dynamic waveguides, generally based on the electro-optic effect. Finally, III–V compounds can be used to fabricate active elements such as lasers or light amplifiers. Therefore this technology offers the broadest spectrum for the realization of complex integrated optics circuits. However, the technology is very complicated because each element (laser, guide and detector) to be integrated on a common substrate must be realized with different material combinations to allow for good performance (high gain, low loss and high absorption).

It is estimated that semiconductor integrated optics is unlikely to be used for another 5–10 years. LiNbO$_3$ has been used in most laboratory demonstrations, and integrated optics elements are now available commercially (Crystal Technology, USA; Barr and Stroud, UK). Because glass is restricted to passive components only, there has been little interest. However, new fiber optics concepts for local area networks or distributed sensors require passive and simple (equivalent to cheap) optical elements (mainly splitters and combiners). It is unlikely that fused fiber couplers can be mass produced and offered at low price. Therefore glass integrated optics has increased in importance within the last few years. Finally the use of the thermo-optic effect in glass (Haruna and Koyama, 1984) enables slow passive dynamic elements to be fabricated.

9.4 Technology

The different materials which can be used for integrated optics are summarized in Table 9.3. We will use the typical representatives given in Table 9.2, i.e. glass, $LiNbO_3$ and InGaAsP, for the three classes of materials.

Table 9.3 Comparison of materials for integrated optics

	Glass	Crystal	Semiconductor
Technology	Simple	Moderate	Complex
Loss	Very low	Low	Medium
Integration density	Low	Low	Medium
Electro-optic and similar effects	Very low	High	High
Optical amplification	None	Low	High
Nonlinear effect	Very low	High	?
Availability	Very good	Medium	Poor

9.4.1 Fabrication of glass waveguides

Two different technologies are used for the fabrication of glass waveguides: the ion exchange process and the silica-on-silicon (SOS) technology.

9.4.1.1 The ion exchange process
The principle of this process is shown in Fig. 9.15. A glass containing ions M_1^+ is immersed in a salt containing ions M_2^+. If the salt is heated above its melting point, a thermal ion exchange can occur: the ions M_1^+ in the glass are exchanged with the ions M_2^+ in the salt melt. By using an appropriate ion combination (e.g. exchange of Na^+ ions in the glass with Ag^+ ions in the melt), the refractive index will be increased. However, an additional important advantage of this technology is that a decrease in the index is also possible. A summary of usable ions is given in Table 9.4, together with the possible index differences and ionic radii. If two ions with a large difference in ionic radius are exchanged, high mechanical stress will occur in the glass and this generally destroys the surface. It is also important that the materials used are easy to handle, e.g. they are nontoxic. Therefore Table 9.4 also gives the lethal dose for

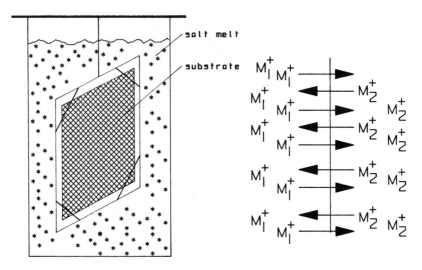

Fig. 9.15   Principle of thermal ion exchange in glass.

Table 9.4 M^+ ions for the salt bath

Ion	Ionic radius (pm)	Coordination number	Δn	$LD_{50}/salt$ (mg kg^{-1})
Li$^+$	59	4	0.02	710/Li$_2$CO$_3$
	76	6		
Na$^+$	99	4	0.002–0.02	1955/NaNO$_3$
	102	6		
K$^+$	138	6	0.009	1894/KNO$_3$
Rb$^+$	152	6	0.01	1200/RbCl
Cs$^+$	167	6	0.04	1200/CsNO$_3$
Ag$^+$	126	6	0.10	2820/Ag$_2$O
Tl$^+$	150	6	0.10	25/Tl$_2$SO$_4$

LD_{50}, dose which is lethal to 50% of animals tested.

the various salt baths. As can be seen, Ag$^+$ ion exchange is the most desirable, and Tl$^+$ exchange should be avoided.

The ion exchange technique shown in Fig. 9.15 is usually very slow, and the fabrication of multimode waveguides takes a long time (some days). Thus the field-assisted ion exchange technique shown in Fig. 9.16 is used for these applications. The principle is the same, but the front and back of the substrate are separated electrically and the exchange salt is at the front only. The exchange is accelerated by applying a voltage (a field of about 50 V mm^{-1} is commonly used) between the front and the back of the substrate. Whereas in thermal exchange both sides of the substrate are treated in the same manner, field-assisted exchange produces a higher index at the surface and could give a

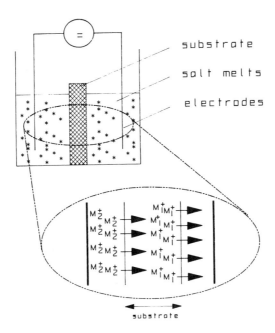

Fig. 9.16   Field-assisted ion exchange in glass.

lower index at the back of the substrate. This again may lead to opposing surface tensions in the substrate, and if it is too thin it will bend. The thermal and field-assisted processes also result in different index profiles, as can be seen in Fig. 9.17. The thermal exchange produces an exponential decrease in the refractive index, whereas the field-assisted exchange gives a step-like profile. This step-like profile can be changed to a Gaussian profile by annealing. The

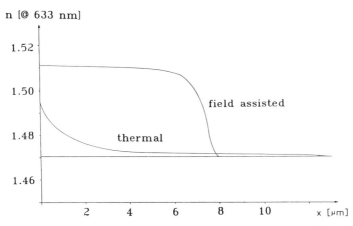

Fig. 9.17   Refractive index profiles generated using thermal and field-assisted ion exchange in glass.

reduction in processing time achieved with field-assisted exchange is about an order of magnitude compared with thermal exchange. In the case of multimode waveguides in particular (and multimode fibers, i.e. $50/125\,\mu m$ graded-index fibers), only field-assisted exchange is recommended.

Various investigations of waveguides fabricated using ion exchange have been reported. However, when the experimental results are compared many contradictions can be seen with respect to processing parameters and waveguide properties. This can be explained by the choice of substrate material, which generally has unknown composition and is sometimes unsatisfactory for ion exchange. A summary of various substrate materials which have been used for Na^+–K^+ exchange is given in Table 9.5. Obviously the experiments cannot be compared. To avoid these problems, three different glasses have been developed by Schott Glaswerke and are commercially available. All three glasses are of optical quality and are produced with low tolerances.

Table 9.5   Properties of glasses commonly used in the fabrication of waveguides by ion exchange

Glass	Type	n_d	Ion	Ion concentration (wt%)	Polyvalent impurities
Window/ microscope slide	Soda lime	1.51	Na^+	10–14	High
TiF 6	Phosphate	1.62	Na^+, K^+	23	Low
K 8	Borosilicate	1.52	Na^+, K^+	15	Low
SV–2	Aluminosilicate	—	Na^+, K^+	13	—
S52–2	Aluminoborosilicate	—	Na^+, K^+	6	—
OFE–1	Aluminoborosilicogerm	—	Na^+	7	—
BK7	Borosilicate	1.52	Na^+, K^+	17	Low
Pyrex	Borosilicate	1.47	Na^+	7	High
D 263	Borosilicate	1.52	Na^+, K^+	13	Middle
S 8011	Silicate	1.53	Na^+	15	Low

BGG 21 is a glass optimized for Cs^+ ion exchange. Because of the low diffusion constant of Cs^+ ions this glass is used for the fabrication of single-mode waveguides. The properties of the glass are highly controlled and therefore the parameters for the ion exchange can be calculated to produce a given refractive index distribution or change by using the diffusion constant, which is given as a function of temperature in Fig. 9.18. The glass has a very good transmission (less than $0.01\,dB\,cm^{-1}$) and is fitted to quartz glass fibers ($n_d = 1.463$) to avoid any reflection losses at the fiber–waveguide interface.

Two other glasses, BGG 31 and BGG 35, have been developed for the fabrication of multimode waveguides using Ag^+ ion exchange. It has been

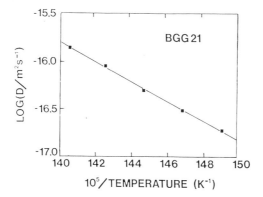

Fig. 9.18   Diffusion constant of Cs^+ in BGG 21 as a function of temperature.

reported that when Ag^+ is used as the exchange ion, absorption occurs owing to the presence of metallic silver in the waveguide. A typical example is given in Fig. 9.19 for the technical glass B270; the reduction in transmission caused by the presence of silver is clearly seen. However, the compositions of BGG 31 and BGG 35 avoid this problem. BGG 31 is optimized for smaller refractive index changes, as can be seen in Fig. 9.20. By choosing an appropriate salt melt composition, the refractive index change can be set to the required value. BGG 35 is used for waveguides with refractive index changes as high as 0.1.

The salt melts used for the ion exchange are quite aggressive, particularly at the high temperatures required. Therefore the glass has to be stable to avoid any surface change because this would cause additional scattering loss. In the fabrication of strip waveguides a suitable masking material is required in addition to the glass. Such a masking material must be able to withstand the

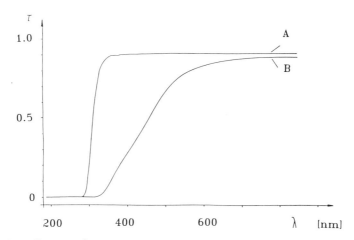

Fig. 9.19   Effect of Ag^+ ion on the transmission behavior of a slab of B270 glass 2 mm thick: curve A, before ion exchange; curve B, after ion exchange.

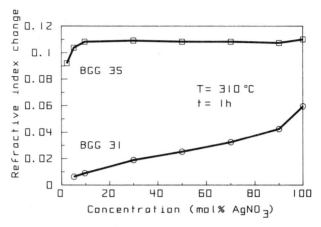

Fig. 9.20 Change produced by Ag^+ ion exchange in the refractive index of BGG 31 and BGG 35 glasses as a function of the composition of the salt melt.

aggressive salt melt and protect the substrate surface from ion exchange and must also be easily removable after the exchange process. Various masking materials have been investigated. A suitable material is titanium, which is stable in the melt and can be dissolved in certain chemicals which do not affect the glass.

9.4.1.2 Silica-on-silicon technology

SOS technology has been developed in parallel by NTT (Kawachi *et al.*, 1985) and CNET (Valette *et al.*, 1983, 1985). The principle of the NTT process is shown in Fig. 9.21. A thin layer of pure silica is deposited on a silicon

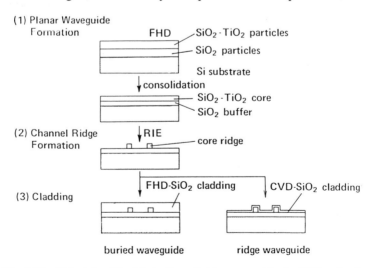

Fig. 9.21 Principle of the fabrication of strip waveguides by SOS technology.

substrate using a flame hydrolysis technique (FHD). This layer is used as a buffer between the optical waveguide and the silicon, i.e. it acts as the optical substrate. The guide itself consists of titanium-doped SiO_2; the doping with titanium increases the refractive index. Strip waveguides are formed by reactive ion etching and are then covered with pure FHD-deposited SiO_2 as a superstrate. Both multimode and single-mode waveguides with very good performances have been achieved using this technology. Losses as low as $0.1 \, dB \, cm^{-1}$ have been reported.

As will be discussed later (Section 9.7), SOS technology offers a further advantage: grooves for the alignment of fibers, which will reduce fiber–waveguide coupling problems, can be produced easily.

9.4.2 Titanium in-diffusion into LiNbO₃

The process of in-diffusion of metals into $LiNbO_3$ was first investigated at Bell Laboratories (Schmidt and Kaminow, 1974). The most suitable metal is titanium. The whole process is shown in Fig. 9.22. A mask is deposited on a substrate with a plane-polished surface ($LiNbO_3$ substrates with diameters of up to 3.5 in are now available) using conventional photolithography. This photoresist mask is used to put a structured thin titanium film (20–70 nm thick) on the $LiNbO_3$ surface. The metallic film is in-diffused at about 1000 °C

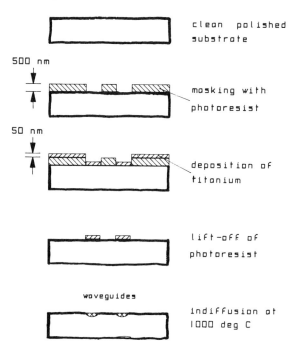

Fig. 9.22 Titanium in-diffusion into LiNbO₃.

for 5–8 h. In this way a waveguide is built. The refractive index difference that can be achieved is about 0.05 but is usually less. Because $LiNbO_3$ is a two-axis crystal, the waveguides show birefringence.

One problem is the so-called out-diffused waveguide. During the high temperature in-diffusion process lithium ions out-diffuse from the crystal surface, forming a higher-index layer which acts as a surface slab waveguide. Leakage may occur from the strip waveguide into this slab. The problem can be avoided by using a water-saturated atmosphere during the diffusion process.

Some other problems also occur with $LiNbO_3$.

(a) The occurrence of optical damage in $LiNbO_3$ depends on the presence of impurities (mainly Fe^{2+}). If optical damage is present, high power densities cannot be guided through $Ti:LiNbO_3$ waveguides because the waveguiding facility is temporarily destroyed. Experimentally the power limits are about $10 \,\mu W$ for single-mode waveguides at 633 nm. The effect vanishes at wavelengths well above $1.3 \,\mu m$. As already stated, the effect depends strongly on the crystal quality. $LiNbO_3$ of integrated optical quality is commercially available, but the problem still exists.

(b) The process parameters required to form a certain waveguide depend strongly on crystal quality. Unfortunately $LiNbO_3$ crystal can be pulled with different Li:Nb ratios. Therefore for the titanium in-diffusion process it is necessary to know the exact Li:Nb ratio of the crystal to be processed.

These difficulties are not insurmountable for fundamental experiments, but so far they have prevented the high yield mass production of such devices.

$LiTaO_3$ can be used instead of $LiNbO_3$. However, because of the low Curie temperature of this material (around 650 °C compared with 1250 °C for $LiNbO_3$) the crystal has to be poled after the diffusion process.

9.4.3 III–V compounds

In the case of III–V compounds, e.g. InGaAsP, several different technologies can be used without any preference. These technologies are already applied in the production of optoelectronic circuits such as semiconductor lasers or light-emitting diodes (LEDs). Because they have already been described in detail elsewhere (Casey and Panish, 1978), they are not discussed here.

As stated earlier, III–V compounds are very promising materials for integrated optics circuits. However, more effort is required to overcome the technological problems. In addition, the main application of III–V integrated optics will be in optical communications (although preliminary results for sensors have been presented (Isaac et al., 1987)). Therefore we will not discuss this material further.

9.5 Losses

Obviously the same loss mechanisms as in optical fibers occur in integrated optics circuits, i.e. scattering, absorption and radiation.

Scattering is caused by two different effects: volume scattering and surface scattering. Whereas volume scattering effects exceed surface scattering effects in fiber optics, the reverse is true in integrated optics. This is because the fibers are reduced in dimension during the fabrication process, i.e. the large preforms are pulled to very small fibers. Thus any surface defect is reduced. However, integrated optics are produced on a 1:1 scale. As noted earlier, even a low roughness at a waveguide–air interface causes large losses. Buried waveguides can be used to overcome this problem. The use of a diffused graded-index distribution also decreases the effect of geometrical distortions.

Because of the short waveguide length in integrated optics the absorption losses can usually be neglected.

Radiation losses may occur at waveguide imperfections, i.e. if the waveguide geometry changes abruptly (because of a masking error for example), and are unavoidable at the boundary of a straight and a bent guide. However, radiation losses are severest at sharp bends. The minimum radius of curvature for negligible radiation loss depends on the waveguide structure, i.e. the index difference, the wavelength, the index distribution and the mode number. The theory is very complicated and the limits are generally found empirically.

There is a trade-off between the minimum radius of curvature (which is needed for a high integration density) and the ease of fabrication, i.e. the waveguide dimensions. As already noted, the waveguide dimensions depend on the refractive index difference. If the difference is large, the dimensions for single-mode waveguides become very small (too small for any fabrication process) and the scattering becomes large, but the radius of curvature can be made very small. Therefore it is necessary to find a compromise. This also depends on the waveguide material used. Ion exchange in glass allows refractive index differences of up to 0.1, titanium in-diffusion in $LiNbO_3$ gives differences of 0.05 and III–V compounds give differences of 0.1 or more. Therefore the radius of curvature is usually of the order of centimeters in $LiNbO_3$, millimeters in glass and hundreds of micrometers in III–V compounds.

9.6 Processing steps

To build integrated optics waveguides it is not sufficient just to create an area of high refractive index within a substrate of lower index. Many different processing steps are necessary to fabricate complex integrated optics circuits. This is shown schematically in Fig. 9.23. In addition to the fabrication of the

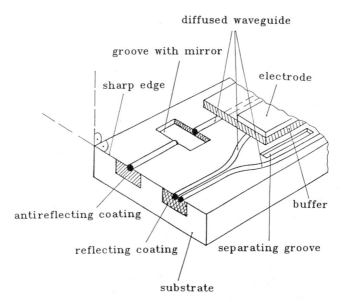

Fig. 9.23   Diagram of the various processing steps for the realization of an integrated optics circuit.

waveguide an etching process is required either to interrupt the waveguides (groove with mirror) or to avoid interaction between two adjacent waveguides (separating groove). Thin film technology is also necessary to provide antireflecting coatings, mirrors or buffer layers. Buffer layers are needed if the waveguide is not buried and metallic electrodes have to be deposited on top of the waveguides. These metallic electrodes can attenuate the guided light and therefore must be separated from the guide by a dielectric buffer layer with a low optical loss. Finally preparation of the edge of the waveguide is not a trivial problem because the edge between the front-end and the substrate surface has to be very sharp to prevent destruction of the waveguide end.

9.7 Coupling

So far in this chapter we have assumed that the light is already traveling in the integrated optics waveguide. In the case of III–V compound integrated optics this assumption may be valid because light can be generated and detected in the integrated optics circuit itself. However, in the case of glass or LiNbO$_3$ waveguides the light has to be coupled in and out.

Several schemes have been used. The prism coupler provides a simple method for experiments. A second possibility is the holographic grating coupler. However, the efficiency depends strongly on the optimization of the grating period with respect to the waveguide, i.e. the guided mode. Therefore

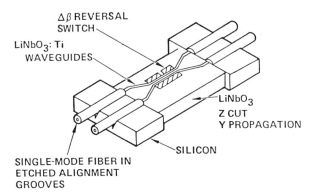

Fig. 9.24 Butt-coupling of fibers with integrated optics waveguides using V grooves etched in silicon for alignment.

this method is not very suitable for the investigation of unknown waveguides. In addition, the fabrication (which generally requires interferometry) is very complicated.

The most convenient method is end-fire coupling using a microscope objective lens or, in the case of commercial applications, a fiber as shown in Fig. 9.24. (Usually only the microscope coupling is known as "end-fire coupling", and the direct fiber access is called "butt-coupling".) In both cases polishing of the end-face of the substrate presents severe problems, and additional problems arise when butt-coupling is used:

(1) alignment of the fiber with respect to the integrated optics waveguide is difficult because the guide is invisible in most cases;

(2) the fiber must be fixed without disturbing the alignment, and the glue used (which is usually ultraviolet hardening) must have a very low shrinkage or the alignment will vary causing increased coupling losses;

(3) the mode fields of the integrated optics waveguide and of the fiber should be identical or very similar to ensure low coupling losses.

A number of methods of overcoming the alignment problem have been proposed. SOS technology offers the option of fabricating fiber-alignment grooves beside the waveguides. An example is shown schematically in Fig. 9.25 (Kawachi *et al.*, 1985). Because the grooves are fabricated using the same processing steps and the same mask, ideal alignment is guaranteed in the lateral direction. However, in the transverse direction the thickness of the buffer layer must be controlled to submicron accuracy, which is not easy to achieve. Nevertheless, low coupling losses have been demonstrated experimentally.

An alternative solution has been proposed for ion-exchanged multimode waveguides. V grooves are embossed into the substrate by precision molding,

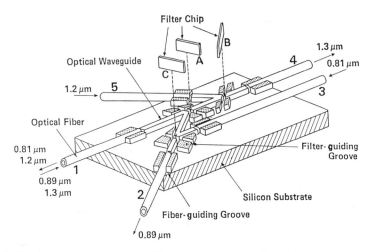

Fig. 9.25 Alignment grooves for fiber–waveguide coupling fabricated by the SOS process. The example shows an optical filter arrangement used for demultiplexing.

and these are used to align the fibers with respect to the waveguide (Beguin *et al.*, 1988). Very low coupling losses with this technique have been demonstrated in experimental investigations of multimode star couplers (up to 1–16) (Beguin *et al.*, 1988). However, a compromise is necessary because glasses optimized for precision molding are not usually optimal for the production of waveguides by the ion exchange technique. In addition, because of the tolerances of the embossed grooves the technique is suitable for multimode waveguides only.

Source–fiber coupling is easy for coupling between the source and an integrated optics circuit. Therefore the fiber-pigtailed integrated optics circuit is the most practical configuration for commercial applications.

The mode field of an integrated optics waveguide can be made comparable with that of a fiber by using the double-diffusion technique of ion exchange technology. After the first ion exchange, in which the guide is fabricated just beneath the surface, the mode field is usually elliptical. This elliptical field can be changed to a circular field by performing a second process step which re-exchanges the ions at the surface. The processing parameters have to be determined empirically, but once this has been done the process is reproducible. Very good results have been obtained by a number of groups (e.g. Ikeda *et al.*, 1987; Beguin *et al.*, 1988).

9.8 Integrated optics circuits in or as sensors

So far we have only discussed the fundamentals and realization of integrated optics. However, what are the advantages of using integrated optics circuits in or as sensors? The main advantages are miniaturization, the need for fewer adjustments and the development of new optical structures. These result in cost reduction and technical improvement.

In the following we will discuss examples of integrated optics circuits in sensors, of which some have been fabricated as prototypes and some are still at the proposal stage.

9.8.1 Evanescent field sensor

Evanescent field sensors play an important role in fiber optic sensors (Paul and Kychakoff, 1987), and configurations using integrated optics have been proposed. A typical arrangement with a Mach–Zehnder interferometer is shown in Fig. 9.26 (Harmer, 1985). One arm of the interferometer is protected from its surroundings and the other is exposed. Because the optical field is not

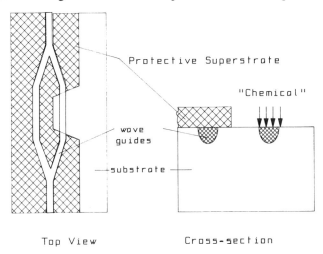

Top View   Cross-section

Fig. 9.26 Chemical sensor using the evanescent field in a Mach–Zehnder interferometer configuration.

totally restricted to the waveguide but some of the field is traveling as an evanescent wave at the guide–surface interface, any change in the surrounding medium will influence the guided mode. In this manner chemicals can be identified through their refractive indices. Although absolute measurements are very difficult, a high relative sensitivity can be achieved. An estimate of the sensitivity is given by

$$\frac{I_x}{I_0} = \frac{1 + \cos \varphi}{2}$$

$$\varphi = 2\pi \frac{L_2 n_2 - L_1 n_1}{\lambda_0}$$

where I_0 is the light intensity coupled to the Mach–Zehnder interferometer and I_x is the output intensity which depends on the phase difference φ between the two arms. φ depends on the difference between the optical lengths of the arms ($L_1 n_1$ and $L_2 n_2$ respectively). If it is assumed that the mode propagation depends linearly on the refractive index of the surface (which is not strictly true), index differences as low as 10^{-5} can be detected.

This principle has also been used successfully for the hydrogen sensor shown schematically in Fig. 9.27 (Nishizawa *et al.*, 1985). It consists of a single-mode Y junction in which one arm acts as the reference and the second as the sensor. The sensor arm is coated with a thin layer of WO_3 (directly above the waveguide) on top of which is a thin layer of palladium. The palladium layer acts as a catalytic layer through which only hydrogen ions can penetrate. The WO_3 and the hydrogen react and the colorless WO_3 is reduced to a colored $H_{2x}WO_3$ layer, which will absorb some of the light guided by the waveguide.

Another sensor based on the evanescent field uses frustrated total reflection to measure the refractive index of a liquid (Tamela *et al.*, 1987); it

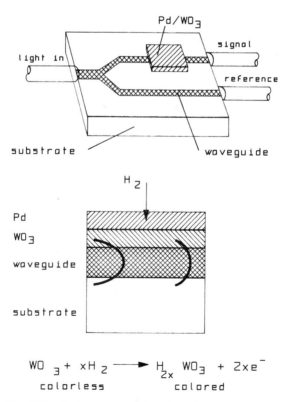

Fig. 9.27 Hydrogen sensor based on the evanescent field.

operates in a similar manner to the sensor described above, but the waveguide edge rather than the waveguide surface is used as the sensing area. This gives a very small sensing surface, which may be useful in special cases but reduces the sensitivity.

9.8.2 Integrated optics and the optical gyroscope

One of the main motivations for integrated optics came from the development of optical gyroscopes which are discussed in detail in Chapter 11 and have been reviewed by Pavlath and Suman (1984). Two different approaches are important with respect to integrated optics: components for fiber gyroscopes; the gyroscope on a chip.

9.8.2.1 Components of the gyroscope
The use of integrated optical circuits in fiber gyroscopes is shown diagrammatically in Fig. 9.28. The upper diagram shows the main components of an optical gyroscope and the lower diagram shows the integrated optics version. It must be emphasized that the integrated version is very small compared with the bulk optics version and that only the fibers have to be aligned to the integrated optics circuits whereas in the bulk optics version each element has to be aligned (and has to maintain this alignment). However, integrated components have not yet achieved satisfactory performances. Two

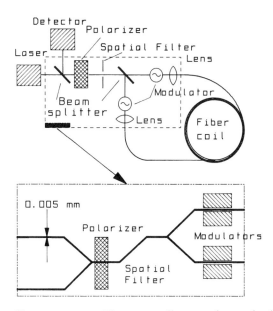

Fig. 9.28 The fiber gyroscope. The upper diagram shows the bulk optics. In comparison only a small area is needed to realize the equivalent structure with integrated optics (lower diagram).

main problems, involving the mode filter and the polarizer, have not yet been solved satisfactorily. Therefore present-day prototypes use two integrated optics circuits connected by a polarizing fiber about 1 m long. The first circuit is a simple Y branch (i.e. the left-hand side of the circuit shown in Fig. 9.28) and the second circuit is another Y branch with phase modulators (i.e. the right-hand side of the circuit shown in Fig. 9.28).

Gyroscopes using frequency-shifted light offer some advantages. However, the realization of a Bragg cell in integrated optics is difficult. Although several successful experiments using a spectrum analyzer have been reported (Barnoski, 1979), they have been restricted to slab waveguides. A strip waveguide version is needed for a fiber optic gyroscope because it is necessary to couple the frequency-shifted light to a single-mode fiber. Preliminary results have been reported (von Helmolt, 1981), but the efficiency was inadequate.

Other schemes have been proposed which may offer advantages if the complicated optics can be realized by compact integrated optics circuits (Imai *et al.*, 1987).

9.8.2.2 Gyroscope on a chip
The first review of the possibilities of developing an all-integrated optic gyroscope was given by Lawrence (1983). The version proposed was based on a resonator rather than an interferometer. A detailed description of this type of optical gyroscope is given elsewhere (Bernard and Schlaak, 1984). The

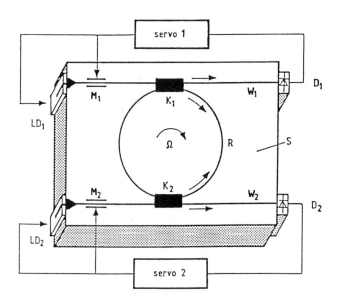

Fig. 9.29 Schematic diagram of an integrated gyroscope: W_1, W_2, waveguides; R, ring guide; K_1, K_2, directional couplers; M_1, M_2, waveguide modulators; LD_1, LD_2, laser diodes; D_1, D_2, detectors; S, chip substrate.

principle of the integrated gyroscope is shown in Fig. 9.29. The main circuit is the ring resonator which is coupled to two waveguides. As already discussed, the coupling is difficult. Keeping the resonator at a constant resonance is also a problem but, as shown in Fig. 9.29, this is overcome by using a relative measurement where the resonance is detected by two different light sources (laser diodes LD_1 and LD_2) at a given wavelength.

The sensitivity of this type of gyroscope depends on the area enclosed by the waveguide ring. Therefore a large substrate area is preferable. However, this is limited by masking technology because it is necessary to fabricate single-mode waveguides (with widths of the order of micrometers) with smooth edges (roughness less than 100 nm). Direct writing with an electron beam machine can offer substrate sizes up to 2 in. However, the software required to draw circles or bends is not usually available, because electron beam machines are designed for electronic circuit masking in which smooth bends are not required.

In principle, rotation sensors based on resonant ring structures offer the same sensitivity as fiber gyroscopes. However, the technological problems are much more severe although the compactness of such a gyroscope is challenging.

9.8.3 Fabry–Pérot sensors

A special class of fiber optic sensors makes use of the Fabry–Pérot effect (Kist and Sohler, 1983). This fiber optic sensor, which has a special interrogation scheme, is one of the few which do not require optically neutral transmission lines to and from the optical sensor. Therefore this concept plays an important role in the field of fiber optic sensors.

Integrated optics can be used in two ways in this sensor. In the "conventional" design, as discussed above for the gyroscope, all the optics needed to feed the light into and detect the light from the sensor can be integrated, thus avoiding a bulky and very unreliable arrangement. However, we will concentrate on a Fabry–Pérot sensor using integrated optics. The following parameters can be detected using this type of sensor: temperature; pressure (equivalent to force, acceleration, acoustic parameters); electric field; magnetic field (i.e. current). Both temperature and pressure can be measured using glass as the sensitive medium (Martens, 1984). However, an electro-optic material such as $LiNbO_3$ must be used for the measurement of electric and magnetic fields. In the case of $LiNbO_3$ the sensitivity is highest for temperature and lowest for magnetic fields.

A typical arrangement is shown in Fig. 9.30. A Fabry–Pérot resonator is fabricated by titanium in-diffusion into $LiNbO_3$. The resonator is realized by putting semireflecting mirrors at the ends of the waveguide. To achieve high reflectance, the mirrors should be placed perpendicular to the waveguide which is rather difficult. In some special requirements for evaluating the signal,

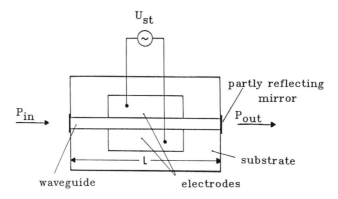

Fig. 9.30   The principle of the Fabry–Pérot resonator as a sensor.

two electrodes are placed on the substrate forming a phase modulator. Such a configuration should be avoided if possible, because electrical connections are needed at the sensor and the main advantage of an optical sensor (no electrical or metallic connection between the sensor and the evaluation equipment) is lost. However, the sensor shown in Fig. 9.30 will also work without the electrodes. The operation of such a sensor has been described elsewhere (Kist and Sohler, 1983), and therefore we will not discuss it further here but will concentrate on the possibilities offered by integrated optics for a device of this type.

The first possible configuration is shown in Fig. 9.31. Several identical Fabry–Pérot sensors are placed close to each other. In this way the spatial change of the parameter to be sensed can be detected. For example, a laser beam running across the substrate surface and increasing the temperature locally will be detected with respect to intensity *and* direction.

The dynamic range of many interferometric fiber optic sensors is insufficient. Therefore several similar sensors with varying sensitivities are

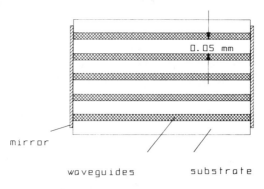

Fig. 9.31   A multiple Fabry–Pérot resonator arrangement as a sensor for spatially resolved measurements.

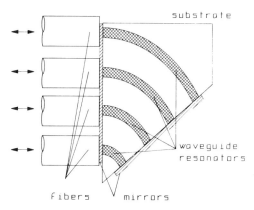

Fig. 9.32 Multiple Fabry–Pérot sensors with different resonator lengths, i.e. different sensitivities.

used together, but this is not easy to achieve because of packaging problems. In integrated optics this can be solved as shown in Fig. 9.32. The Fabry–Pérot sensors are curved and are of different lengths. Because the sensitivity is proportional to the length of the sensor, the arrangement satisfies the requirements. Obviously many similar arrangements can be considered. However, the main advantage is the compactness of the device and the planar technology.

9.9 Other applications

Numerous other applications of integrated optics circuits in sensors or as sensors have been demonstrated or proposed. In the following we will discuss some of them to emphasize the potential of this technology.

9.9.1 Frequency multiplexing

As discussed in Chapter 14 sensor multiplexing is very important. Frequency multiplexing is one of the possibilities offered for sensor multiplexing. Usually the multiplexing of optical sources with different frequencies is relatively easy but demultiplexing is difficult. Several proposals have been made for the use of integrated optics for demultiplexing. The devices have been realized in SOS technology (but can be transferred to any other technology).

(1) Valette *et al.* (1987) have proposed a planar design based on a diffraction grating. The basic design of the demultiplexer is shown in Fig. 9.33.

(2) A strip waveguide component (Fitchew *et al.*, 1987) which offers the advantage of tunability is shown in Fig. 9.34. It consists of an interferometer which produces a 20 GHz resonant periodic filter.

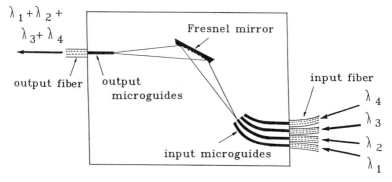

Fig. 9.33 Optical wavelength demultiplexer realized by planar slab waveguides in SOS technology.

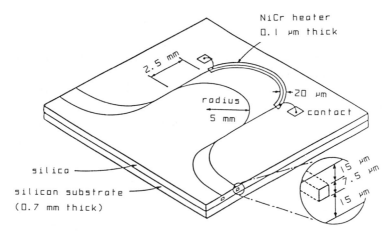

Fig. 9.34 A demultiplexer based on a tunable interferometric structure realized in SOS technology.

(3) An arrangement which has already been shown as an example of the advantages of SOS technology over fiber–chip coupling (Fig. 9.25) should also be noted.

9.9.2 Displacement sensors

Displacement sensors are usually based on Michelson interferometers. One arm of the interferometer is identified as the sensing arm, and if its length is changed a change in the output signal will be detected and can be evaluated. Two examples have been demonstrated, again based on a slab waveguide and a strip waveguide scheme.

Figure 9.35 shows the arrangement of a displacement sensor based on a slab configuration and realized in SOS technology (Lizet *et al.*, 1987).

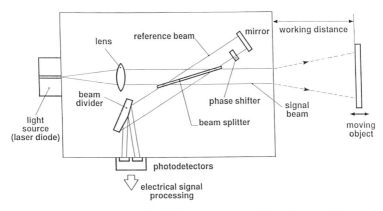

Fig. 9.35 Schematic diagram of a displacement sensor based on a slab waveguide configuration and realized in SOS technology.

Detection of the interference of π-shift signals with two photodetectors enables the direction of the movement to be evaluated. The second approach uses $LiNbO_3$ technology and is in principle a strip waveguide version of the previous device. The very simple arrangement is shown in Fig. 9.36 (Hosokawa *et al.*, 1988). Both types of sensor can be used to measure vibrations or even pressure if a suitable transducer is used (i.e. a moving membrane).

9.9.3 Laser Doppler velocimetry

Laser Doppler velocimetry (LDV) plays a very important role in modern diagnostics (Nishihara *et al.*, 1982; Kaufmann, 1986). The use of fibers was an

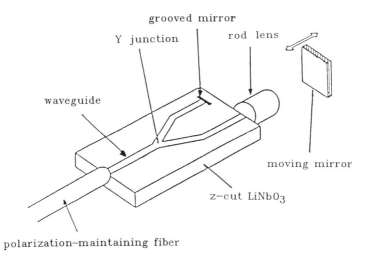

Fig. 9.36 Displacement sensor using strip waveguides in $LiNbO_3$.

important step forward because the LDV instruments became more flexible. However, some bulky optics at the measurement head still restrict the number of applications. Therefore several attempts have been made to build an integrated optics circuit to miniaturize the bulk optics. A typical example is described by Toda *et al.* (1987). Because of the complexity of both the system and the integrated optics chip it will not be discussed further.

9.10 Outstanding problems

Although integrated optics has been under development for some time, there are still many (sometimes fundamental) problems to be solved. The simple integrated optics arrangement shown in Fig. 9.37 demonstrates these problems. One of the most severe restrictions on integrated optics is shown in

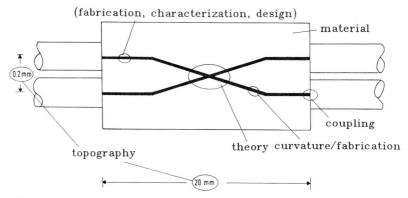

Fig. 9.37 Outstanding problems in integrated optics demonstrated using a "simple" waveguide crossing.

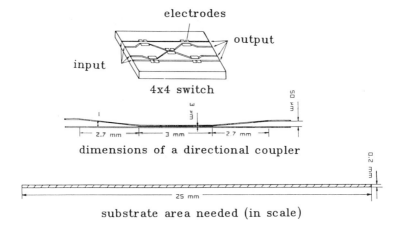

Fig. 9.38 Problem of the topology of integrated optics.

detail in Fig. 9.38. The guides are very small. Even if complex structures like a 4×4 matrix are realized, the substrate area needed in the lateral direction is also very small and is mainly determined by the dimensions of the fibers to be coupled to the guides. However, because small radii of curvature are not allowed and the coupling lengths in directional couplers are of the order of millimeters, the device length is of the order of centimeters. In the example shown in Fig. 9.38 the 4×4 matrix needs a substrate area of $0.2 \, \text{mm} \times 25 \, \text{mm}$. Thus a high integration density cannot be realized and the complexity of the integrated optics circuit is limited mainly by the device length or by the maximum substrate length which is available.

9.11 Conclusions

In principle integrated optics offer a very high potential in the area of optical sensors (i.e. Fabry–Pérot sensors or ring resonators for gyroscopes) and fiber optic sensors (i.e. the fiber gyroscope). However, many problems remain to be solved before integrated optics can be used commercially. The most important of these problems are fiber coupling, the production of suitable masks, loss reduction, and appropriate packaging and housing.

Acknowledgments

The author would like to thank the following colleagues who helped to collect the material presented here: A. Brandenburg, FhG-IPM, FRG; R. Jansen, Corning, France; M. Kawachi, NTT, Japan; A. Nutt, NSG, Japan; S. Valette, LETI, France; E. Voges, University of Dortmund, FRG.

References

Barnoski, M. K. (1979). Integrated optic spectrum analyzer, *IEEE Trans. Circuits Syst.*, **26**, 1113–1124.

Beguin, A., Dumas, T., Nissim, C. and Jansen, R. (1988). Fabrication and performance of low loss optical components made by ion exchange in glass, *Int. Conf. on Optical Fiber Sensors, New Orleans, LA*.

Bernard, W. and Schlaak, H. (1984). Integrated optical rate sensor development, *Proc. Symp. on Gyro Technology, Stuttgart*.

Casey, H. C. and Panish, M. B. (1978). *Heterostructure Lasers*, Parts A and B, Academic Press, New York.

Eberhard, D. and Voges, E. (1988). Fiber optics interferometer with digital heterodyne detection using lithium niobate devices, *Int. Conf. on Optical Fiber Sensors, New Orleans, LA*.

Enokihara, A., Izutsu, M. and Sueta, T. (1988). Integrated optic fluid sensor using heat transfer, *Appl. Opt.*, **27** (1), 109–113.

Ezekiel, S. and Arditty, H. (1982). *Fiber Optic Rotation Sensors*, Springer, Berlin.

Feit, M. D. and Fleck, J. A. (1978). Light propagation in graded index optical fibers, *Appl. Opt.*, **17** (24), 3990–3998.

Fitchew, K. D., Toba, H. and Oda, K. (1987). Frequency response of thermo-optic tuning mechanism of planar silica optical multiplexer, *Opt. Lett.*, **12** (10), 781–783.

Harmer, A. (1985). Battelle Institute, Geneva, Personal communication.

Haruna, M. and Koyama, J. (1984). Thermo-optic waveguide interferometric modulator/switch in glass, *Proc. Inst. Electr. Eng., Part H*, **131**, 322–324.

Haruna, M., Nakajima, H. and Nishihara, H. (1985). Optical π-arc waveguide interferometer in proton-exchanged $LiNbO_3$ for temperature sensing, *Appl. Opt.*, **24** (16), 2483–2484.

von Helmolt, C. H. (1981). Integrated optic strip waveguides driven by surface acoustic waves, *J. Opt. Commun.*, **1** (4), 142–154.

Hosokawa, H., Takagi, J. and Yamashita, T. (1988). Integrated optic microdisplacement sensor using a Y-junction and a polarization maintaining fiber, *Int. Conf. on Fiber Optic Sensors, New Orleans, LA*.

Ikeda, Y., Okuda, E. and Oikawa, M. (1987). Graded index optical waveguides and planar microlens arrays and their applications, *Proc. EFOC/LAN 87*, pp. 103–107.

Imai, Y., Koseki, H. and Ohtsuka, Y. (1987). Heterodyne fiber-optic gyroscope using orthogonally polarized two-frequency beams, *Appl. Opt.*, **26** (15), 2962–2965.

Isaac, J. J. *et al.* (1987). *An Integrated Optical Pressure Sensor in III–V Material*, pp. 213–216, Scottish Electronic Technology Group, Glasgow.

Kapron, F. P., Keck, D. B. and Maurer, R. D. (1970). Radiation loss in glass optical fibers, *Appl. Phys. Lett.*, **17** (10), 423–425.

Kaufmann, S. L. (1986). Fiberoptics on laser Doppler velocimetry, *Lasers and Applications*, pp. 71–73.

Kawachi, M., Yamada, Y., Yasu, M. and Kobayashi, M. (1985). Guided-wave optical wavelength-division multi/demultiplexer using high-silica channel waveguides, *Electron. Lett.*, **21**, 314–315.

Kist, R. and Sohler, W. (1983). Fiber optic spectrum analyzer, *J. Lightwave Technol.*, **1** (1), 105–110.

Lawrence, A. (1988). *The Micro-Optic Gyro*, Internal report, Northrop Precision Products Division.

Lizet, J., Gidon, P. and Valette, S. (1987). Integrated optics displacement sensor achieved on silicon substrate, *Proc. 4th European Conf. on Integrated Optics, Glasgow*, pp. 210–212.

Marcatili, E. A. J. (1969). Dielectric rectangular waveguide and directional coupler for integrated optics, *Bell Syst. Tech. J.*, **48**, 2071–2102.

Martens, G. (1984). Measurement of pressure by photoelastic effects, *Sensors Actuat.*, **6**, 181–190.

Miller, S. E. (1969). Integrated optics: an introduction, *Bell Syst. Tech. J.*, **48** (7), 2059–2069.

Nishihara, H. *et al.* (1982). Optical fiber laser Doppler velocimeter for high resolution measurement of pulsatile blood flows, *Appl. Opt.*, **21** (10), 1785–1790.

Nishizawa, K., Sudo, E., Maeda, M. and Yamasaki, T. (1987). Waveguide type hydrogen sensor, *Proc. European Conf. on Optical Communications, Barcelona*, pp. 99–102.

Paul, P. H. and Kychakoff, G. (1987). Fiber-optic evanescent field absorption sensor, *Appl. Phys. Lett.*, **51** (1), 12–14.

Pavlath, G. A. and Suman, M. C. (1984). Fiber-optic gyroscopes: advances and future developments, *J. Inst. Navig.*, **31** (2), 70–83.

Schmidt, R. V. and Kaminow, I. P. (1974). Metal diffused optical waveguides in $LiNbO_3$, *Appl. Phys. Lett.*, **25** (8), 458–460.

Schmidt, R. V. and Kogelnik, H. (1976). Electrooptically switched coupler with stepped delta-β-reversal using Ti-diffused LiNbO$_3$ waveguides, *Appl. Phys. Lett.*, **28** (9), 503–506.

Tamela, S., Honkanen, S., Tervonen, A. and Leppihalme, M. (1987). An integrated optical waveguide refractometer, *Proc. 4th European Conf. on Integrated Optics, Glasgow*, pp. 148–151.

Thylen, L. (1983). The beam propagation method; an analysis of its applicability, *Opt. Quantum Electron.*, **15**, 433–439.

Toda, H., Haruna, M. and Nishihara, H. (1987). Optical integrated circuit for a fiber laser Doppler velocimeter, *J. Lightwave Technol.*, **5** (7), 901–905.

Valette, S. *et al.* (1983). Integrated optic spectrum analyzer using planar technology on oxidized silicon substrate, *Electron. Lett.*, **19** (21), 883–885.

Valette, S., Lizet, J. and Mottier, P. (1985). Integrated optical circuits achieved by planar technology on silicon nitride waveguides, *Opt. Eng.*, **24**, 235.

Valette, S., Gidon, P. and Jadot, J. P. (1987). New integrated optical multiplexer–demultiplexer realized on silicon substrate, *Proc. 4th European Conf. on Integrated Optics, Glasgow*.

Index

319